MARINE
CHEMISTRY

(IN TWO VOLUMES)

DEAN F. MARTIN

DEPARTMENT OF CHEMISTRY AND
INSTITUTE OF MARINE SCIENCE
UNIVERSITY OF SOUTH FLORIDA
TAMPA, FLORIDA

VOLUME 2
Theory and Applications

PRELIMINARY EDITION

MARCEL DEKKER, INC., New York

1970

TO BARBARA

PREFACE

As the preface to Volume 1 noted, the field of marine chemistry may be divided, for the sake of convenience, into two subject areas: theory and analytical methods. In Volume 1, the analytical methods were considered; in this volume, the results of theoretical aspects and the applications that follow from experimental observations are considered.

Volume 2 has been developed as a result of an introductory course in marine chemistry (offered at the advanced undergraduate and graduate levels) that is intended primarily for those persons who have not had an extensive background in chemistry, but who have had a more intensive background in other fields. It would be difficult to obtain substantial agreement as to what the precise contents of such a course should be, and certain problems do become self-evident upon teaching this course in marine chemistry.

The first problem encountered is that comprehensive treatises are unsuitable as texts for this kind of study. Such comprehensive works include *The Ocean*, written by Sverdrup, Johnson, and Fleming and published in 1942; *The Sea*, particularly Volume 2, edited by Hill and published in 1963; and *Chemical Oceanography*, edited by Riley and Skirrow and published in 1965. Although such books provide a useful background, they may be of limited utility at the outset of an introductory course. The second problem is the varied backgrounds of the students and of other persons who are interested in an introduction to marine chemistry. It is assumed that they have had a recent year of college chemistry. This in itself means that their knowledge of chemistry, particularly of the theoretical aspects, is much more extensive than it would have been 5, 10, or 15 years ago. They have, for instance, been exposed to the foundations of thermodynamics, though the applications of these principles to marine chemistry may not have been immediately apparent to them. The students' varied backgrounds pose an additional problem in that certain aspects of marine chemistry, such as the concept of an ecological system, some mixing processes in the marine environment, and so on, may be new to them. Finally, the problems of time and space become paramount in preparing this introductory course in marine chemistry, and as a result many topics that are of consequence must be less well emphasized or regrettably omitted.

There has been a trend toward a greater reliance on theory, and the present text takes another step in this direction. It adopts an approach that might be termed one of "total integration": that is, the facts, theory, and implications or applications are integrated as completely as possible. It is my firm belief, based on several years of experience, that the emphasis on theory does a better job of "teaching the facts" than does the classical approach of "considering only facts." I recognize though, as all teachers must, that this is a matter of emphasis and that the emphasis will vary from person to person. It would be surprising if the blend of theory and fact in this volume were universally acceptable. However, it is my belief that this blend is a useful one and that the possibilities and opportunities for variation are ample for any instructor who uses this text.

The material in this volume is presented as follows:

In Chapter 1, the unique characteristics of water substance are considered as part of the physical and chemical properties of sea water. There is considerable emphasis upon the hydrogen bond and its consequences, particularly as it affects the properties of water. There is a summary of the structure of liquid water and some of its consequences, notably thermal anomalies and the implications of these. Other properties of sea water are introduced in a logical sequence, concluding with some of the gross constancies of sea water. These constancies include chemical composition, limited temperature range, pH, and buffer action. This leads to a consideration of the mixing processes in the marine environment that support these constancies and those phenomena, such as the thermocline, that serve as a barrier to the mixing processes (Chapter 2).

In Chapter 3 (Energy Flow in the Marine Ecological System), the concept of an ecological system is introduced, as well as the theme, which is prevalent throughout the book, of the interactions of organisms, chemicals, and the environment, including the geological aspects of the environment. The concept of energy flow is introduced and tied in with the concept of a biogeochemical cycle.

In Chapter 4, the interactions of components of the ecosystem are discussed and two pertinent questions are considered: How did sea water and air obtain their present compositions, and how are these compositions maintained? The theoretical model ocean suggested by Sillén is introduced and is compared with the real ocean. The deviations between the two oceans are considered, and this sets the stage for consideration of those nutrients that represent deviations from the chemical constancy.

Chapters 5, 6, and 7 consider the nutrient cycles of silicon, phosphorus, and nitrogen, respectively. All of these chapters maintain the central theme of the interaction of various components of the marine ecological system.

Chapter 8 deals with the major biogeochemical cycles of the carbon system: the intense biological, the geological, and the combined biological-geological-economic cycles. Some implications of these cycles include the consequences of fossil-fuel burning, the problems arising from carbon dioxide interactions in the atmosphere and in the ocean, the origin and the diagenesis of marine carbonates, and the dolomite problem.

The intense biological cycle is discussed in more detail in Chapter 9 (Organic Productivity). This chapter is concerned with the organisms that are involved in the primary productivity of the sea, the so-called fertility of the sea, with the methods of determining this fertility, and with the general geographical variations of productivity. Chapter 9 also serves as a basis for the consideration of food resources of the sea (Chapter 11).

In Chapter 10, mineral resources of the sea, as well as the sea's general resources, are considered along with both present and future problems concerning the mining of the sea and the extraction of its mineral resources. The problems discussed include those of legal, geological, and chemical aspects. Chapter 11, the final chapter, considers the problems of obtaining food from the sea in the form of plants, aquatic animals, and phycocolloids, shows the interactions of food and chemicals found in the sea, and concludes with a discussion on drugs from the sea.

This volume has some features that are worth noting here:

1. Material is presented in the light that theory, not facts, will change. Emphasis is given to the facts upon which theory is founded, and where possible, facts are presented first. The experimental basis of the information is emphasized, and so the pertinent material in Volume 1 is referenced as much as possible.

2. The text mentions the principal investigators with whom particular views are associated. The reasons for this are to give credit to these scientists, to bring science alive for the students, and to provide a key to future extended readings. It is a regrettable consequence of this practice that in so doing, many errors of omission must be made. It is hoped that it will be recognized that this is an inevitable result and that the omission of a given name reflects only a limitation of space.

3. Considerable emphasis is placed upon the interactions of organisms, chemicals, and environment. This constitutes the formerly mentioned "central theme" which pervades this text and which follows the views of Odum and others. The use of this central theme is not uncommon in books on ecology, but does seem to be uncommon in books concerned with chemistry. It is hoped that this emphasis will provide a balanced view of many fields.

4. The biogeochemical cycles of the sea are stressed, as well as the important roles these cycles play. For example, the significance of the sulfur biogeochemical cycle probably can not be underestimated. It appears to many, including the author, that the oxygen composition of the atmosphere is maintained, not by the activity of phytoplankton, but by the activity of sulfate-reducing bacteria (Chapter 4).

5. Each chapter concludes with a summary of the notable concepts that have been introduced within that particular chapter, which acts also as a useful introduction to the subsequent chapter.

6. Most of the references listed at the end of each chapter denote recent publications, including those of 1970. This should not be construed as a deemphasis of older work. Extensive reference to older work is given in the major comprehensive treatises included in the reference lists, as well as in the other publications cited.

7. Many contemporary problems of marine chemistry, though obviously not all, are included in this text. For example, a current

problem of concern is the imbalance of the nitrogen cycle, which is the problem of denitrification, and so consideration is given both to the organisms responsible for this process and to the locations at which it must be occurring.

Problems inevitably arise in the preparation of any textbook—the major problem, as mentioned previously, being the inability to cover all topics of interest and the resultant necessity of omitting certain of these topics.

One of the topics omitted in this textbook is an extensive consideration of the instrumentation involved in analysis. This omission is made with regret, though problems of instrumentation are woven throughout the individual chapters. Regret is tempered with the hope that it will be appreciated that many major items of instrumentation are not in general use because of their extensive cost, though it is recognized that these same items are used in major oceanographic laboratories.

Some newer methods of detection also are not considered in this volume, though references to these are provided. The use of specific ion electrodes is a case in point. It has been only recently that these electrodes seem to be used in oceanography. The fluoride electrode seems to have some utility, according to a recent article in *Science;* however, the use of the calcium electrode has received a mixed reaction. It is anticipated that these electrodes, or other similar devices, will become more generally useful.

In summary, an attempt has been made to present the essentials of marine chemistry in as economical and attractive a fashion as possible. It is hoped that the "total integration" approach to the subject will encourage the reader to think for himself and that the experience will be a satisfying one for both student and instructor.

I will appreciate it if readers would inform me of any textual errors, or if they could suggest ways of improving the presentation, or even if they would let me know of something within this volume that they like.

ACKNOWLEDGMENT

A large number of persons helped directly and indirectly with the evolution of this manuscript, and I regret that they can not all be mentioned personally. The comments of students who used early mimeographed editions were most valuable. I am grateful to my colleagues for helpful criticism and advice, particularly to Harold J.

Humm, William H. Taft, and Thomas L. Hopkins. The support and encouragement of members of the administration of the University of South Florida are also gratefully acknowledged.

Several typists worked on earlier drafts of this work (Mrs. Katherine Berry, Mrs. Betty Thrower, and Mrs. Adora Winans). I am indeed grateful to Mrs. Aura Ferrell, who typed the final manuscript.

Finally, I am particularly grateful to my wife, Barbara B. Martin, who provided me with substantial technical assistance and encouragement.

DEAN F. MARTIN

CONTENTS

Preface   v

CHAPTER 1   Physical and Chemical Properties of Sea Water   1
CHAPTER 2   Mixing Processes in the Marine Environment   39
CHAPTER 3   Energy Flow in the Marine Ecosystem   77
CHAPTER 4   The Model Ocean   105
CHAPTER 5   The Silicon Cycle   145
CHAPTER 6   The Phosphorus Cycle   183
CHAPTER 7   The Nitrogen Cycle   225
CHAPTER 8   The Carbon Cycles   267
CHAPTER 9   Organic Productivity   317
CHAPTER 10 Resources of the Sea   357
CHAPTER 11 Food from the Sea   397
APPENDIX   Plankton Terminology   435

Author Index   439
Subject Index   445

PHYSICAL AND CHEMICAL PROPERTIES

OF SEA WATER

1.1 Unique Characteristics of Water Substance

As noted in the preceding volume, it is useful to regard
sea water as being a solution of eleven major constituents.
Although the convenience of this view is unquestioned, it may
be a dangerous view because there is a tendency to overlook
what should be an obvious fact: sea water with salinity of
35°/oo is actually 96.5°/o by weight water. Furthermore, in
emphasizing the properties of this solution, we face the
danger of not recognizing the unique characteristics of water
or water substance (to encompass the liquid, solid, and
gaseous forms). Water substance has a number of "abnormal"
properties that have important oceanographic and meteorologic
significance.

The abnormal properties of water are a direct consequence
of the structure of water and the nature of the component elements. The gaseous water molecule is angular, and the bond
angle is $104°$ 40' (Fig. 1-1). The electrons are distributed
unequally in this molecule, so much so that we assign a
partial positive charge to each hydrogen ($\delta+$) and a partial
negative charge to the oxygen ($\delta-$). Each positive center (or

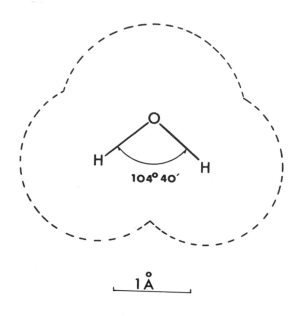

$$104° \, 40'$$

$$1 \overset{\circ}{\text{A}}$$

FIG. 1-1

The water molecule. The dashed lines indicate the effective sizes of individual atoms.

hydrogen atom) in a given molecule is attracted to and forms

a weak link with a negative center (or oxygen atom) in another

molecule. The weak link, in which a hydrogen joins two oxygen

atoms, is called a hydrogen bond.[1] The strength of this bond

is about 10 per cent of that of a covalent hydrogen-oxygen

bond. Water behaves as it does because of the consequences of

hydrogen bonding. These include the following:

1. The hydrogen bond causes large irregular aggregates of

   molecules. Ultimately, in ice, each oxygen is involved

in two hydrogen bonds and thus is surrounded with four
hydrogen atoms (Fig. 1-2).

2. The bond angle is distorted from $104° \ 40'$ to $109° \ 28'$,
typical of a molecule with a tetrahedral geometry, and a
large open structure results for solid water substance.

3. Because of the extensive aggregation, liquid water substance behaves as if it were a much larger molecule than
would be expected from the formula H_2O. As a result,
typical properties of water appear startlingly abnormal
when compared with those of a nonpolar substance such
as methane (Table 1-1). For example, the boiling point
of water is about $180°C$ higher than might be expected; if
hydrogen bonding suddenly ceased, the oceans would vapo-
rize instantly. The heats of fusion and vaporization are
abnormally high, which makes water substance useful for
refrigeration and air-conditioning functions,

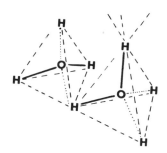

FIG. 1-2

Tetrahedral geometry of water showing hydrogen bonds
(dotted line) and covalent bonds (solid lines).

TABLE 1-1

Comparison of Physical Properties of Water and Methane

Physical Property	Water $(H_2O)_n$	Methane (CH_4)
Molecular weight	$n \cdot 18$	16
Melting point	$0^\circ C$	$-182.5^\circ C$
Heat of fusion	79.63	14.5
Heat capacity, cal/g/$^\circ$C	1.0	0.5
Boiling point	$100^\circ C$	$-161.5^\circ C$
Heat of vaporization, cal/g	536	122

respectively (Note 1). At sea, the heat of fusion is responsible for a temperature-controlling effect as heat is released upon the freezing of ice or absorbed upon melting. The heat of vaporization is extremely important in heat and water transfer to and from the atmosphere. The abnormally large heat capacity is responsible for the remarkable climate-moderating influences large bodies of water have on adjacent land masses. The abnormality of many of these properties can be rationalized in terms of the _extra_ energy needed to overcome the effects of hydrogen bonding.

4. Because of the open structure of ice (Fig. 1-3), ice floats and water has a temperature of maximum density

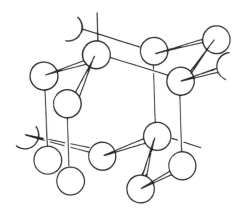

FIG. 1-3

Ice structure with hydrogen atoms omitted for sake of clarity.

above the melting point. The last result is a consequence of the two opposing effects: (1) collapse of the
open low-density ice structure which results in an increase in density with increasing temperature; and
(2) the normal thermal expansion of a liquid, which results in decreasing density with increasing temperature.
Below 4°C, the first effect predominates; above 4°C the
second effect predominates. The temperature of maximum
density of distilled water is 4°C (Fig. 1-4); this temperature decreases with increasing salinity, and is below
the normal freezing point for salinities greater than

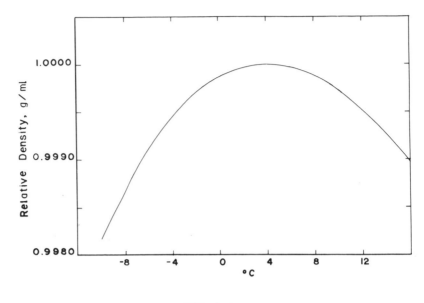

FIG. 1-4

Variation of relative density (g/ml) of water with temperature.
Values are based upon the mass of one ml of water at 3.98°C
as unity.

$20^{\circ}/oo$. Thus, the phenomenon, temperature of maximum

density, has much greater significance in the mechanism

of mixing in lakes than in oceans (Chapter 2).

There are two important chemical properties of water:

solvation and solvolysis. Solvation is the chemical combi-

nation of species with solvent molecules. Because of its

polar nature, water has an unusually high dielectric constant

of 80 (Note 2). This, in effect, means that water has an un-

usual capacity to dissolve inorganic compounds because water

molecules surround anions or cations, insulate them from each

6

other and overcome the forces of attraction that hold these

substances in an ionic lattice. In addition to solvation of

the ions (Eq. 1-1), water can cause solvolysis (Eq. 1-2),

which involves cleavage of the hydrogen-oxygen bond

$$MX + nH_2O \rightleftarrows M(OH_2)_{n-x}^+ + X(H_2O)_x^- \qquad (1\text{-}1)$$

to form acids or bases (see Vol. 1, Chap.3)

$$PO_4^{3-} + H_2O \rightleftarrows HPO_4^{2-} + OH^- \qquad (1\text{-}2)$$

These, then, are three significant features of water sub-

stance: it is highly associated, it has a tendency to form an

open structure; and it has unusual solvent characteristics.

The structures of solid and gaseous phases of water substance

are known, but much less is known about the structure of

liquid water. The next section summarizes our state of know-

ledge.

1.2 Structure of Liquid Water and Thermal Anomalies[2]

Drost-Hansen[2] has published reviews of the structural

models of water and the significance of reported thermal

anomalies in the properties of water and aqueous solutions.

It appears that many properties of water exhibit relatively

abrupt transitions at certain distinct temperatures (cf.

Fig. 1-5). A number of examples of these thermal anomalies or

"kinks" have been collected by Drost-Hansen and his coworkers,

who tentatively ascribe the origin of the anomalies to higher-

order phase changes in the structure of water. Several

generalizations have been made about the thermal anomalies.[2]

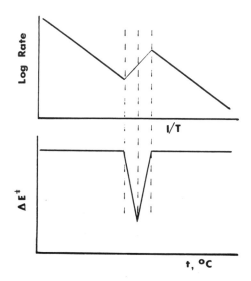

FIG. 1-5

Schematic representation of one type of thermal anomaly. Rate plot (upper) appears as two parallel lines with displacement near "kink" and is compared (lower) with variation of energy of activation with temperature. (After Drost-Hansen[2].)

1. The change in property with temperature is more or less abrupt and occurs within ± 1-$2°$ of a "centered" transition temperature.

2. The "centered" transition temperature at which thermal anomalies are most frequently observed are $15°$, $30°$, $45°$, and $60°C$. Two additional anomalies may occur near $80°C$ and near 140-$170°C$.

3. Thermal anomalies or "kinks" seem to occur for the properties of aqueous solutions of either electrolytes or

nonelectrolytes. Thermal anomalies in the viscosity of pure bulk water evidently do not occur, according to Korson, Drost-Hansen, and Millero,[3] who conducted precise measurements over small temperature intervals. On the other hand, there is good evidence for thermal anomalies in the properties at water-air, water-solid, or other water-interface surfaces.

4. The transition temperatures of properties of aqueous solutions seem to be unsensitive to the nature and concentration of the solute.

5. The kinks are observed for equilibrium properties, transport phenomena, as well as surface and interfacial phenomena.

6. Thermal anomalies are observed for biological processes, particularly when water is intimately associated with various interfaces. Examples include cell division and growth which seem to be especially sensitive probes of thermal anomalies. Growth is generally retarded in the vicinity of the kink, and optimum growth is observed roughly halfway between consecutive kinks.[4] For example, Streptococcus faecalis has two growth optima, near 26 and 34°C, with a notable minimum near 29°C.[4]

The existence, if real, of thermal anomalies is interpreted as implying the occurrence of higher-order phase transitions and structured units of a certain size range. That is, the structure of water undergoes more or less sudden changes with change in temperature. How complex these changes are and the nature of these changes are uncertain. The biological and physical significance is evident (Note 3). Moreover, if the reality of thermal anomalies is granted, as seems reasonable, their existence in any theory of water structure must be accomodated. Theoretical models fall into two groups, uniformist and mixture models.

Uniformist or average models. According to this view, water lacks local domains of structure and is to be regarded as an unstructured liquid. At a given time, one individual water molecule behaves essentially like any other molecule in the bulk liquid. In support of this view, there is the reported inability of certain techniques (e.g. Raman spectroscopy) to identify definite structures within liquid water (Wall and Hornig[5]). On the other hand, this model is not consistent with the implications of thermal anomalies.

Mixture Models: broken-down ice lattice models. These models imply the existence of two species of water - a bulky species, which consists of some kind of structural unit, and a dense species, e.g. individual water molecules. The models imply that an equilibrium exists between the two species of water.

Actually, there are three mixture models which differ primarily in the size and nature of the bulky species. This bulky species is based on a <u>broken-down ice lattice model</u> (cf. Danford and Levy[6]), a <u>cluster model</u> (cf. Nemethy and Scheraga[7]), or a <u>clathrate-cage model</u> (cf. Frank and Quist[8]).

According to the first model, monomeric water molecules occupy positions in the interstices of ice-like structures. The cluster model presumes the existence of a range of clusters composed of water molecules which have 0-4 hydrogen bonds per water molecule; the average cluster at room temperature was estimated to be 50 water molecules. The clathrate-cage model presumes the existence of discrete sites for "guest" particles (foreign ions, molecules, or water molecules) in a "host" lattice. Such sites are not presumed in the cluster model.

These three models would be in accord with the implications of thermal anomalies. The structural units responsible for these anomalies are thought[2] to range from 20 molecules to possibly 100-200. It is a point of some interest that current theories differ in physical models to a wide extent but all have remarkable agreement between predicted and observed numerical values for certain physical properties. Obviously, each model has its proponents and its utility.

With this background, we may examine some physical properties of sea water. Properties of interest include density,
compressibility, velocity of sound, transparency, and salinity.

1.3 The Density of Sea Water

The density of sea water is a parameter of critical interest because it affects the loading of ships, the stability
of water strata (which in turn significantly influences chemical and biological processes), and the field (or distribution)
of pressure in the ocean.

In view of the importance of the density of sea water it
is a matter of interest that the absolute density of sea water
is unknown. Moreover, it is likely to remain unknown because
of the practical difficulties. (The details are given by Cox,
et al.[9])

The values of densities that are usually quoted in the
literature are not densities (with units of g/cm^3). Rather,
the values are specific gravities, i.e., the ratio of the
density of a given sample to that of "pure" water at $4^{\circ}C$, the
temperature of maximum density. The specific gravity is a
ratio and is a pure number without units. Many oceanographers
have erroneously quoted units of g/cm^3 for the specific gravity.
Unfortunately the problem has been compounded in four ways.

1. An additional unit was introduced. The "specific volume"
   was defined as the reciprocal of the specific gravity of
   sea water; unfortunately, this reciprocal of a dimension-

less number was (and is) given units of cm^3/g.

2. A correction factor was introduced, i.e., multiplying
   specific gravities (and dividing specific volumes)
   by the factor 1.000028, which was the accepted value of
   the volume of a liter, expressed in cubic decimeters,
   dm^3. The conversion factor was actually an average value
   and was probably accurate to 5 ppm, though the results of
   the density measurements are thought to be reliable within
   1 ppm. In 1964, however, the definition of a liter was
   redefined.[9] It is now the special name given to the cubic
   decimeter, and the milliliter and cubic centimeter are now
   synonymous.

3. The composition of "pure" water is not constant and the
   proportion of isotopic hydrogen and oxygen is not constant,
   though this was not known prior to the 1920's. The variations affect the density. In fact, repeated distillation
   can alter the density of "pure" water, up to 20 ppm, because of the fractionation of isotopes.

4. Typically, "pure" water is assumed to have a density of
   1.0 g/cm^3 at $4^\circ C$, but the true value is about 0.99999
   (which would introduce an error of 30 ppm).

These difficulties can only be resolved by recognition
and solution of the central problem. Precise measurement of
the specific gravity of sea water samples requires a determination of the density of <u>defined</u> reference water.

This particular difficulty seems to have been solved because precise experimental details[9] have been given for the preparation of pure water for a relative density standard. The original article must be consulted for details, but it may be sufficient to note certain points of interest here. Deep waters of the Mediterranean Sea and the North Pacific Ocean seem to be the most uniform bodies of water known; hence an average sample should come from one of these locations. The triple distillation procedure which was used did not alter the isotopic composition of the water and all 60 samples obtained from an initial 20-liter sample had the same density (within 1 ppm).

Though the difficulty of finding a relative density standard is solved, another remains. The specific gravity of sea water samples is rarely measured directly, and there is an uncertainty about the absolute density of the standard water that was used in the 1902 study of Forch, Knudsen and Sorensen which formed the basis of all subsequent work on sea water densities.[9]

By way of background, usually the specific gravity is computed from the chlorinity (as determined by a Knudsen titration) or the salinity (obtained from conductivity or refractive index measurements) plus the in situ temperature. The density ρ of sea water, in a given location and depth (in situ) depends upon the temperature t, the salinity S, and the pressure $\underline{p}$. This is indicated by the symbol $\rho_{S,t,p}$. The specific gravity anomaly, $\sigma_{S,t,p}$, is often used (Eqn. 1-3), instead of the specific gravity.

$$\sigma_{S,t,p} = (\rho_{S,t,p} - 1)1000 \qquad (1-3)$$

If $\rho_{S,t,p} = 1.01204$, then $\sigma_{S,t,p} = 12.04$; and if $\sigma_{S,t,p} = -0.32$, then $\rho_{S,t,p} = 0.99968$. If the specific gravity is given at atmospheric pressure, the specific gravity anomaly is abbreviated σ_t; if it is designated at atmospheric pressure and $0^{\circ}C$, the symbol σ_o is used.

Typically, the in situ density is obtained from tables of density which give the variation of $\rho_{S,t,p}$ with salinity, temperature, and pressure; many tables are the results of three different fundamental determinations by M. Knudsen (1902), C. Forch (1902), and V. W. Ekman (1908).[10] It is advantageous when evaluating these properties of sea water to have several sets of independent tables available, if for no other reason than to check the possibility of systematic errors. In all cases, these tables should be examined critically in terms of the definition of the "pure" water standards. For example, Knudsen's Hydrographic Tables gives the values of σ_t for all reasonable temperatures and salinities in the ocean.[11] Recent compilations of pressure-volume-temperature data have been prepared by Newton and Kennedy[12] and by Wilson and Bradley.[13]

These tables indicate that the maximum value (at a depth of

10,900 m) of $\sigma_{S,t,p}$ is 75.7 or $\rho = 1.0757$. The range for $\rho_{S,t,p}$ is 0.9960 to 1.0757. The density of water at greatest depth is only a few percent greater than at the surface, but the effect is important, as we shall see later in this chapter. The values of σ_t found at the sea surface range from 0.9969 to 1.0283.[16] A ship which has a displacement of 1000 m^3 at a given loading line would weigh 996.9 metric tons in the first instance and 1,028.3 metric tons in the second instance.[16] Given the same freight, the free board (distance between upper deck and water line) would be shorter in fresh water than in sea water and shorter yet in sea water during the winter. Therefore, some vessels carry several different loading marks (Fig. 1-6; Note 4).

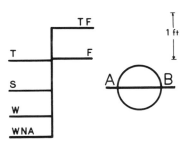

FIG. 1-6

Representation of the Plimsoll line (Note 4).

PHYSICAL AND CHEMICAL PROPERTIES OF SEA WATER

The usefulness of these tables is evident, but the accuracy is open to question for two reasons. First, as noted before, the density standard of the early work is unknown; presumably, tap water was distilled and there could be an uncertainty of 5-20 ppm in the density values. In other words, the supposedly significant numbers to the right of the decimal point in the specific gravity anomaly may actually be meaningless. Secondly, the relationships by which chlorinity is related to salinity which is related to density are approximations. These approximations are probably inadequate for the precise work that is now possible and need to be reexamined. Two parameters of interest in this connection are compressibility and salinity.

1.4 The Compressibility of Sea Water

The true compressibility of sea water is described by means of the coefficient of compressibility which represents the relative decrease in specific volume at a given temperature if the hydrostatic pressure is increased by one unit of pressure (Eqn. 1-4).

$$\alpha_{S,t,p} = \alpha_t - \mu p \alpha_t \qquad (1-4)$$

Here, $\alpha_{S,t,p}$ is the specific volume _in situ_, α_t is the specific volume of water at atmospheric pressure, μ is the coefficient of isothermal compressibility, and p is the pressure in bars (Note 5).

Sea water is very nearly incompressible. The coefficient of compressibility is about 0.000046/bar under standard conditions. There are two significant features of this value. First, the value is small but significant because of the large volume of the world ocean; if the value of the coefficient, μ, were zero, sea level would be about 90 feet higher. Secondly, the value of μ decreases with increasing temperature, salinity, and pressure. The compressibility of substances normally increases with an increase in temperature; water is anomalous because of the molecular structure (Section 1.1).

It should be noted that in addition to the isothermal compression of water, there is an adiabatic compression due to quick changes in pressure, e.g., sound waves. The coefficient of adiabatic compressibility, K, gives the change in specific volume as a function of pressure change for pressure unit. The value of K, which may be computed from values of μ, was a fundamental parameter for the determination of sound velocities in the ocean. Currently, however, direct measurements of sound velocities provide values that are more reliable than the computed values.[10]

The compressibility of sea water is of interest in attempts to explain ocean currents, which requires a knowledge of the field (or distribution) of force. Understanding the field of force requires knowledge of the fields of gravity, mass, and pressure. In turn, the specific volume in situ, $\sigma_{S,t,p}$, is preferred for describing the field of mass and pressure. An accurate analysis of these fields requires accurate data for the compressibility of sea water.

Values of compressibility and thermal expansion of sea water are critical because the effects of these two parameters on density have been used to evaluate densities at nonambient pressures and temperatures. (The alternate, of course, is direct measurement, as Wilson and Bradley[13] have done.) Unfortunately, numerical values of the compressibility of sea water have been disputed recently[10] and these values probably deserve close examination in view of their critical importance.

On the other hand, the study of partial molal values of salt solutions and sea water may be a fruitful approach to the problem and could lead to insights into the nature of ion-water interactions. This is a logical approach because the effect of compression is to force solvent molecules and ions closer together. The partial molal volume of a salt $\overline{V}^o$ at infinite dilution would be the volume change produced when one mole of a salt is placed in an infinite amount of water. The numbers are evaluated by precise measurements of densities of salt solutions and are of interest for two reasons. First, the rate of change of $\overline{V}^{o}$ with temperature ($d\overline{V}^{o}/dt$) can be related to compressibilities. Secondly, the value of $\overline{V}^{o}$ can be separated into component volumes and provide an insight into the nature of ion-water interactions.

For example, according to one study[14] it is possible to recognize four components of the partial molal volume: (1) the intrinsic or actual volume of an ion, which corresponds to the volume the ion would have in a crystal lattice; (2) a second (or electrostricted) volume, due to those water molecules that are strongly oriented to and firmly attracted to the ion; (3) a disordered volume or region which surrounds the second volume; and, possibly, (4) a caged volume, due to the formation of structured or caged water around the third volume. The last component or volume may be significant for ions of high charge.

1.5 Velocity of Sound

As noted in the preceding section, the velocity of sound may be calculated from the adiabatic compressibility, though direct measurement is the more common practice.

The velocity of sound V in sea water is about 1500 m sec^{-1} or about 4.5 times the velocity in air. The value of V is sensitive to changes in temperature ($\Delta V/\Delta t = 3m \ sec^{-1} \ ^{o}C^{-1}$), and pressure ($\Delta V/\Delta p = 1.8m \ sec^{-1}/100$ db and is less sensitive to changes in salinity ($\Delta V/\Delta S^{o}/oo = 1.3m \ sec^{-1} \ s^{-1} \ ^{o}/oo$).

PHYSICAL AND CHEMICAL PROPERTIES OF SEA WATER

An accurate knowledge of the sound velocity is obviously
a requirement for range determinations, as in navigation and
estimation of bottom depth. It is also of interest for echo
sounders in detecting underwater objects, schools of fish,
discontinuities in water layers (e.g., a layer of fresh water
from a river overlying salt water), and changes in the nature
of the bottom (rock reflects most of the sound hitting the surface, mud absorbs most of the sound, and mud overlying rock
could give two echoes on depths.) Finally, the speed of sound
is of interest in measuring salinity with velocity meters,
though precision is limited ($\pm 0.2^{o}/oo$).[10]

1.6 Optical Properties

Three optical properties of sea water are of especial
interest - reflection, refraction, and extinction. These
properties influence the color of sea water, the intensity and
spectrum of light (which in turn influence photosynthesis, the
basis of all life in sea water), and the temperature of sea
water (diurnal and seasonal variations). In addition, optical
properties of sea water are used to distinguish water masses,
to trace oceanic currents, and to detect biological and
geological variations in a water column.[15]

Reflection is an important parameter in the heat budget
of the ocean because the amount of radiant energy absorbed per

unit volume depends upon two factors: the amount of energy re-
acting with the surface and the fraction reflected. Reflection
of solar radiation depends upon the altitude of the sun and the
sea surface (assuming clear sky). At the sea surface the
fraction of radiant energy absorbed depends upon the angle of
incidence and on the refraction (Fig. 1-6), according to
Fresnel's law (Eqn. 1-5), which is valid for smooth surfaces.[16]

$$r^2 \simeq \left[\frac{1-n}{1+n} \right]^2 \tag{1-5}$$

Here r^2 is the fraction of energy reflected and n is the refractive index of sea water. Because the surface of sea water
is not smooth, observed reflection values differ from the
calculated values. At sun elevations greater than 40°, less
than 5% of the incoming radiation is reflected; at lower
elevations, typical of polar regions, the reflection increases
markedly. When seas are running high, major foam areas
develop with concomitant increasing reflectivity, and as much
as 40% of the incoming radiation can be reflected.[16] Finally,
as noted earlier, the incoming radiation depends on the altitude of the sun, the time of day, the season, the geographical
latitude, and the atmospheric conditions (including the
extent of pollution and cloudiness).

Refraction of the nonreflected light favors penetration to
a certain depth because the light beam is bent toward the

vertical and the light path is shortened. The dependence of refraction on salinity forms the basis of a salinity determination (Vol. 1, Chap. 6).

Extinction. After radiation penetrates into the ocean, it is scattered; a small fraction radiates back as diffuse underlight, part is absorbed and converted into heat or chemical energy.

The color of the ocean, or more technically, color impression seen by an observer, is mainly determined by the diffuse underlight. Sea water which has been carefully filtered is a deep blue, which is truly the "desert" or barren color of sea water. The color of sea water may differ from this color for several reasons, including the following[15]:

1. The presence of certain yellow-colored organic substances, collectively called humic acids, results in a green color. These materials are dissolved and light scattering by particulate matter may be negligible.

2. The effect of light scattering by particulate matter depends upon the size of the particles; as the size increases the intensity of the blue coloration diminishes because the scattered light is white. The larger particles may be colored, and color reflection as well as selective absorption of radiation become factors in determining the color of the water.

3. Plankton "blooms" or dense concentrations in sea water
   give rise to discoloration of water. Often these outbreaks occur with such regularity as to cause the seas to
   be named for the color of the plankton species. The Red

   Sea and the Gulf of California (formerly the Vermillion

   Sea) are examples of this.

The absorption of light by sea water is of interest for
several reasons.

First, many constituents are determined by colorimetric
methods (Vol. 1, Chapter 8). The absorption of distilled water
and of well-filtered sea water are the same above 6000 $\overset{o}{A}$, but
in the visible region sea water has a maximum and a minimum absorption. Figure 1-7 shows the percent transmittance of a
1-meter length of water at various wavelengths in comparison
with a visible spectrum color chart. In effect, sea water is
blue because there is absorption of light in visible regions
other than blue.

Secondly, the photosynthetic process and primary production depend upon the availability of light of a suitable
wavelength and intensity, as well as the photosynthetic action
of a plant.[17] About 10% of the incoming radiation power has
a blue-green component. Of the rest, about 5-8% is reflected,
about 50% is infrared radiation (and is

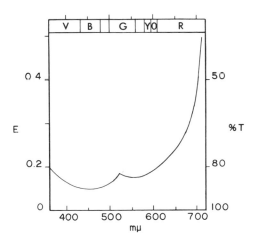

FIG. 1-7

Extinction E (and percent transmittance, % T), as a function
of wavelength for a filtered 1-meter length of sea water. A
color absorption chart is included for comparison.

absorbed strongly in the first meter of sea water), and about

20% is an ultraviolet component which may penetrate

some tens of meters (if no humic acids are present). The

narrow blue-green band of light may penetrate a few hundreds

of meters.

Thirdly, the penetration of blue-green light permits

visibility, which is important to most predators in the sea.

1.7 Salinity

The saltness or salinity is perhaps the most notable property of sea water from a chemist's viewpoint. Salinity is a
consequence of the interaction of the atmosphere and sea water
and the earth's crust. The nature of this interaction is explored in more detail in Chapter 4. For the moment, it is
appropriate to review certain terminology and concepts related
to salinity.

From a practical standpoint, it is useful to define two
groups of constituents based on a generally accepted boundary
concentration of 1 mg/kg of sea water (1 ppm). There are
eleven main constituents (Table 1-2) and the rest are trace
constituents. The concentrations of the trace constituents
are subject to relatively large changes, usually because of
biological processes. The concentrations of the main constituents generally are not subject to major relative changes and
this has led to the concept of constant composition (Vol. 1,
Chapter 1). For historical reasons, there have been at least
four definitions of salinity.[18]

Salinity (I) was the first definition based on total
salts (Forch, Knudsen, and Sorensen, 1902):

"the total amount of solid matter in grams contained

in one kilogram of sea water when all the carbonate has

been converted to oxide, all the bromine and iodine

PHYSICAL AND CHEMICAL PROPERTIES OF SEA WATER

TABLE 1-2

Major Constituents of Sea Water

Constituent	Concentration[a]		
		C	
	g/kg sea	moles/liter	logC
Water		54.90	1.74
Chloride	19.353	0.5483	-0.26
Sodium	10.76	0.47015	-0.33
Sulfate	2.712	0.02824	-1.55
Magnesium	1.294	0.05357	-1.27
Calcium	0.413	0.01024	-1.99
Potassium	0.387	0.00996	-2.00
Bicarbonate	0.142	0.00234	-2.63
Bromide	0.067	0.00083	-3.08
Strontium	0.0080	0.0015	-3.82
Boron	0.0045	0.00043	-3.37
Fluoride	0.001	0.00007	-4.15

[a]For water of salinity $35^\circ/oo$

    replaced by chlorine and all of the organic matter

    oxidized."

This definition reflects the experimental difficulties of

determining salinity directly by weighing ignited salts re-

maining after evaporation. The major difficulty is the fact

that hydrated magnesium chloride undergoes hydrolysis and

forms magnesium oxide and gaseous hydrogen chloride. This

difficulty can be overcome: Morris and Riley[19] devised a

method for direct gravimetric determination of salinity; the results were within 0.015% of the results obtained by conductivity or titration.

Salinity (II), also an empirical relationship, associates salinity (I) and chlorinity (as estimated by the Knudsen titration; Vol. 1, Chapter 5). Salinity (II) is defined by the relationship (Eqn. 1-6).

$$\text{Salinity (II)} \; = \; 0.03 \; + \; 1.805 \; \times \; \text{chlorinity} \qquad (1\text{-}6)$$

Most of the salinity data prior to 1960 conforms to this definition. The chlorinity was defined (Jacobsen and Knudson, 1940)[18] in terms of a permanent silver standard as "the number giving the mass with unit gram of 'atomsewichtssilber' just necessary to precipitate the halogens in 0.3285234 kg of sea water sample." On the basis of this definition, there was no need to revise chlorinity values with each new evaluation of atomic weights. On the other hand, there is some objection to the "salinity constant," 0.03. This value is the salinity of the diluting river water (Baltic rivers in the original definition) and this salinity varies with location.

Salinity (IIA) was proposed to overcome the objections to the salinity constant (Eqn. 1-7).

$$\text{Salinity (IIA)} \; = \; 1.80655 \; \times \; \text{chlorinity} \qquad (1\text{-}7)$$

The constant is eliminated, and the effect ($\pm 0.004^{\circ}/oo$) on salinities in the range $30\text{-}40^{\circ}/oo$ would not be detected in typical determinations. Also, there would be no effect on densities calculated from Knudsen's tables.

Salinity (III) and Salinity (IV) are definitions based on the salinity-conductivity relationship using older (1934) or more recent (1962) data, respectively. These definitions reflect improvements in the techniques for measuring the conductance of sea water precisely. Probably, future water standards will be defined in terms of chlorinity as well as conductivity.

The methods used to determine salinity have been summarized earlier (Vol. 1, Chap. 6) and Johnston[18] and Cox[10] have discussed the instrumentation and techniques in more detail. While the value of salinity is certainly of interest, the variation of salinity is of more interest, as we shall see in the next section.

1.8 Salinity Distribution

The trends and variations in the distribution of salinity are of interest for two major reasons: (1) as an indication of physical processes involved and movement of water masses (Chapter 2); (2) because of the effects of salinity on marine and brackish water invertebrates and fishes (cf. Kinne[20]) and other organisms.

For example, the salinity growth curve for Gonyaulax tamarensis (Fig. 1-8) has an optimum near 20°/oo and a tolerance range of 7-40°/oo.[21] This dinoflagellate is associated with paralytic shellfish poisoning on the Atlantic coast of Canada and is obviously able to exist in estuaries with reduced salinity. In contrast, Gymnodinium breve, a toxigenic

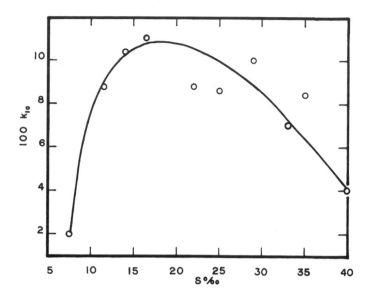

FIG. 1-8

Growth constant, $\underline{k}$ (Eqn. 9-6), as a function of salinity for <u>Gonyaulax</u> <u>tamarensis</u> (after Prakash[21]).

dinoflagellate found in Gulf of Mexico coastal waters, has an optimum salinity of about $34^{\circ}/oo$, and a narrower salinity tolerance. Evidently, this organism is prevented from causing shellfish poisoning by an ecological factor, the salinity tolerance.[22]

Variations in the salinity distribution can be understood in terms of the oceanic water budget.[16] There are certain constant values (typical of a steady-state approximation): the total volume of water, the total amount of dissolved salts, and the average salinity $(35^{\circ}/oo)$. The vertical and horizontal

variations in salinity are due to the incursion of physical
processes in local areas: removal of water (through evaporation
or freezing) increases the salinity at the surface; addition of
water (precipitation, river discharge, and ice melting) decreases the salinity. Differences in salinity areas from these
processes are reduced by mixing.

The oceanic water budget is summarized by the relationship (Eqn. 1-8):

$$W_e = (E - P) + (F - M) + (G - L) + R \quad (1-8)$$

Here, $\underline{W}$ is the total water exchange. The first term (Eqn. 1-8)
represents the exchange between the atmosphere and the ocean,
i.e., the difference between evaporation $\underline{E}$ and precipitation $\underline{P}$. The second term represents the gain or loss due to
ice formation $\underline{F}$ or melting $\underline{M}$. The third term represents the
contribution by currents as a gain $\underline{G}$ or a loss $\underline{L}$. The last
term represents the total river discharge from the continents
(about 27,000 km^3/year).

Zonal distribution

The large-scale distribution of salinity is governed by
the value of the first term, because the second and third
terms are zero for large areas, and the value of R is small relative to the first term. The latitudinal zone distribution
curve (salinity as a function of latitude, Fig. 1-9) shows
minimum surface salinities with equatorial and high latitudinal zones where precipitation is in excess. Maximum surface

31

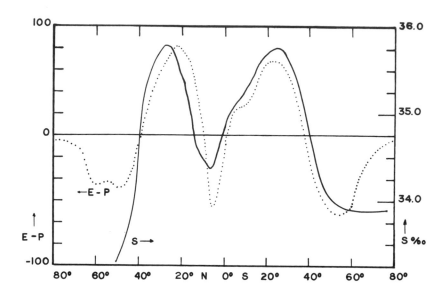

FIG. 1-9

Zonal distribution in the annual mean of evaporation (E)-
precipitation (P) in centimeters per year and salinity at
the ocean surface, including the marginal seas. (After
Dietrich.[16])

salinities are found in subtropical zones where evaporation is

in excess. The good correlation between (P - E) and salinity

may be seen from a comparison of the two quantities at various

latitudes (Fig. 1-9).

Obviously, the second, third, and fourth terms of the

water exchange equation (1-8) become significant under differ-

ent conditions.

1.   The second term becomes significant in understanding

surface salinities of subpolar regions.

2. The third term becomes significant in understanding the
    greater salinities of the Atlantic vis-à-vis those of
    the Pacific Ocean. The high salinity of the Mediter-
    ranean represents one contributing factor; salt transport
    by currents in and contiguous with the Atlantic is
    another.

3. The fourth term becomes significant in understanding the
    lower salinities of the Baltic.

Vertical Distribution[16]

There is good evidence that zooplankton aggregate at
salinity or temperature interfaces and that such interfaces
may be preferential sites for certain marine organisms.[23]
Whether this effect is a salinity effect or related to thermal
"kinks" (Section 1.2) is unknown at this time, though the
question will undoubtedly be the subject of future research.

The vertical distribution of salinity is more complex
than surface distribution, but some general trends may be
suggested. Even though the temperature of sea water usually
decreases with depth, the salinity of the water may increase
in order to maintain stable density strata, though this is not
a requirement.

Thus, the halocline, or well-defined change of salinity
with depth, is usually positive.

This situation is observed in the North Atlantic Ocean,
though high salinity water from the Mediterranean intrudes at

considerable depth and causes complexities in the salinity distribution.

The vertical salinity distribution in three other areas (North and South Pacific, South Atlantic) is characterized by an intermediate salinity minimum. For example, this layer (S, 34.2-34.6^o/oo) is encountered at about 700-800 m over the entire width of the Atlantic between about 20°N and 40°S. South of 40°S, the depth of the intermediate layer decreases and ultimately approaches the surface near the polar front. A similar, though less pronounced, pattern is observed for the North and South Pacific. The pattern occurs because the intermediate layer water originates at high latitudes, where the salinity is low, and passes through high-salinity surface and bottom layers at middle and low latitudes.

1.9 Summary

These, then, are some of the significant physical and chemical properties of sea water. These properties are a consequence of the unique features of water substance (due to its molecular structure and the existence of hydrogen bonding) and the chemical composition of sea water.

It is logical to inquire as to how sea water arrived at the present chemical composition; which seems to have remained constant for a long time (Chapter 3). In subsequent chapters, we shall examine the nature of certain cyclic processes, such as the nutrient cycles. Final chapters will be concerned with the implications and applications of the more theoretical chapters.

We may anticipate a consideration of these topics by noting two important subjects that demand prior consideration: mixing processes in the marine environment (Chapter 2) and energy flow in the marine ecosystem.

NOTES

1. The heat of fusion is the amount of heat needed to convert a given weight of substance from solid to liquid at the normal melting point. The heat of vaporization is the amount of heat needed to convert a given weight of substance from liquid to vapor at the normal boiling point.

2. The dielectric constant is the ratio of the capacitance of a condensor in a medium to the capacitance of the same condensor in air.

3. Many biological implications have been discussed by Drost-Hansen;[24] additional implications will be described in future communications by W. Drost-Hansen and A. Thorhaug.

4. The design represented in Fig. 1-6 is called the Plimsoll line or Plimsoll's mark, named for Samuel Plimsoll (1824-1898). In about 1875, he was able to persuade the British Parliament to pass a law forcing the marking of ships to

the load limit. Prior to this law, many English ships went to sea dangerously overloaded and some were over-insured.

A ship can be loaded to the line marked TF when in tropical fresh water; to T in tropical zones; to F in nontropical fresh water; to S in summer; to W in winter; to WNA in the winter in the North Atlantic. The circular symbol indicates that the marking is in accordance with the rules of the American Bureau of Shipping.

5. One bar is equal to 10^6 dyn/cm^2 or 0.987 atm. The practical unit is a decibar, db (= 0.1 bar). The depth in meters and the pressure in decibars are numerically the same.

REFERENCES

1. G. C. Pimentel and A. L. McClellan, The Hydrogen Bond, Freeman, San Francisco, 1960.

2. W. Drost-Hansen, Adv. Chem. Ser., 67, 70 (1967).

3. L. Korson, W. Drost-Hansen, and F. J. Millero, J. Phys. Chem., 73, 34 (1969).

4. C. B. Davey, R. J. Miller, and L. A. Nelson, J. Bacteriol., 91, 1827 (1966).

5. T. F. Wall and D. F. Hornig, J. Chem. Phys., 43, 2079 (1965).

6. M. D. Danford and H. A. Levy, J. Am. Chem. Soc., 84, 3965 (1962).

7. G. Nemethy and G. H. Scheraga, J. Chem. Phys., **36**, 3382 (1962).

8. H. S. Frank and A. S. Quist, J. Chem. Phys., **31**, 1086 (1959).

9. R. A. Cox, M. J. McCartney, and F. Culkin, Deep-Sea Res., **15**, 319 (1968).

10. R. A. Cox in Chemical Oceanography (J. P. Riley and G. Skirrow, eds.), Vol. 1, Academic Press, New York, 1965, Chap. 3.

11. E. L. Bialek, Handbook of Oceanographic Tables, SP-68, U. S. Government Printing Office, Washington, D. C., 1966.

12. M. Newton and G. Kennedy, J. Mar. Res., **23**, 88 (1965).

13. W. Wilson and D. Bradley, Deep-Sea Res., **15**, 355 (1968).

14. F. J. Millero and W. Drost-Hansen, J. Phys. Chem., **72**, 1758 (1968).

15. N. G. Jerlov, Optical Oceanography, Elsevier, Amsterdam, 1968.

16. G. Dietrich, General Oceanography, Wiley-Interscience, New York, 1963.

17. cf. R. C. Smith, Limnol. Oceanogr., **13**, 423 (1968).

18. R. Johnston, Oceanog. Mar. Biol. Ann. Rev., **2**, 97 (1964); W. S. Wooster, A. J. Lee, G. Dietrich, Limnol. Oceanog., **14**, 437 (1969).

19. A. W. Morris and J. P. Riley, Deep-Sea Res., **11**, 899 (1964).

20. O. Kinne, Oceanog. Mar. Biol. Ann. Rev., **2**, 281 (1964).

21. A. Prakash, J. Fish. Res. Bd. Canada, **24**, 1589 (1967).

22. S. M. Ray and D. V. Aldrich in Toxic Animals (F. E. Russell and P. R. Saunders, eds.), Pergamon, Oxford, 1967, p. 75.

23. W. Harder, Limnol. Oceanog., **13**, 156 (1968).

24. W. Drost-Hansen, New York Acad. Sci., Annals, Conf. Monographs, **125** (Art. 2), 471 (1965).

MIXING PROCESSES

IN THE MARINE ENVIRONMENT

2.1 Introduction

The combination of diverse physical processes that
assists mixing in the marine environment has great significance. These processes contribute to maintenance of the gross
constancies of the environment - the constancy of chemical
composition (of the major constituents), the limited temperature range, the constancy of the pH (Chapter 4), the constancy
of buffer action (Chapter 4), and even the constancy of the
nutrient cycles (Chapters 5-7).

The distribution of a constituent is influenced by two
classes of physical processes, advective and diffusive. Advective processes involve large-scale movement of water masses
and include ocean currents as well as vertical movements of
water masses due to upwelling or sinking. In contrast, diffusive processes involve no overall transport of water masses
and arise from varying magnitudes of turbulent mixing, both in
horizontal and vertical planes.

The properties of the container or major oceans influence
the mixing properties and some of the gross characteristics are

summarized in Tables 2-1 and 2-2. The oceans cover 70.8% of the earth's surface and have a total surface area of 360.8 x 10^6 km^2. A detailed treatment of the properties of the oceans and a quantitative treatment of the mixing processes is given elsewhere.[1]

The mixing processes that will be reviewed here include: wave action, tidal action, turbulent mixing, and ocean currents.

2.2 Wave Action

For the sake of convenience, we may recognize four kinds of wave action due to (1) progressive surface waves, (2) internal waves, (3) so-called long waves, and (4) standing waves. Before considering these, it would be useful to review the characteristics of waves. The general physical laws may be applied to ocean waves, though it is obvious from looking at typical waves that the treatment has limitations.

TABLE 2-1[2]

Surface as a Function of Depth

Zone	Depth, meters	% of Earth Surface
Continental shelf	0-200	7.6 x 70.8
	200-2000	8.5 x 70.8
	2000	83.9 x 70.8
All oceans and seas		70.8

MIXING PROCESSES IN THE MARINE ENVIRONMENT

TABLE 2-2

Characteristics of Major Oceans[2]

Ocean[a]	Area, 10^6 km^2	Volume, 10^{21} liters	Mean Depth, m	Maximum Depth, m
Atlantic	106.2	0.3535	3331	8526
Indian	74.9	0.291	3897	7450
Pacific	179.7	0.7237	4028	11034
All	360.8	1.3691	3795	11034

[a]Includes adjacent seas.

A wave is a progressive vibrational disturbance propagated through a medium without forward movement of individual particles. There are three significant properties of a wave. First, it is a detectable disturbance in space and time. Secondly, the transport of energy is associated with wave motion. Thirdly, it is a periodic disturbance that can be characterized by four parameters: wave length, height and amplitude, period, and velocity. These may be defined in terms of a representation of an ideal oceanic progressive wave (Fig. 2-1).

Wave length, L, is the distance between any two corresponding points, and in the open sea wave lengths exceeding 100 m have been noted.

Wave height, H, probably has been typically overestimated. According to careful observers of wave action,[3] the height

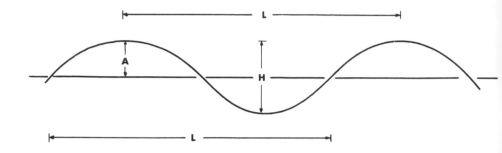

FIG. 2-1

Representation of an ideal progressive oceanic wave.

commonly observed for large waves is typically 2-4 m and does not exceed 12 m. (In exceptional storms or in hurricanes or typhoons, probably wave heights of 25 m might be observed, though the circumstances may limit objectivity.) The energy of the wave is related to the wave's length and height. Smaller waves cannot absorb much energy, and a wave tends to break when its height-wavelength ratio approaches 1:7.

Amplitude, A, is the distance from an equilibrium position (flat water) to the maximum or minimum and is a measure of the (mainly potential) energy of the system. For a symmetric wave, the amplitude is one-half the wave height.

The wave period, T, corresponds to the time required for one complete cycle to occur. The frequency of the wave is equal to the reciprocal of the wave period.

MIXING PROCESSES IN THE MARINE ENVIRONMENT

Wave velocity, c, is equal to the wave length divided by the wave period. Surface velocities can exceed values of 250 cm/sec.

These parameters can be computed (Eqn. 2-1 to 2-6) approximately when the amplitude is small with respect to the length.

$$\text{Wave length, L} \quad = \quad \frac{2\pi c^2}{g} \qquad (2\text{-}1)$$
$$\text{(in meters)}$$
$$= \quad \frac{gT^2}{2\pi} \qquad (2\text{-}2)$$

$$\text{Wave period, T} \quad = \quad \frac{2\, L^{\frac{1}{2}}}{g} \qquad (2\text{-}3)$$
$$\text{(in sec)}$$
$$= \quad \frac{2\pi c}{g} \qquad (2\text{-}4)$$

$$\text{Wave velocity, c} \quad = \quad \frac{(gL)^{\frac{1}{2}}}{2\pi} \qquad (2\text{-}5)$$
$$\text{(in m/sec)}$$
$$= \quad \frac{(gT)^{\frac{1}{2}}}{2\pi} \qquad (2\text{-}6)$$

where g is the acceleration of gravity (9.8067 m/sec^2). The agreement between calculated and reported values is good (Table 2-3). With this background in mind, it is appropriate to consider the mixing effects of four kinds of waves.

43

TABLE 2-3

Observed and Computed Values of Velocities,

Lengths, and Periods of Surface Waves[3]

	Wave Velocity, m/sec			Wave Length, m			Wave Period, sec		
	Ob-served	Computed from Eqn. 2-5	Eqn. 2-6	Ob-served	Computed from Eqn. 2-1	Eqn. 2-2	Ob-served	Computed from Eqn. 2-3	Eqn. 2-4
Atlantic Ocean; Trade Wind region	11.2	10.8	10.5	65	70	61	5.8	6.0	6.2
Indian Ocean; Trade Wind region	12.6	13.1	13.7	96	88	104	7.6	7.3	6.9
S. Atlantic Ocean, West Wind region	14.0	15.5	17.1	133	109	163	9.5	8.6	7.8

Progressive oceanic surface waves[4] have wave lengths which

are extremely short relative to the depth of water (Note 1).

The important consideration is the extent of displacement of

individual particles at a given depth in the surface wave.

The particles move in an appropriately circular path and the

extent of displacement may be described in terms of the radius

of the circular orbit (Fig. 2-2). The radius of this orbit

decreases rapidly with depth as does the velocity of indivi-

dual particles. Roughly speaking, at a depth corresponding to

one wave length, the motion of individual particles would be

imperceptible (as seems to be the experience of submariners).

Most of the oceanic waves should have a wave period of less

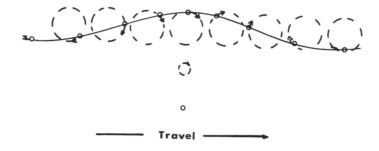

Travel →

FIG. 2-2

Representation of orbital displacement of water molecules in
a progressive wave. Orbital diameter decreases with depth.

than 10 sec, and motion of particles would be imperceptible

at 100 m. (For pertinent calculations, see Sverdrup et al.[3])

However, mixing at considerable depths is provided by internal

waves.

Internal waves are undulating waves that form between

subsurface water layers of differing density.[5] The density

differences may be caused by temperature differences, as in

fresh-water lakes, or by temperature and/or salinity differ-

ences, as in the sea. The displacement of the internal waves

may be greater than surface waves, though the wave velocity is

less. Displacements can be 50 m or more.

There are a number of causative factors, including melting

water in polar regions, large-scale water discharge, water flow

impinging on an obstruction such as a continental shelf, vari-

ations in atmospheric pressure, and strong winds.

Internal waves can be detected by a variety of methods. These include aerial photography, temperature-sensing units (using thermistor beads), dye markers, and sound transmission methods.[5] These waves are important because they affect oxygen and nutrient transport and mixing at considerable depth in ocean waters. For example, Emery[6] provided evidence indicating the existence of standing internal waves in a deep basin near Southern California. In this instance, the waves appeared to have an amplitude of 130-200 m and existed at 1000 m.

"Long" waves arise when the depth of water is not great with respect to the wave length, as would be true in coastal waters. As a surface wave rapidly approaches the shore, particles no longer move in a circular motion and the velocity of particles near the bottom of the orbit is retarded relative to that at the top. As a result, the orbit becomes increasingly elliptical and ultimately the wave becomes unstable and "breaks" on the shore.

There are several consequences of the tremendous disturbances of water masses due to the "long" wave. The shallow waters become thermally homogeneous and the tendency toward stable layering of waters is minimal. The agitation of the water mass obviously aids oxygen, nutrient, and possibly food transport. On the other hand, agitation may cause movement of sediment and result in abrasion of organisms as well as increased turbidity and decreased photosynthesis. In addition, these waves also have a tendency to produce <u>long shore</u>

<u>currents</u> which run parallel to the shoreline and which can

cause sediment transport, beach erosion, and buildup.

<u>Standing waves</u>[3] or <u>seiches</u> typically occur in lakes and

bays and are significant because they assist in mixing water

layers and suspending particulate matter. Relatively little

energy (e.g., from minor periodical variations in barometric

pressure) is needed to maintain seiches that may be regarded

as the result of two progressive waves that pass in opposite

directions and interact (Fig. 2-3).

2.3 <u>Tidal Action</u>

Tide is the periodic vertical rise and fall of sea water

due to the attractive forces of (mainly) the moon and sun upon

different parts of the earth (Note 2). A tidal current (or

tidal stream) is a horizontal movement of the water which

accompanies a tide.

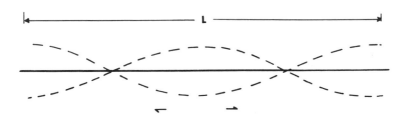

FIG. 2-3

Representation of a standing wave.

The timing of the tides is closely identified with the motions of the moon because the tide-producing force of the moon is about 2.2 times that of the sun, and the general effect may be seen in a simplified representation (Fig. 2-4). Consider only the moon-earth system for the moment, with the moon exactly over the equator. It is apparent that the tide-producing forces are in the direction of centrifugal force in the hemisphere opposite the moon and are in the direction of gravitational force in the hemisphere near the moon. As a result, high tides occur on the sides nearest to and furthest

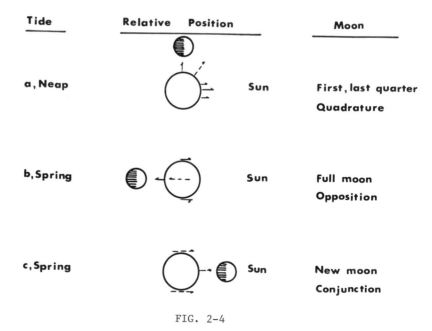

FIG. 2-4

Representation of a tide cycle, showing relative positions of moon, sun, Earth. (Dashed line indicates net force.)

from the moon and low tides occur in the intermediate areas.
As the earth rotates every location should experience a semidiurnal type of tide, i.e., two high tides and two low tides.
This is not the case because the tidal pattern is a function
of the declination of the moon, the relative position of the
sun, and the nature of the basin. The last factor is particularly significant and gives rise to the truism that one cannot predict the tidal pattern of the future for a location for
which the tidal pattern of the past is unknown.

There are three classes of tides (at a given location):
semidiurnal, diurnal, and mixed (Fig. 2-5). The semidiurnal

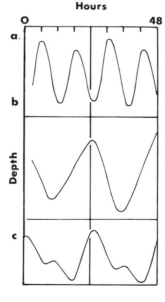

FIG. 2-5

Representation of classes of tides: a, semidiurnal;
b, diurnal; and c, mixed.[7]

type uniformly has two high and two low tides in a given tidal day; an example is Boston Harbor. The diurnal type has only one high and one low tide each tidal day; examples are found in the Java Sea, the Gulf of Tonkin, Pakoi, China,and locations in the northern Gulf of Mexico. The mixed type usually has two high and two low tides, though the tide may become diurnal, but there may be large inequalities in the heights of high and low waters. Examples are the tides at Tampa Bay, Los Angeles, Honolulu, and Seattle. The type of tidal current corresponds largely to the type of tide at a given location.

It is also useful to classify the ranges of tidal variation within the lunar month (29.53 days). The ranges can be correlated with the relative positions of the earth, moon, and sun.

The spring tides occur throughout the year during new moon and full moon when the sun and moon are aligned (Fig. 2-4 b,c). Smaller neap (from the Anglo-Saxon nep, small) tides occur during the quadratures (first, last quarter) when the tide-producing effects of the sun and moon oppose each other. Perigean tides occur when the moon is nearest to the earth and the semidiurnal range increases. Apogean tides occur when the moon is farthest from the earth.

Details of tidal cycles and tidal predictions are given elsewhere.[3,7] Specific data concerning tides and tidal currents are issued annually by various governments.

MIXING PROCESSES IN THE MARINE ENVIRONMENT

There are two major effects of tidal action, biological and physical. The former includes biological clock effects (feeding, mating, and general movement cycles) due to tidal rhythms, and the latter includes a range of effects such as alteration of the shoreline, reduction of the earth's rotation and revolution, speed, and, of course, mixing of water masses. The mixing influence of tides varies considerably with location, and the open oceans and narrow sounds represent two extreme cases.

The gross circulation pattern of the major oceans is not of tidal origin. The cyclic nature of tidal movement precludes any _net_ transport of water. On the other hand, regular tidal currents, which occur everywhere in the oceans at all depths, contribute to a breakdown of stratification. The mixing results more from the turbulence associated with tidal currents than from the current velocities, which seldom exceed 10 cm/sec and are often only 2 or 3 cm/sec.[2]

2.4 Turbulent Mixing or Eddy Diffusion[2,8]

Even in the laboratory, it is impossible to achieve perfect laminar flow, i.e., water layers moving at a uniform velocity in an orderly manner without local fluctuations of velocity or turbulence. If laminar flow of water occurred in the sea, the exchange of nutrients would be extremely slow as it would depend upon molecular diffusion.

In the oceans, the flow of water is nonlaminar because of the large scale of motions, and turbulent movements or "eddies" occur. Turbulent mixing or eddy diffusion is important as a transport mechanism because the rate of transference of a substance is vastly greater than molecular diffusion. There is a wide spectrum of turbulent motion (up to 100 km in diameter), and it is not a totally random process.

Turbulent mixing in vertical and horizontal planes differs substantially because of two factors: the large width-to-depth ratio and the existence of stable density gradients. The latter factor strongly inhibits vertical but not horizontal turbulence.

Turbulent mixing in the vertical plane arises from three processes:

1. wind stress on the surface layer acts through wave motion;
2. the action of bottom friction on currents results in a vertical shear;
3. horizontal pressure gradients cause vertical shear in currents.

Turbulent mixing in the horizontal plane arises from three causes:

1. wind stress on the surface layers has horizontal variations;
2. lateral stresses occur at coastal boundaries;

3.   horizontal shear occurs in currents or between adjacent

currents.

2.5   Ocean Currents

    Ocean currents represent the most important mixing force

yet considered because they are responsible for the ponderous

circulation of the oceans. The volumes of water transported

by these currents is fantastically great. For instance, the

Gulf Stream attains the greatest volume near Chesapeake Bay

where the flow is about 70 million m^3/sec, or roughly 80 times

the flow of all world streams. Currents such as the Gulf

Stream exert a marked influence on the climate of coastal

regions along which they pass. For example, the climate of

Great Britain and even Iceland is much milder than if there

were no Gulf Stream. Surface currents affect the pressure

pattern, evaporation rates, and the life of the surrounding

waters (Note 3).

    An ocean current is a well-defined mass of water with

essentially horizontal motion over an extensive region. The

direction toward which the current moves is called the set and

the velocity is often called the drift. A permanent oceanic

current undergoes little gross periodic or seasonal change;   a

seasonal current undergoes substantial gross changes in set or

drift because of seasonal winds (Note 4).

The principal generating forces of ocean currents are wind and density differences. Significant factors in the pattern of ocean currents include depth, underwater topography, extent and placement of land masses, and deflection by the earth's rotation (coriolis force). It is convenient to consider two types of currents, wind-driven and density, before looking at the measurement of oceanic currents.

Wind currents. These arise from the stress of wind blowing across the surface layer of water, which induces movement of successive layers of water, the velocity of movement decreasing with depth. It is assumed that primary generating force is due to the presence of small ripples on the water surface rather than large waves. Generally speaking, a wind current requires a steady wind of about 12 hours duration.

In the open oceans, the surface water does not flow in the direction of the prevailing wind but at an angle because of the coriolis force (Note 5). Ideally, the surface current should flow at a maximum deflection angle of 45° to the direction of prevailing wind -to the right in the northern hemisphere, to the left in the southern hemisphere. The angle of deflection should increase with depth in a spiral fashion (the Ekman spiral, Note 6), and at a depth of about 60 m the set should be reversed 180°. This view is based on a theory proposed by S. Ekman in 1905 to rationalize the deviation of ice movements with wind direction.

The increased deviation should arise because of two effects. First, the effect of the wind force decreases with
depth and the current velocity should, ideally, decrease loga-
rithmically with depth. Secondly, the deflection, due to the
coriolis force, should increase with depth because the water
velocity will decrease as the depth increases. In reality, the
density of the water is not constant with depth and the coefficient of eddy diffusion also varies with depth. As a result,
the surface currents tend to deviate by 15-20° from the wind
direction, and the spiral relationship has a general validity
to a depth of 100-200 m.

If the surface currents are wind-driven, it should be
possible to rationalize the gross features in terms of the
prevailing winds.[10] That this is generally true will be seen
in a review of the general patterns of surface ocean currents.

General patterns of surface currents. These may be seen from
a climatic-type presentation (Fig. 2-6). These wind-driven
currents should be influenced by the prevailing winds, by the
geography of the bordering land masses, and by the coriolis
force. Certain general patterns seem to emerge.

1. There is a general clockwise circulation pattern (gyral
    or gyres) in the northern hemisphere (North Atlantic and
    North Pacific) and a counterclockwise pattern in the
    southern hemisphere (South Atlantic, South Pacific, and
    Indian Oceans). The South Pacific gyral, for example, is

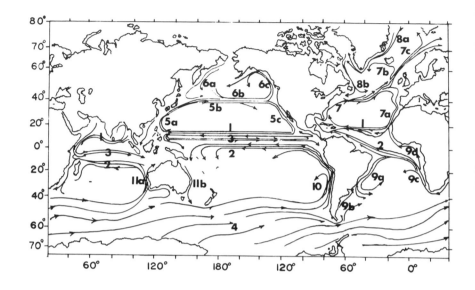

FIG. 2-6

Average surface currents of the world's oceans. (After
Williams[9]). 1, North Equatorial; 2, South Equatorial;
3, Equatorial Countercurrent; 4, West Wind Drift; 5a,
Kuroshio; 5b, North Pacific; 5c, California; 6a, Oyashio;
6b, Subarctic; 6c, Alaska; 7, Gulf Stream System; 7a,
Canary; 7b, Irminger; 7c, Norway; 8a, E. Greenland; 8b,
Labrador; 9a, Brazil; 9b, Falkland; 9c, Benguela; 9d,
Guinea; 10, Peru; 11a, W. Australia; 11b, E. Australia.

composed of the following currents: South Equatorial,

Peru, East Australia,and West Wind Drift.

2.   The major gyrals have westward intensification in all

major oceans,which can be rationalized in terms of the

coriolis force and the wind structure.[10,11] The centers

of the gyrals are displaced to the west, and the western

boundary currents tend to be narrower and faster than the
corresponding eastern boundary currents.

3. The wind structure has a number of separate systems.
    These may be represented in a highly idealized form (Fig.
    2-7). First, there is a group of easterly winds, called
    the Trades, north and south of the equator (20°N-20°S).
    Secondly, prevailing westerly winds occur at latitudes
    between roughly 40°-60° both in the northern and southern

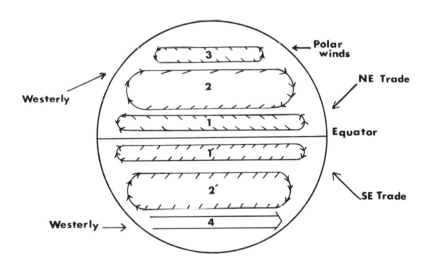

FIG. 2-7

Highly idealized representation of prevaling winds and
effects on surface currents in a hypothetical ocean:
1 and 1', north and south tropical gyral; 2 and 2', north
and south subtropical gyral; 3, north subpolar gyral;
and 4, antarctic or circumpolar current.

hemispheres. Finally, the easterly polar winds are found
just south of the Arctic Ocean.

4.   At the region of the comparatively light winds of the
      equatorial low, equatorial countercurrents are set up.

5.   The three southern oceans (South Atlantic and Pacific,
      Indian Oceans) border on a circumpolar current, the West
      Wind Drift, which is largely a closed circulation.

Density currents. These currents and the deep circulation of
the oceans result in part from the wind stress and in the main
from those factors or processes that lead to a change in
density. These factors include the gross temperature differences between the poles and the equator, the excess of evaporation near the equator, and an excess of precipitation near
the poles (Fig.1-9). As Wyrtki noted, the role of winds in
relation to the general circulation in the oceans probably has
been overemphasized.[12] At the same time, it is probably true
that winds have an indirect influence that extends beyond the
100-200 m Ekman layer and that they do induce vertical motion.
Wyrtki[12] has presented a four-layer model of wind-driven and
thermohaline circulation which is in general agreement with the
circulation pattern resulting from water mass analysis. According to this model,[11] the circulation must occur in a meridional plane between two thermal regions - heating in the low
latitudes, cooling in the high latitudes. It was assumed that

there are four major processes involved in the circulation
pattern (Fig. 2-8).

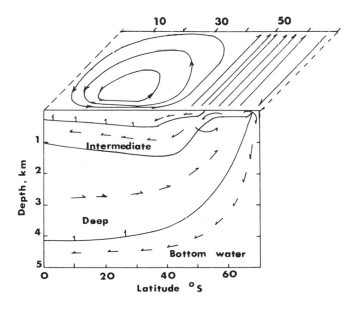

FIG. 2-8

Four-layer model of circulation in meridional plane
and surface in southern hemisphere ocean. (Vertical
exaggeration 1:1100. After Wyrtki.[12])

1. Heating and surface spreading: water at the surface layer
   is heated and spreads poleward.

2. Sinking: densest water at the highest latitude sinks and
   forms a deep layer.

3. Deep spreading: water in the deep layer spreads toward
   the equator.

4.   Ascending: deep water ascends through the thermocline
      into the surface layer.

The deep-sea circulation of the Atlantic Ocean is more
active than that of the Indian and Pacific Oceans for three
reasons. First, most of the important centers of thermohaline
convection exist in the Atlantic. Secondly, the South American
continent is a barrier that forces large volumes of surface
water from the South Atlantic surface currents into the North
Atlantic. Finally, the large volume of surface water lost from
the South Atlantic is compensated by North Atlantic deep water
which flows southward into the South Atlantic. On the way
south, the deep water receives a contribution from highly
saline Mediterranean water. The volume of the latter may be
small but the salinity contribution is significant.

Measurement of currents.[13] Probably more instruments and devices are used for measuring ocean currents than for most
oceanic measurements. Ocean current measurements may be
divided into two categories: direct and indirect.

Direct measurements involve the assessment of the effects
of the current on (1) the drift of a free body or (2) on a
fixed body. In the past much of the data used to prepare
average surface current charts were obtained from the first
effect, specifically ships' logs. The method consisted in comparing two vector quantities - the actual distance traveled
versus the calculated distance (based on the ship course and

speed). The vector distance, corrected for the effect of wind, was ascribed to surface currents. Also, surface currents have been detected and the drift and set estimated through the drift of drift bottles, debris, marker dye, or radioactive material. The ship's log or drift method provides gross or average changes, which may be an advantage because the effects of tidal currents are averaged out. The use of marker dye or radioactive material has the advantage of showing mixture and movement in three dimensions.

Other examples of the measurement of currents by means of the drift of a free body involve the use of a self-contained instrument capsule[14] such as the Swallow-type naturally buoyant float. This device emits acoustical pings from a self-contained sound source. The device can be followed for several days as it drifts at a preselected depth; the drift can be estimated within about 0.01 km under ideal conditions.

Currents are also measured through analysis of the effect on a fixed object or by instruments. These include (1) ship-attached propeller-type meters (Ekman type), used for subsurface measurements, which record the revolutions of a propeller per unit time as well as the current direction; (2) self-contained propeller-type meters (e.g., the buoy-operated Roberts radio current meter) which telemeter data, either to the ship or to a buoy; (3) meters that use underwater cameras to record deflection of compasses, propellers, and vanes.

Indirect measurements involve (1) instrumental measurement or (2) assessments of the distribution (and movement) of water masses.

The first method uses self-contained instrument capsules. These may be anchored in specific locations or dropped to the bottom of the sea, where they can remain for a period of days to several months. At a desired time, the capsule is called to the surface by ship-transmitted acoustical command. Data may be accumulated by computer-compatible, magnetic-tape recorders located within the capsule. Current may be measured indirectly by the rate of cooling of hot wires or thermisters or by means of the GEK (geomagnetic electrokinetograph) method. The GEK is a measurement of the difference in potential difference between two separated electrodes. The potential difference results from the passage of conducting salt water through the earth's vertical magnetic field. A 1-knot current would induce a potential of about 1 mV between two electrodes 100 m apart.

The second method, assessment of subsurface flow patterns, involves tracing the distribution of salinity along lines of constant density. Temperature, salinity, and pressure must be measured at various depths in known stations along a straight line or over a grid. The details of the calculation are given elsewhere.[3] The method has been very important, though it has some serious limitations, not the least of which is the assumption that the empirical salinity-temperature-depth-density relationship is sufficiently accurate (Section 1.3).

2.6 Other Mixing Processes

Two other mixing processes, upwelling and the development of a seasonal thermocline, should be considered. It may be fairly argued that the seasonal thermocline actually constitutes a barrier to mixing. As such it is a negative mixing process until the fall and winter breakup. Nevertheless, the seasonal thermocline is involved in mixing, if only negatively, and deserves consideration here.

Upwelling. This is a process by which subsurface sea water is displaced toward the surface. Usually, the process is the result of persistent winds which blow nearly parallel to the shore. Surface water is then deflected off shore, and subsurface water upwells. Upwelling may also be caused by cyclonic gyrals and by a junction of deep and diverging currents.

Upwelling has several important characteristics, including the following:

1. Coastal upwelling is most pronounced along the western coasts of continents - California, Peru, western Australia, and regions of southern and northern Africa. On the other hand, the southwest monsoon winds during the summer cause

the coastal upwelling off the east coast of Africa (Soma-
liland) and the east coasts of India and several Southeast
Asia nations.

2.   Upwelling brings colder and denser water to the surface,
     and the water temperatures at early summer may approach
     those typical of winter. A combination of wind and
     density currents may be developed along shore. Fog may
     develop as a result of upwelling.

3.   Large quantities of nutrient-rich waters (containing
     phosphate, nitrate, etc.) are brought to the surface as a
     result of upwelling. The surface region can be very
     fertile as a result and can be economically significant
     as the enriched waters become prime fishing grounds or
     the location of giant kelp beds, to cite only two examples.

Thermocline. This has two meanings. It is a vertical negative temperature gradient (change of temperature with depth)
in a layer of water that is appreciably greater than the gradients in the overlying and underlying waters; also, it is that
layer in which the temperature decrease is greater than that
of the water above or below the layer. The principal thermo-
clines are either seasonal, due to heating surface water in
the summer, or permanent. There is, in addition, a temporary
or shallow thermocline, due to diurnal heating of the surface
waters.

MIXING PROCESSES IN THE MARINE ENVIRONMENT

The permanent thermocline is virtually unchanged seasonally and results from cold, dense, polar waters flowing toward the equator and sinking below warmer surface waters moving outward from the equator. The top of the permanent thermocline is shallow at the equator and at a high latitude (50°N, 50°S), and has a maximum depth (200 m) at midlatitude (30°N, 30°S), where it is also the thickest (ca. 1,000 m). The thermocline disappears south of 55-60°S and north of 55-60°N latitude.

The seasonal thermocline is found in surface waters except for those waters that are ice infested. There is a four-stage cycle.

1. In spring, air temperature increases and the sea gains more heat than it loses, the water warms, and the top few feet develop a negative temperature gradient (Fig. 2-9a).

2. Mixing of the surface waters occurs which reduces the temperature of the top layer somewhat but which also warms deeper water and creates an isothermal layer (Fig. 2-9b).

3. The second stage continues and the isothermal layer is transported to the maximum depth where it remains from roughly July through September (Fig. 2-9c).

4. In autumn, air temperatures fall, the water loses heat to the atmosphere through radiation and convection. The air is cooled to air temperature and ultimately the

thermocline disappears (Fig. 2-9d) until spring when the cycle begins again.

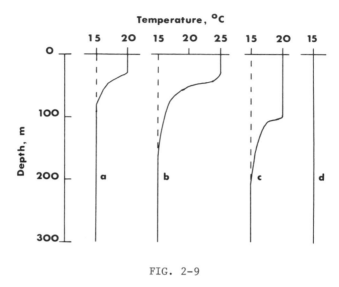

FIG. 2-9

Stages of a middle latitude seasonal thermocline cycle.

2.7 Assessment of Mixing

An assessment of the extent of mixing depends upon being able to identify water masses. This identification is based on distinctive chemical or physical properties. These properties may be conservative (temperature, chlorinity, salinity) and not change except through mixing; they may be nonconservative (dissolved oxygen, micronutrient, and radioisotope concentration) and change independently of mixing. Three examples may indicate how these properties are used to assess the extent of mixing.

Constituent-chlorinity ratio. The constituent concentration-
chlorinity ratio can be a good indication of the extent of
mixing of two different water masses, and as an indication of
the extent of incursion of other processes. For example,
Voipio[15] reported a linear relationship between silicon content
and chlorinity of surface waters in the Gulf of Bothnia
(Bothnian Bay and Sea) and the Baltic. The slope of the relationship was less than calculated from simple mixing of
silicon-rich river waters (which empty into the Gulf) and
silicon-poor sea water from the Baltic. At each chlorinity
there was a deficiency of silicon which was ascribed to removal
in primary production.

The T-S diagram.[9] This has been the standard method for
tracing water masses and assessing mixing. The T-S diagram is
a plot of temperature as a function of salinity, wherein each
point (in order of increasing depth) is connected to give a
smooth T-S curve. Next, curves showing the variation of σ_t
with temperature and depth are drawn on the T-S diagram. The
diagram (Fig. 2-10) may then be interpreted.

A water type is characterized by a unique or single value
of temperature and salinity and corresponds to a single point
on the diagram. A water mass is composed of two or more water
types, has a range of temperature-salinity values, and corresponds to a portion of the T-S curve. A straight line portion
of the T-S curve represents mixing of two water types; a curved

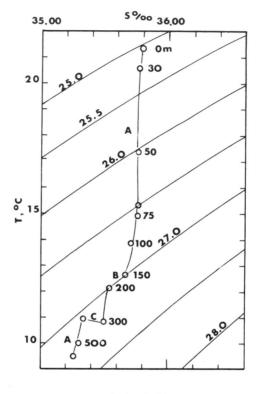

FIG. 2-10

The T-S diagram as an indication of water stability.
Portion A indicates positive stability; B, neutral;
C, negative stability.

portion of the T-S curve represents a mixing of three or more

water types.

The stability of the water column is inferred by comparing

the T-S curve with the σ_t (sigma-t) curve. Neutral stability

(Note 7) is indicated when the two curves are parallel (density

is constant with depth). Positive stability is indicated if

the T-S curve crosses the sigma-t curve in a generally down-
ward direction (i.e., density increases with depth). Negative
stability is indicated if the T-S curve crosses in a decreasing
direction as the T-S curve reverses direction and heads upward
(density decreases with depth).

Radioactive tracer studies. These studies involve either
naturally occurring isotopes or added isotopes. Two naturally
occurring radioactive isotopes which are studied are tritium,
^3_1H, and carbon-14, $^{14}_6C$. The half-life of tritium (12 years)
is so short that this isotope is of interest mainly in studying
short-term circulation.

Carbon-14 is continuously produced in the atmosphere
through the action of high-energy neutrons (formed by the
interaction of cosmic rays with nuclei) and ordinary nitrogen
nuclei (Eqn. 2-7).

$$^{14}_7N + ^1_0n \rightarrow ^{14}_6C + ^1_1H \qquad (2\text{-}7)$$

This carbon is oxidized to carbon dioxide and incorporated
into living organisms and, directly or indirectly, into sea
water. Carbon-14 is radioactive and disintegrates (Eqn. 2-8).

$$^{14}_6C \rightarrow ^{14}_7N + ^0e \qquad (2\text{-}8)$$

There are 15.3 disintegrations of $^{14}_6C$ observed per gram of contemporary carbon per minute, and the age t of a given sample
can be estimated by

$$t = \frac{2.303}{\lambda} \log_{10} \frac{15.3}{D} \qquad (2\text{-}9)$$

knowing the disintegration rate of a given sample $\underline{D}$ and a constant λ (Note 8).

The use of $^{14}_{6}C$ in estimating the mixing time and origin of water masses depends upon three assumptions: (1) that once this isotope has been incorporated into the surface layer no process introduces more; (2) that the mixing of adjacent layers is limited; and (3) that in the surface layer the $^{12}_{6}C/^{14}_{6}C$ atomic ratio is uniform everywhere. These assumptions have varying degrees of validity.

The first assumption is generally reasonable. The possibility of isotope exchange between deep layer water and sea-bed carbonate is generally regarded as negligible. On the other hand, there is a steady increase in the amount of $^{14}_{6}C$ being injected into the atmosphere because of increased burning of fossil fuels and because of nuclear bomb tests.

The second assumption is invalid unless examples are taken from the cone of a thick water mass at the edges of adjacent water layers, because turbulent mixing does occur (Section 2.4).

The third assumption has limited validity because the $^{14}_{6}C$ content of surface samples does vary, owing to upwelling and nuclear bomb tests.

The Atlantic and Antarctic bottom waters have been studied and serve as an example of the use and problems of radiocarbon analysis.

1. The core of the thick North Atlantic deep layer has been sampled and subjected to radiocarbon analysis; the results have been compared to samples from the surface water in the source region; and the average residence time is about 560 years at 30°N. In this instance, there has been no problem with mixing of adjacent layers.

2. The Antarctic bottom current, as mentioned earlier, flows northward, and this has been verified by the use of T-S diagrams. With the radiocarbon method, it appears that the current is moving slowly southward. The anomaly arises because there is considerable mixing of younger overlying water. If the effect of mixing is not considered, the water appears to grow younger down current, and, in the absence of the T-S method, it would appear to be flowing backwards.

2.8 Summary

This has been an admittedly brief review of the important mixing processes: wave action (progressive, internal, long waves, seiches), tidal action, turbulent mixing, ocean currents (both wind and density), upwelling, and the thermocline; the influence of each; and some methods for assessing the extent of mixing. A few of the consequences of mixing have been considered. One, the existence of conservative properties, is considered in more detail in Chapter 4. Another, the effect on nonconservative properties, is considered in Chapters 5-7. Both require a consideration of the flow of energy in a marine ecosystem, which is the subject of the next chapter.

NOTES

1. Waves on the surface of the sea are caused mainly by wind, though other causes are known (volcanic action, submarine, earthquakes, tides). The waves generated while the wind is blowing are termed sea, those that continue in the absence of local wind are termed swell.
    Tsunamis (tidal waves) are ocean waves produced by a sudden major-scale movement of the ocean floor or shore. The tsunamis of the Pacific may have a wave height of only 2-3 ft in deep water; the wave period varies between 15 and 60 minutes, but the average wave velocity may be 490 miles per hour.

2. The tide-generation forces are regularly distributed over the earth, but other factors (size and shape of the basin) influence the tidal pattern.

3. An example is the El Niño phenomenon which occurs near the coast of Peru when the Peru current diminishes or shifts seaward. Surface water temperatures become abnormally high, the indigenous fish die or depart, which affects fishermen and the bird population. The birds deprived of fish also depart or die. "Red Tide" outbreaks, in this

case fish-killing phenomenon, may occur as well. The secondary effects, beach and air pollution, may seem staggering.

4. The term _gross_ must be emphasized because charts of currents are really climatic charts in the sense that they represent mean conditions recorded ober a long period of time. If a current at a particular site were measured continuously, the drift would vary significantly and so would the set; the latter perhaps by as much as 180°.

5. Coriolis (Coriolis') force is named for the French mathematical physicist, who, in about 1840 was the first to show that a body moving on a rotating surface (such as the earth) would be deflected from the original path by the rotation of the surface. Any horizontal motion will undergo a deflection toward the _right_ in the northern hemisphere and toward the _left_ in the southern hemisphere. An excellent mathematical treatment may be found elsewhere.[3,9]

6. According to one view, however, the Ekman spiral is "surely one of the most discussed and least observed of all oceanic phenomena."[17]

7. If lifting of the water mass occurred, neutrally stable water would not tend to return to the original position or continue ascent in the absence of a lifting force; positively stable when raised would tend to fall back and

maybe continue to fall; neutrally stable when lifted would tend to continue the ascent. The stability (Σ) is equal to 10^{-3} $(\sigma_{t_2} - \sigma_{t_1})/(z_2 - z_1)$ where z_2 and z_1 are two different depths with corresponding σ_t values.

8. Typically, a relative value is used, $\Delta_6^{14}C$. The details and background have been summarized in an excellent review by Burton.[16]

REFERENCES

1. The Sea (M. N. Hill, ed.), Vol. 1, Interscience, New York, 1962.

2. K. F. Bowden in Chemical Oceanography (J. P. Riley and G. Skirrow, eds.), Academic Press, New York, 1965, Chapt. 2.

3. H. U. Sverdrup, M. W. Johnson, and R. H. Fleming, The Oceans, Prentice-Hall, Englewood Cliffs, New Jersey, 1942.

4. N. F. Barker and J. J. Tucker, cf. Ref. 1, Chapt. 19.

5. E. C. LaFord, cf. Ref. 1, p. 731.

6. K. O. Emery, Limnol. Oceanog., 1, 35 (1956).

7. American Practical Navigator, H. O. Pub. No. 9, Washington, D.C., 1966.

8. K. F. Bowden, Ann. Rev. Mar. Biol. Oceanog., 2, 11 (1964).

9. J. Williams, Oceanography, Little, Brown, Boston, 1962.

10. W. H. Munk and G. F. Carrier, Tellus, 2, 158 (1950).

11. H. Stromel, Deep-Sea Res., 4, 149 (1957); 5, 80 (1958).

12. K. Wyrtki, Deep-Sea Res., 8, 39 (1961).

13. G. Neumann and W. J. Pierson, Jr., Principles of Physical Oceanography, Prentice-Hall, Englewood Cliffs, New Jersey, 1966.

14. F. E. Snodgrass, Science, <u>162</u>, 76 (1968).

15. A. Voipio, edited by F. A. J. Armstrong <u>in</u> Chemical Oceanography (J. Riley and G. Skirrow, eds.), Academic Press, New York, 1965.

16. J. D. Burton, <u>in</u> Chemical Oceanography (J. P. Riley and G. Skirrow, eds.), Academic Press, New York, 1965, Chapt. 22.

17. C. Wunsch, Science, <u>159</u>, 969 (1968).

ENERGY FLOW IN A MARINE ECOSYSTEM

3.1 Introduction

An ecosystem is a functional system that includes a
natural community and the environment.[1] A marine ecosystem
would have at least five divisions or subdivisions:

1. Physical environment.

2. Bottom materials or substrate.

3. Communities with subdivisions of animal, precipitation
   or plant, and saprobe (bacteria, fungi) communities. Or
   the communities with subdivisions of shore or intertidal
   (littoral), sublittoral (which might include a depth
   range of 0-200 m), pelagic (open water), the bathyal
   (or deep sea, depth 200-300 m), and abyssal (ocean basins
   and the deeps) communities.

   A marine ecosystem also has four groups of constituents:

1. Abiotic substances or basic inorganic and organic compounds which exist in the physical environment and the
   bottom materials.

2. Producers or autotrophic organisms, which are largely
   green plants.

3. Consumers ("animals") heterotrophic organisms ingest and
    utilize other organisms and (chiefly) particulate organic
    compounds.

4. Decomposers or reducers (saprobes) disintegrate complex
    materials of dead protoplasm, utilize some decomposition
    products, and release other products which can be uti-
    lized by the producers.

The interaction of these constituents is represented as a
cycle (Fig. 3-1), and consideration of this interaction leads
to several conclusions:

1. The ecosystem necessarily involves very complex relation-
    ships and interdependences and it is often convenient to
    focus attention on a small unit of study. In this in-
    stance, these systems are ecologically incomplete, though
    this may not be recognized. For example, it is possible
    to have a system containing only producers and decomposers.

2. It is obvious that the physical environment can control
    the activities of producers, consumers and decomposers.
    It is less commonly appreciated that organisms influence
    and control the concentration and distribution of abiotic
    substances. Organisms can affect the silicon content,
    the process of calcium carbonate precipitation, sulfate
    and nitrate reductions, and oxygen concentration, to name

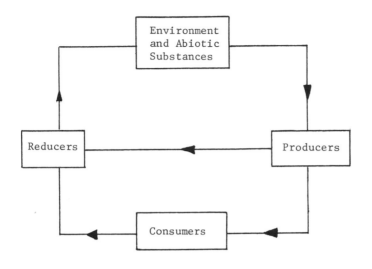

FIG. 3-1

Schematic representation of components of an ecosystem.

a few. Taking a broad view, the composition of sea water
and air is largely determined by the action of organisms.

3.   There is a series of homeostatic mechanisms or a system
of forces and counterprocesses that prevent gross change
in the total ecosystem. It is obviously possible for man
to overcome homeostasis or the balance of nature and effect irreversible alterations in the environment. It
seems that pollution of the sea is a reality, if the ubi-
quity of DDT is a criterion.

4. The organism activity (number and the rate at which they live) depends upon two factors:(1) the rate of abiotic circulation within the system and exchange with other ecosystems;and (2) the rate of energy flow through the system.

The two factors need to be considered in any study of the composition and properties of sea water. Understanding the circulation and exchange of materials presupposes an appreciation of the flow of energy and this factor needs to be considered first. The approach used here will be to review the relationship of heat and energy, the total versus the available energy of a system, some quantitative aspects of chemical equilibria, and finally, to consider the heat flow in a marine ecosystem.

3.2 Heat and Energy

It is appropriate to begin by defining three terms - energy, heat, and work.

Energy is the capacity of matter to produce an effect. The effect may appear as a physical change (or mechanical work), a chemical reaction, or a biological growth. Commonly, energy is considered to fall into one of two classes: stored energy and energy in transition. It is customary to define all energy in transition (i.e., not associated with any matter) as either heat or work.

Heat is energy in transit between bodies at different
temperature. If two bodies at different temperatures are
joined, energy flows from the hotter (source) to the colder
body (sink). By definition, the energy is not called heat before it has started to flow or after it has stopped. Heat is
transferred in three ways – conduction (i.e., through adjacent
layers of matter), convection (i.e.,in a fluid through movement of the fluid), radiation (i.e., through electromagnetic
radiation which does not require a connecting body between the
source and the sink).

Work is a form of energy in transit resulting from a force
acting through a given distance. In most chemical systems,
work is concerned with expansion or contraction of gases re-
acting or formed in the process. The force opposing the expansion is often constant, i.e., the ambient pressure. Heat
differs from work in one significant aspect – the conversion
of heat to work is limited.

Finally, it is useful to review four other terms – system
phase, state,and thermodynamics. A system is a portion of the
universe on which we choose to focus our attention – a system
may be a beaker or a box and its contents, a portion of the
ocean, etc. A phase is a physically distinct homogeneous portion of the system – lump of ice, a solid. Matter can exist
in three states – solid, liquid, and gas. Thermodynamics is a

branch of science that is concerned with the chemical and physical processes which involve the interconversion of energy in its various forms. Thermodynamics does not deal with the rate of a process (the time element) or with the detailed path (mechanism) by which the process occurs.

The first law of thermodynamics is a statement of the principle of the conservation of energy. This may be stated as

"Energy can neither be created or destroyed."

or

"You can't get out more than you put in."

or

$$\Delta E = q - w \qquad (3-1)$$

The last expression can be developed as follows:

Suppose we have a chemical system (represented in Fig. 3-2 as a box) in which a chemical or physical change occurs. Accompanying this change is a change of energy which is represented as ΔE (or sometimes as ΔU). The energy exchange between the system and the surroundings can occur in two ways - as heat absorbed or evolved (q) or as work done by or done on the system (w).

Two conventions apply. First, if heat is absorbed by the system, q is positive and the reaction is said to be endothermic; if the heat is evolved, q is a negative quantity and the reaction is said to be exothermic (Note 1). Secondly, if work

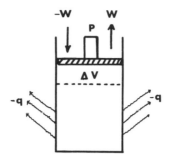

FIG. 3-2

Representation of a chemical system, as a frictionless piston, moving a cylinder. Expansion and contraction shown as w and -w, heat lost from the system as -q.

is done by the system, w is a positive quantity; if work is done on the system, w is a negative quantity.

Two reaction conditions can be envisioned - constant pressure (as is common with a marine ecosystem) and constant volume (as in a rigid container).

In the first instance, if there is a volume change, work is done and this work is equal to PΔV where $\underline{P}$ is the constant pressure and $\underline{\Delta V}$ is the final volume minus the initial volume (Eqn. 3-2).

$$\Delta E \;=\; q - w \;=\; q - P\Delta V \qquad\qquad (3-2)$$

Because most reactions do occur at constant pressure, it is useful to rearrange the expression (Eqn. 3-2) and call the heat associated with this change, q_p, by another name the enthalpy change (= ΔH)

$$q_p \;=\; \Delta E \;+\; P\Delta V \;=\; \Delta H \qquad\qquad (3-3)$$

The quantity ΔH is more commonly called the <u>heat of reaction</u>, which is unfortunate because it is an ambiguous term.

In the second instance, if there is no volume change, ΔV is equal to zero, as is w, and the expression becomes

$$\Delta E = q_v \qquad\qquad (3\text{-}4)$$

where q_v represents the heat measured under conditions of constant volume.

There are certain other points that deserve comment. First, both the quantities ΔE and ΔH depend upon the initial and final states, not upon the path. This means that regardless of whether the reaction occurs in one step or many, the values of ΔE and ΔH depend only upon the states of the reactants and the products. Secondly, the discussion was concerned with the <u>change</u> in energy, ΔE, and the enthalpy <u>change</u>, not with the absolute values, <u>E</u> and <u>H</u>. The change is emphasized because it is not possible to define energy on an absolute basis and because the important quantity in a chemical reaction is the change in a thermodynamic quantity.

These two points lead to a consideration of applications of ΔH.

3.3 <u>Application of ΔH Values</u>

The applications or the utility of ΔH values include the following:

As an indication of spontaneity of change. The enthalpy change may be a measure of the driving force of a reaction. There is an observed tendency for exothermic reactions (ΔH = negative value) to be favored over those system changes that occur with an increase in enthalpy (ΔH = positive value).

As a measure of stability. The term "stability" is probably one of the more misused words in chemistry. An unambiguous meaning is possible if stability is defined in terms of ΔH values for an exactly specified system. Thus, we may say that a substance is stable or unstable with respect to decomposition into certain products under specified conditions. If ΔH has a large negative value for those products and conditions, it would follow that the reaction should be spontaneous and that the substance should be unstable under the specified circumstances. For example, to say that liquid hydrogen peroxide is unstable is meaningless, unless the conditions and products are specified. Hydrogen peroxide at $25^{\circ}C$ and 1 atm pressure is stable with respect to decomposition into its constituent elements (Eqn. 3-5); it is decidedly

$$H_2O_{2(\ell)} \rightarrow H_{2(g)} + O_{2g} \quad \Delta H = +44.8 \text{ kcal} \quad (3\text{-}5)$$

$$H_2O_{2(\ell)} \rightarrow H_2O_{(\ell)} + \tfrac{1}{2}O_2 \quad \Delta H = -23.4 \text{ kcal} \quad (3\text{-}6)$$

unstable with respect to decomposition into liquid water and oxygen (Eqn. 3-6) and may decompose with explosive force.

Estimation of other parameters. The enthalpy change may be obtained experimentally and may be used to estimate other thermodynamic parameters - free energy and entropy of a reaction (Section 3.5). These parameters may be used to understand the exceptions noted in the first example.

Other applications. Enthalpy change values may be used in estimating bond dissociation energies, or bond energies, or crystal lattice energies. Though obviously important, the consideration of these applications is not within the scope of this treatment (Note 2).

3.4 Measurement of ΔH Values

The utility of enthalpy change values is evident, and the question arises, how are these values obtained? Two ways - experiment and calculation - are available.

Experimental evaluation. It is often possible to measure precisely the heat associated with a defined reaction. The heat measured in a microcalorimeter is q_v (Eqn. 3-4), but the value needed by those interested in the marine ecosystem would be q_p or ΔH. The change of enthalpy is obtained by correcting q_p for the work done by the system.

To illustrate the method, consider the process (Eqn. 3-7)

$$CH_{4(g)} + 2O_{2(g)} \rightarrow CO_{2(g)} + H_2O_{(\ell)} \qquad (3-7)$$

For this process, q_v is equal to -211 kcal. This value may be
corrected by adding the value of $P\Delta V$ at $25^{\circ}C$ and 1 atm pressure.
Each mole of gaseous reactant or product occupies about 24.5
liters. Thus $P\Delta V$ would be equal to 1 atm (-2 x 24.5 liters),
or -49 liter-atm, or -1.2 kcal (since 1 liter-atm corresponds
to 24.2 calories). Thus,

$$q_p \quad = \quad \Delta H \quad = \quad q_v \quad + \quad P\Delta V$$
$$= \quad -211 \quad + \quad (-1.2) \text{ kcal}$$
$$= \quad -212 \text{ kcal} \tag{3-8}$$

Calculation. It is evident that there is no need to determine
the enthalpy change for these reactions that have been studied.
The pertinent data have been reported. But is it necessary to
determine the enthalpy change for every reaction, and what
about reactions that cannot be studied? The answer in both
instances is the application of Hess' law. This states, in
effect, that ΔE and ΔH are functions of state not of path. If
a reaction can be envisioned as occurring in a series of steps,
the overall enthalpy change is the sum of the enthalpy changes
of the individual steps. Obviously, this law has wide application.

As an example, consider the oxidation of methane to produce carbon monoxide (Eqn. 3-9) instead of carbon dioxide
which is produced in a calorimeter. In effect we are interested in a reaction which doesn't occur typically, but which is of

$$CH_{4(g)} + 1\tfrac{1}{2}O_{2(g)} \rightarrow CO_{(g)} + 2H_2O_{(\ell)} \qquad (3\text{-}9)$$

practical significance. Some estimations of the amount of organic carbon in the sea are probably in error because of incomplete combustion, and corrections must be made for the amount of carbon monoxide produced.

To return to our reaction (Eqn. 3-9), we can visualize this reaction as occurring in two steps: (1) oxidation of methane to carbon dioxide and water (Eqn. 3-7); and (2) decomposition of this carbon dioxide (Eqn. 3-10).

$$CO_{2(g)} \rightarrow CO + \tfrac{1}{2}O_2 \quad \Delta H = +68.3 \text{ kcal} \qquad (3\text{-}10)$$

Combination of the two reactions and combination of the two enthalpy changes yield the desired reaction (Eqn. 3-9) and the pertinent enthalpy change, $\Delta H = -144.7$ kcal (Note 3).

3.5 Total, Fixed, and Free Energy

As noted in the previous section, the change in enthalpy is not always an indication of the spontaneity of a reaction. It is useful to introduce a different parameter, the free energy of the system. If energy is defined as the capacity to do work, then the free energy, $\underline{G}$ (or $\underline{F}$), is defined as the component of the total energy that determines the capacity of a substance to participate in an exchange of energy, i.e., a chemical reaction.

By way of analogy (Note 4), money might be defined as the capacity to purchase goods and services. Total income might

be defined as total capacity to purchase. But, there is a
difference between income and take-home pay (or free income),
just as there is a difference between total energy and free
energy. A person also has certain unavailable (or organizational) income, which is a function of his environment and
which includes taxes and union or professional expenses. A comparison may be made between money and energy systems (Eqs.
3-11, 3-12).

$$\text{Total income} = \text{Free income} + \text{Organizational income} \tag{3-11}$$

$$\text{Total energy} = \text{Free energy} + \text{Organization energy} \tag{3-12}$$

$$H = G \text{ (or } F\text{)} + TS \tag{3-13}$$

The more appropriate expression also is given (Eqn. 3-13).

For any reaction, the free energy change (ΔG or ΔF) determines the capacity of the reaction to occur. The total
energy change (ΔH) is the energy change observed when the reaction actually occurs. The organizational (or unavailable)
energy is TS, where T is the absolute temperature ($^{\circ}K$) and S
is the entropy. One factor that determines the organizational
or unavailable energy is degree of disorder. The entropy,
then, is a measure of the degree of disorder and is a minimum
for a crystalline solid at $0^{\circ}K$. The degree of disorder also
is a function of the temperature and this is a second factor
that determines the organizational energy.

A further comparison of the four quantities (Eqn. 3-13) is possible. Three quantities (H, G, S) are <u>extensive</u> properties of a substance; all depend upon the amount of substance under consideration. Thus, H and G are expressed in units of calories (or kilocalories) per mole; S is expressed as entropy units (e.u. = calories per degree per mole). The absolute temperature, T, is an intensive quantity and, thus, is independent of the amount of substance.

The change sign and magnitude of the extensive properties also are of interest. For a hypothetical reaction (Eqn. 3-14)

$$aA + bB \rightarrow cC + dD \qquad (3\text{-}14)$$

the free energy change is

$$G = (cG_C - dG_D) - (aG_A + bG_B) \qquad (3\text{-}15)$$

and similar expressions may be written for the enthalpy and entropy changes. This leads to the expressions (Eqn. 3-16,-17)

$$\Delta H = \Delta G + T\Delta S \qquad (3\text{-}16)$$

$$\Delta G = \Delta H - T\Delta S \qquad (3\text{-}17)$$

A spontaneous reaction should be one for which ΔG and ΔH have large negative values and for which $T\Delta S$ is a positive quantity. The pertinent relationships are also summarized schematically (Fig. 3-3; Note 5).

At this point, the second law of thermodynamics may be stated in terms of an equation (3-17, or better, as Eqn. 3-13) or in terms of equivalent statements.

FIG. 3-3

Schematic summary of thermodynamic parameters. Note the
horizontal and vertical columns are additive. (The work
function A is also termed the Helmholtz free energy.)

"Every system will tend to change to a condition
of maximum probability."

or

"You can't get out as much as you put in (except
at absolute zero)."

or

"A perpetual motion machine cannot be made."

Every system left to itself will tend to change in such
a way as to approach a state of equilibrium. Some practical
examples include the following spontaneous processes.

1. Organic compounds in the sea are oxidized by the
    atmosphere.

2. A solute diffuses from a more concentrated solution into
    a more dilute portion, leading to a uniform concentration.
    This is one of the slower mixing processes of the sea, as
    noted in Chapter 2.

3. Heat passes from a hot body (warmed sea surface) to a cold body (lower layer of the sea), leading to a temperature uniformity. The development of a thermocline is an example (Section 2.6).

4. A chemical reaction changes from an initial state to a state of equilibrium (carbonate and/or silica buffering of the ocean pH).

It is appropriate to review the relationship of equilibria and free energy, not only because of the importance of equilibria but also because values of free energy change are obtained from equilibrium constants. Given the free energy changes and the enthalpy change (obtained from a calorimeter), entropy change may be calculated at a given temperature.

3.6 Free Energy and Equilibria

The equilibrium constant as defined previously (Vol. 1, Chapt. 3) is used as a quantitative measure of the extent to which a chemical reaction occurs. These constants can be manipulated to define equilibria that may not be conveniently measured. For example, consider the reaction

$$a\text{A} \ + \ b\text{B} \ \rightleftharpoons \ c\text{C} \ + \ d\text{D} \qquad\qquad (3\text{-}18)$$

for which the equilibrium constant which may not be conveniently measurable is:

$$K_1 \ = \ \frac{(\text{C})^{c} \ (\text{D})^{d}}{(\text{A})^{a} \ (\text{B})^{b}} \qquad\qquad (3\text{-}19)$$

This reaction is the algebraic sum of two other reactions (Eqn. 3-20, 3-21).

$$aA \; \rightleftarrows \; cC \; + \; rR \tag{3-20}$$

$$K_2 \;=\; \frac{(C)^{\underline{c}} \; (R)^{\underline{r}}}{(A)^{\underline{a}}} \tag{3-20a}$$

$$rR \; + \; bB \; \rightleftarrows \; dD \tag{3-21}$$

$$K_3 \;=\; \frac{(D)^{\underline{d}}}{(B)^{\underline{b}} \; (R)^{\underline{r}}} \tag{3-21a}$$

and it follows that

$$K_1 \;=\; K_2 K_3 \tag{3-22}$$

It also follows that K_1 can be evaluated if the values of K_2 and K_3 are known.

It also follows that the manipulation of equilibrium expressions may become cumbersome. The difficulty is obviated by use of the relationship between the equilibrium constant and the free energy change (Eqn. 3-23).

$$\Delta G^o \;=\; -RT \ln K \tag{3-23}$$

or

$$\Delta G^o \;=\; -2.30^o gK \tag{3-23a}$$

where R is the universal gas constant (1.98 cal/^{o}K/mole and where the superscript zero refers to the standard temperature, 25°C. For the example considered,

$$\Delta G_1^o \;=\; \Delta G_2^o \; \Delta G_3^o \tag{3-24}$$

It is evident that a large negative value of ΔG^o corresponds to a large positive value of K, and also that a large positive value of ΔG^o corresponds to a large negative value of K. For example, if the value of K is 10^{10}, ΔG^o would be -13.7 kcal/mole, and the reaction would proceed virtually to completion. Also, if the value of K is 10^{-10}, ΔG^o would be +13.7 kcal/mole and the reaction would not proceed to any significant extent.

3.7   Energy Flow in the Ecosystem

As noted in the introduction, the rate of flow of energy and the rate of circulation of abiotic materials in the eco-system are two critical factors. The most significant distinction between the two factors is: materials circulate, energy does not. The elements in abiotic substances (carbon, hydrogen, nitrogen, oxygen, phosphorus, silicon) may be used over and over as they are converted from abiotic substances to living organisms and back upon death and decomposition. The flow of energy is one way because energy is used once, is converted to heat, and is effectively lost from the ecosystem. (Technically, of course, the physical environment is modified slightly.) The loss of energy is balanced by the continuous flow of solar energy into the ecosystem.

The flow of energy in an ecosystem may be represented schematically (Fig. 3-4).

Degradation is a significant feature of this flow of

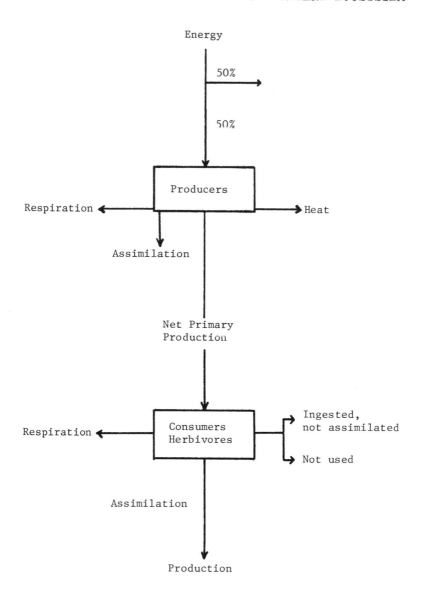

FIG. 3-4

A simplified diagram of energy flow in an
ecosystem. (After Odum[1])

energy. There is loss of energy at each stage in the energy-transfer sequence (or food chain): sunlight → producers → herbivores (plant eaters) → primary carnivores (which eat the herbivores) → secondary carnivores (which eat the primary carnivores), etc. Thus, the producers, or green plants, absorb only about half of the mean radiant energy reaching them. Moreover, only 1-5% of the absorbed energy is transmitted, i.e., converted into food energy in the form of productive vegetation.

The food chain in the marine ecosystem is limited essentially to three or four links because of the energy degradation. At each link the energy is reduced by one order. For example, given 100 kcal of net primary production (Note 6) from the producers (Fig. 3-4), only about 10 kcal would be reconstituted into primary herbivores, and about 1 kcal of the original 100 would be reconstituted into new organic compounds in the primary carnivores. Much of the energy is lost at each stage as heat (as is consistent with the second law of thermodynamics, Eqn. 3-17). Despite the energy loss, the communities or the individual organisms do not run down and reach maximum entropy or disorder (Eqn. 3-17). This trend is reversed by the continued absorption of energy through the chain as food (or negative entropy).

Standing crop. It is important to know the relationship between energy flow and the standing crop, which may be defined

(1) the number of organisms per unit area at a given time, or
(2) the average number over a longer period. The energy-flow
diagram (Fig. 3-4) might be redesigned in terms of pipes
and boxes.[1] A pipe of varying diameter would represent the
relative energy coming in or leaving a given stage; the volume
of a box would represent the living weight of the standing
crop (the biomass). The energy flow decreases with each
successive energy transfer stage (or trophic level), and often
the standing crop also decreases.

The standing crop biomass, however, is very dependent
upon the size of the individual organisms in the standing crop.
The inverse size-metabolic rate relationship applies here.
The smaller the organism, the greater the metabolic rate per
gram of weight. Consequently, the energy degradation per unit
weight is greater. For example, the metabolism of one gram of
algae may be equal to many grams of tree leaves. Relative to
the consumers in the ecosystem, the producers may be mostly
very small organisms which have a much greater average energy
flow (assuming the producer-consumer are directly linked).

How can the greater weight of larger consumer organisms
be supported by the smaller biomass of smaller producer
organisms? Largely by harvesting at frequent intervals. A
consumer organism, such as man or zooplankton, can obtain as
much food from a population of phytoplankton harvested frequently as from a crop of grain harvested only after a long

97

period of time. The problem, of course, is that the zooplankton, but not man, has a method of harvesting the phytoplankton
economically.

Biogeochemical cycles. As noted in Section 3.1, the movement
of materials and the flow of energy are equally important considerations. Up to this point, the emphasis has been concerned with the flow of energy, and it is appropriate to
consider briefly the movement of materials in the ecosystem.
All chemical elements in the marine ecosystem are involved in
biogeochemical cycles, a series of processes involving the
movement of elements from organisms to environment and back.
Basically, there are two types of cycles, sedimentary and
gaseous. The nitrogen cycle (Chapter 7) is an example of the
gaseous type; the sulfur, silicon (Chapter 5), and phosphorus
(Chapter 6) cycles are examples of the sedimentary type.

The interrelationship of the biogeochemical cycle and the
energy-flow scheme is indicated in Fig. 3-5. In effect,
materials exist in pools or reservoirs (in solution, sediment,
air, or organisms; as compounds or in elemental forms). The
ecologist recognizes two types of pools: a nonbiological pool,
which is large and slow moving; and an active pool, which is
smaller but which exchanges more rapidly between the producer
and consumer. In relative terms, the nonbiological pool may
be thought of as an unavailable reservoir in that the materials
are not instantly available to the organism; the active pool

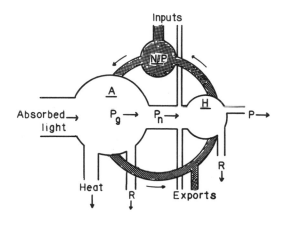

FIG. 3-5

Representation of the interaction of a biogeochemical cycle (stipled circle) and a unidirectional energy-flow system. N.P., nutrient pool; A, autotrophs; H, heterotrophs; P_g, gross production; P_n, net production that may be consumed; (H), stored or exported. (After Odum[1])

is a cycling or available reservoir in that the materials are instantly available to the organism.

The sulfur cycle (sedimentary type) is an excellent example to consider because it illustrates these points and because it is markedly affected by biological reactions. Sulfate ion (SO_4^{2-}) is the major available species in solution that is reduced by heterotrophic plants (Step 1, Fig. 3-6). In being reduced, the sulfur is incorporated into certain amino acids which are converted to protein. Plants and animals that contain these proteins either excrete these proteins (Step 2) or

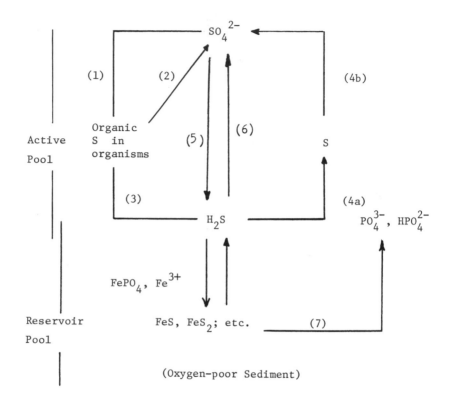

FIG. 3-6

The sulfur cycle (after Odum[1]).
(See text for explanation of numbers).

are decomposed by heterotrophic microorganisms and hydrogen

sulfide (H_2S) is released (Step 3). Some H_2S is oxidized to

sulfate ion by specialized colorless, purple, and green sulfur

bacteria (Step 4); and some is oxidized by aerobic sulfide

oxidizers (thiobacilli bacteria, Step 6). Some hydrogen sulfide is also formed by reduction of sulfate by anerobic sulfate
reducers (desulfovibrio bacteria) in the sediments (Step 5).
Under oxygen-poor or anerobic conditions, much of the sulfide
may not be oxidized and becomes part of the reservoir pool.
In the presence of sulfides, insoluble ferric phosphate is converted to soluble phosphate (HPO_2^{2-}, PO_4^{3-}) and iron sulfides
form (Step 7). The sulfur cycle then has regenerated phosphate, and in effect regulates the phosphorus nutrient cycle.

These are the gross aspects of the sulfur biogeochemical
cycle. Though much is known of the overall aspects, much less
is known about the details. This cycle does serve to illustrate the role of organisms in affecting the concentrations
of constituents in the ecosystem and it does suggest the need
to explore this role in further detail. Redfield,[2] among
others, has summarized evidence that indicates that organisms
over the ages have strongly influenced, if not controlled, the
chemical composition of the world ocean.

This raises the question, what is the composition of sea
water and how did it get that way? We shall try to answer
this question in the next chapter.

3.8 Summary

In this chapter, we have considered the nature of a
marine ecosystem, and the components of that system - the

environment and abiotic materials, the producers, the consumers, and the decomposers. The most significant features
seem to be the flow of energy through the systems and the
circulation of abiotic materials within the system. We have
considered the nature of energy and some of the gross features
of the field of thermodynamics. Finally, we have introduced
the concept of energy flow through the marine ecosystem and
considered its implications in terms of the degradation of
energy, the food chain, the standing crop versus energy flow,
and the involvement of abiotic substances, the environment,
and organisms in biogeochemical cycles.

NOTES

1. The convention conforms to the idea that in an exothermic
    reaction the potential energy of the system is lowered.

2. One useful source is Wall.[3]

3. It is useful to define an arbitrary reference scale, even
    though changes of energy are of interest. Thus zero
    enthalpy is assigned to each element at 25°C when it is
    in the standard (or typical) state of the most stable
    form of that element at 25°C. It is then possible to
    define the heat of formation of a substance as the change
    in enthalpy associated with the formation of one mole of

the substance from its constituent elements, each in its standard state.

4. I am indebted to J. A. Allen[4] for this analogy.

5. The interpretation of entropy is discussed extensively by H. A. Bent.[5]

6. Net production is the difference (positive or negative) in the organic matter present at two successive occasions. Some authors prefer to restrict the term primary productivity to the accumulation of organic matter by plants and to apply the term assimilation to production by non-photosynthetic organisms.

REFERENCES

1. E. P. Odum, Fundamentals of Ecology, 2nd ed., Saunders, Philadelphia, 1959; E. P. Odum, Ecology, Holt, Rinehart and Winston, New York, 1963.

2. A. C. Redfield, American Scientist, 46, 205 (1958).

3. F. W. Wall, Chemical Thermodynamics, A Course of Study, 2nd ed., Freeman, San Francisco, 1965.

4. J. A. Allen, Energy Changes in Chemistry, Allyn and Bacon, Boston, 1966.

5. H. A. Bent, The Second Law, Oxford, New York, 1965.

4

THE MODEL OCEAN

4.1 Introduction

While considering the marine ecosystem, many persons have
asked two fairly obvious questions: (1) how did sea water and
air attain the present composition and (2) how are these compositions maintained? It is recognized that the ratios between various ions, e.g., $Mg^{2+}:Na^+:Cl^-$, and the pH value in the
open sea are remarkably constant under comparable conditions.
Moreover, there are no compelling reasons to believe that these
ratios or the pH value have changed much during the past few
hundred million years[1]; and the sea has probably existed for
about 2 billion years.

At first glance this constancy seems astounding. In the
first place, the amount of nonvolatile dissolved solids in the
present oceans is slight in comparison with the sediments of
the earth. For example, the dissolved solids, as oxides,
could cover the earth to a uniform depth of perhaps 20 m, but
a uniform layer of sediment would be thousands of meters
thick, and the radius of the earth would be 6,400,000 m. This
point is of interest because the ions in the sea come in part
from weathering, from the continued interaction between the sea

and the earth's crust: Water evaporates from the sea, con-
denses as rain, interacts with rocks and soil, and drains into
rivers which carry ions and suspended material to the sea,
where there is an interaction and where sediments deposit.
The amounts of material thus carried to the ocean have been
enormous during, say, 100 million years. Table 4-1 lists the
present amount of ions in the sea versus the amounts added by
rivers during a 100-million year-period. Typically, the
amounts added are much larger than those now present in the
ocean. Sodium and chloride are exceptional and probably represent sea spray washed back.

TABLE 4-1[3,4]

Amounts of Ions in the World Ocean versus

Amounts of Ions Added by Rivers in 100 Million Years

| | Dissolved Ion[a] | | | | | | | |
	Na^+	Mg^{2+}	Ca^{2+}	K^+	Cl^-	SO_4^{2-}	CO_3^{2-}	NO_3^{3-}
Present amount	129	15	2.8	2.7	150	8	0.3	0.01
Amounts added during 10^8 years	196	122	268	42	157	84	342	11

[a]Units, moles/cm^2 of total earth surface.

In the second place, there are a variety of chemical reactions apart from weathering. Other reactions include the processes of the biogeochemical cycles, additions from the atmosphere as dust and in rain, underwater volcanism, and interaction with suspended solids (Note 1).

There have been several attempts to establish that the constancy is due to (1) a "geochemical balance" and (2) a large, complex,and interacting series of biogeochemical cycles (Section 3.7).

The geochemical balance was suggested by Goldschmidt[5] and was based upon the assumed interaction of igneous rock and volatiles (Eqn. 4-1) during the early stages of the earth (Note 2).

Igneous rock + Volatiles → Sea water + Sediments + Air   (4-1)

The volatiles would include water, HCl, CO_2, and compounds of sulfur, boron, nitrogen, fluorine. The composition of sea water was well known, the average composition of igneous rocks was known for the major elements, but the composition of the sediments was poorly known at the time. Goldschmidt concluded that 0.6 kg of igneous rock had reacted to form a liter of sea water,about 0.6 kg of sediments (and about 3 liters of air).

Recently, the geochemical balance was refined by Horn and Adams[6] and it appears that 1.2 kg of igneous rock reacted to form one liter of sea water. Either the Goldschmidt or the

Horn-Adams approach leads to a self-consistent set of data, (Table 4-2) though the latter approach brings 55 elements into material balance. Either approach involves a tacit assumption that the process (Eqn. 4-1) is one way.

There are reasons to believe that Eqn. 4-1 represents a two-way process and that the reverse reaction is occurring. The work of M. Ewing, B. Heezen, and others (at Lamont Geological Observatory, Columbia University) indicates that there is a Mid-Atlantic ridge, a submarine range over 3,000 m above the ocean floor which approximately bisects the Atlantic from north to south. These workers have found that the ridge is a part of a world-girdling ridge system found in all major oceans. There is evidence to support a contention that these ridges represent cracks in the earth's crust and that these rifts are significant features of the proposed continental drift.[7,8] Related to this is the newer view of the ocean bottom,[7,8] that it is not old and unchanging, but is constantly being reformed (Note 3).

It appears to many that a new ocean crust is being generated at a midocean rift, that the ocean floor is spreading outward at the rate of about 1-4 cm per year, and that the older floor is moving beneath the continent. Sediment and entrapped sea water descend to hotter regions, and the reverse process (Eqn. 4-1) occurs as igneous rocks are formed (from interactions of magnesium and sodium ions in the sea water with

TABLE 4-2

Material Balance of Selected Elements for the
Formation of One Liter of Sea Water[3]

Element or Compound	Now[a]		From[a]		
	Air[b]	1 liter Sea Water	Sediments[b]	Igneous Rock[b]	Volatile[b]
H_2O		54.90			54.90
Si as SiO_2			6.06,12.25	6.06,12.25	
Al as $Al(OH)_3$			1.85,3.55	1.85, 3.55	
Na as NaOH		0.47	0.29,1.00	0.76, 1.47	
Cl as HCl		0.55	-,0.40	0.01, 0.02	0.54, 0.94
K as KOH		0.01	0.40,0.78	0.41, 0.79	
Mg as MgO		0.05	0.48,0.82	0.53, 0.87	
Ca as CaO		0.01	0.55,1.08	0.56, 1.09	
O as O_2	0.027,0.022				0.0027,0.022
S		0.03	0.04,0.05	0.01, 0.02	0.06, 0.06

[a]Unit, moles/liter of sea water formed.

[b]First number Goldschmidt;[5] second number, Horn-Adams.[6]

clays in the crust and overlying material). The reverse process could also occur if, as proposed, the newer ocean crust,
sediments, and entrapped sea water sink vertically through
engulfment trenches into warmer regions.

As it happens, the geochemical balance does _not_ require
the assumption that Eqn. 4-1 is either a one-way or a two-way
process. Obviously, the balance is achieved assuming a one-
way process, as Horn and Adams[6] have demonstrated. The balance is also achieved assuming a two-way process which has
reached a steady state, according to Sillén.[3] He has devised
a recycling model: the volatiles of the ocean are continuously
attacking igneous rock, both types (basaltic on the sea floor
and continental), to produce sediments which are carried back
to the depths where both types of igneous rocks are formed.

In an effort to rationalize what reactions could stabilize
the composition of sea water, Sillén proposed an imaginary experiment of making a model ocean. The model ocean would contain the same components and the same amounts as the real
system. There would be one important difference: in the model
ocean a state of true equilibrium would be assumed.

It may be admitted at the outset that major portions of
the real sea water system will _not_ be in a state of equilibrium. The surface layer for example, will not be at equilibrium, and substantial changes in the nitrogen, phosphorus,
silicon, and organic carbon concentrations are expected. The

surface layer, however, constitutes approximately 5%
of the total volume of sea water, and we are surely justified
in choosing to examine the other 95% of sea water.
Also, it may be admitted that any life process will upset the
equilibrium condition. But again we are surely justified in
choosing to focus our attention on the bulk of sea water.

Any consideration of an equilibrium model requires a definition of the system. The pertinent parameters of the system
are listed in Table 4-3, and the major constituents of sea
water have been listed in Table 1-2.

TABLE 4-3

Properties of the Equilibrium System of Sea Water[1]

Property	Value
Total volume	$1.37 \times 10^9 km^3$
	1.37×10^{21} liters
Average temperature	$5°C$
Average density	1.024 g ml^{-1}
Average pressure	200 atm
Average depth	$3,800$ meters
Average pH $= -\log_{10}(H^+)$	8.1 ± 0.2 $(5°C)$
Average pE $= -\log_{10}(e^-)$	12.5 ± 0.2 $(5°C)$

There are three basic objections to the development of the
equilibrium model using the data in Table 4-3 alone.

First, these data represent average values, and the

ranges are substantial. For example, the temperature range is 0 to 30°C, and the pressure range is 1 to 1100 atm. These ranges would preclude the validity of an equilibrium model were it not for the action of currents and other physical processes. For example, in a stationary column of water at constant temperature, any sparingly soluble solid such as calcium carbonate would be more soluble at the bottom of the column of water, owing to the increase in solubility with pressure; and at the top of this water column, the sparingly soluble solid would precipitate under conditions of lowered pressure. This would be tantamount to achieving a perpetual motion device. The action of currents is to lift a layer of water, saturated with a sparingly soluble solid, from the depth to a layer under lower pressure where the solid precipitates.

Secondly, these data do not indicate the extent of mixing in the ocean (Chapter 2). This is, however, a thoroughly stirred system in terms of the length of the experiment. Even granting a rotation period as long as 1,000 years, a half million rotations would be achieved in 500 million years. Also, the observation that the composition of interstitial water in some deep-sea sediments is unchanged over periods of 10^5 years suggests that these sediments are essentially in a state of equilibrium.[9]

Finally, the total volume and composition data are

cumbersome, and Sillén followed the practice of Goldschmidt in
considering one liter of sea water, together with the appropriate share of the atmosphere (approximately 3 liters) and the
sediments (about 0.6 kg). This model is represented as
Fig. 4-1.

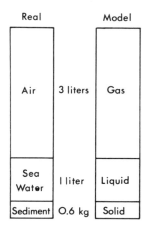

FIG. 4-1

Schematic comparison of real and model systems. Model system
has various elements (except nitrogen) brought into true
equilibrium; average values are assumed; organisms absent.

4.2 The Model Ocean[1-3]

The model ocean is developed by adding elements as hydrox-
ides or oxides to 54.90 moles of water (Table 4-4). As each
component is added, a dissolution or a recombination process
occurs, and it is presumed that equilibrium would be established. Consider the results of Steps 2-6.

113

TABLE 4-4

Steps in Forming the Model Ocean

Step	Constituent	Amount, mole
1	H_2O	54.90
2	SiO_2	6.06
3	$Al(CH)_3$	1.85
4	NaOH	0.76
5	HCl	0.55
6	KOH	0.41
7	MgO	0.44
8	CaO	0.10
9	Carbonate, $CaCO_3$	0.37
	or $CaCO_3$	0.46
	$MgCO_3$	0.09
10	H_3BO_3	0.00043
11	O_2	0.027
12	FeOOH	0.55

After Step 2, there are two phases (in addition to the gaseous phase): a solid phase (about 6.06 moles of quartz) and an aqueous phase. In the latter phase silica is present as dissolved $Si(OH)_4$ ($10^{-3.74}\underline{M}$ at 25° or $10^{-4.10}\underline{M}$ at 0°), according to Van Lier.[1] This compares well with the reported concentration in deep Antarctic waters. The lower concentrations in surface waters, as well as the fluctuations, have been attributed to diatom blooms, though control by clay minerals may be a factor (Section 4.3).

There would be two solid phases after Step 3 and the addition of 1.85 moles of aluminum hydroxide. One phase would

be quartz and the other should be kaolinite, $Al_2Si \cdot O_5(OH)_5$.
The nature of the dissolved aluminum species is uncertain,
particularly as to whether it exists mainly as a mononuclear
species or as a polynuclear species. The concentration of
soluble aluminum should be $10^{-7.7}-10^{-7.0}$ $\underline{M}$,[10] though greater
concentrations have been reported earlier ($10^{-6.7}-10^{-4.0}$ $\underline{M}$).
These uncertainties are regrettable because soluble forms of
aluminum are significantly involved in the formation of
silicate minerals.

Steps 4-7 would have three consequences: first, the ionic
strength would be essentially that of sea water. Secondly, a
reconstitution of silicate minerals that comprise the solid
phases would occur and kaolinite would be converted to other
aluminosilicates, some examples of which are listed in
Table 4-5. Thirdly, there would be an ion-exchange equilibrium between cations (sodium, potassium, calcium) in the solid
phase and those in solution. The significance of the last
consequence is developed in the next section.

Steps 9-11 also would have three consequences: (1) reconstitution of aluminosilicate minerals; (2) introduction of a
new phase, and (3) control of the pH. Let us consider these
in order. The first consequence was considered previously:
ion-exchange with the aluminosilicates listed in Table 4-5 will
occur to some extent. In addition, there is the possibility
that some magnesium carbonate would react with calcium
carbonate (Eqn. 4-2).

TABLE 4-5

Some Silicate Minerals[1,2] (Note 1)

Mineral	Idealized Formula	Structure Type
Kaolinite	$Al_2Si_2O_5(OH)_4$	layer
Glauconite	$K_{0.62}Na_{0.09}Ca_{0.06}Mg_{0.40}^-$	layer
	$Fe_{1.16}Al_{0.86}Si_{3.65}O_{10}(OH)_2$	
Phillipsite	$(M'Si,M''Al)AlSi_2O_3(H_2O)_3$	zeolite
	$M' = Na,K; M'' = Ca,Ba$	
Montmorillonite Na-form	$Al_2Si_4O_{10}(OH)_2$	layer
	$Na_{0.33}Al_2(Si_{3.67}Al_{0.33})O_{10}(OH)_{10}$	
Chlorite	$Mg_3(OH)_6Mg_3Si_4O_{10}(OH)_{10}$	layer
Muscovite	$KAl_2(AlSi_3)O_{10}(OH)_2$	layer
Illite	$K_{0.50}(Al_{1.38}Fe_{0.37}^{III}Fe_{0.04}^{II}Mg_{0.34})-$	
	$(Si_{3.41}Al_{0.59})O_{10}(OH)_2$	

$$2CaCO_{3(s)} + Mg^{2+} \rightleftarrows CaMg(CO_3)_{2(s)} + Ca^{2+} \qquad (4-2)$$
$$\text{(calcite)} \qquad\qquad \text{(dolomite)}$$

The position of equilibrium is a matter of controversy. It is uncertain whether calcite would be transformed to dolomite or whether the dolomite would be transformed to calcite. Sillén avoided the issue by using 0.37 mole of $CaCO_3$ added as the stable form, calcite.

The third consequence of adding carbonate and boric acid is the establishment of the pH of sea water, and this deserves a more extensive consideration before we consider the effects of other components of the model ocean.

4.3 The pH of Sea Water

As noted previously (Vol. 1, Chapt. 3) there are three definitions of pH: Sørensen's definition (Eqn. 4-3), the infinite dilution activity scale (Eqn. 4-4) and the operational definition (Eqn. 4-5), which depends upon the properties of a standard emf cell and upon the comparison of the pH of the

$$pH = -log[H^+] \qquad (4-3)$$

$$pH = -log(H^+) = -log\alpha_H + -log[H^+] \qquad (4-4)$$

$$pH_x - pH_s = -(E_x - E_s)(RTF^{-1}ln\ 10)^{-1} \qquad (4-5)$$

unknown solution (pH_x) with the pH of a standard buffer (pH_s). The second definition is not applicable to sea water; the first and third definitions are. Sørensen's definition may be used with the ionic medium scale because with this scale by definition $-log[H^+]$ is equal to $-log(H^+)$, where the bracket and parenthetical species refer, respectively, to the activity and the concentration of the species.

There are three notable observations about the pH of sea water.

1.   The average pH is 8.1 ± 0.2.

2.   The buffering capacity of an <u>isolated</u> one-liter sample of sea water is very limited: about 3×10^{-3} moles of hydrochloric acid will change the pH from 8 to 3 or less.

3.   The sea water system is extensively buffered, i.e., the pH of the entire ocean is remarkably resistant to change by additions of naturally occurring acids or bases.   Let us examine these observations in order.

First of all, the pH of sea water is not what it is because the oceans contain "everything." It is apparent from Table 1-2 and from consideration of acids and bases (Vol. 1, Chapt. 3) that there are three types of acids in sea water: (1) oxyacids (H_2CO_3, HCO_3^-, H_3BO_3, $H_2BO_3^-$, etc.) (2) hydrated metal ions (such as aluminum) that react with water (Eqn. 4-6) and (3) very weakly acidic cations.

$$M(H_2O)_x^{n+} + H_2O \; \rightleftarrows \; M(H_2O)_{x-1}(OH)^{(n-1)+} + H_3O^+ \qquad (4\text{-}6)$$

The second group typically includes small ions with a formal positive charge of 2 or greater.   The third group includes the alkali or alkaline-earth metal ions (except beryllium).   Those ions of the second group are present in too small a concentration to make a contribution to the pH of sea water.   Moreover, the concentration of oxyacids of phosphorus, silicon, and nitrogen is too slight to affect the pH of sea water (though in isolated portions this may not be the case).

Thus, according to the prevalent view, the pH of sea water is governed by the buffering action of the carbonic acid-bicarbonate-carbonate system and to a lesser extent the boric acid-borate system. The variations of these equilibria and pH and the pertinent calculations have been summarized previously (Vol. 1, Chapt. 2).

This explanation rationalizes the first observation about the pH and leads us to the second observation: the limited buffering capacity of an isolated liter of sea water. At the pH of sea water, the concentration of bicarbonate is about 2.5×10^{-3} M. If this solution is treated with 3×10^{-3} moles of hydrochloric acid, the pH is reduced to less than 6. This is a measure of the limited buffering capacity of an isolated liter of sea water.

How are we to reconcile this limited buffering capacity with the observed acid-base stability of sea water? To a certain extent, the thorough mixing process in the oceans (Chapter 2) and the biogeochemical cycle of carbon (Chapter 8) lead to what appears to be a buffering effect by carbonate. This would rationalize a short-term effect.

Sillén,[1] however, has suggested an alternate explanation which would account for the long-term buffering capacity. A pH-dependent ion-exchange equilibrium between solution and aluminosilicates (Eqn. 4-7) is the major buffering system in the ocean, and the carbonic acid–bicarbonate–carbonate system is really a pH indicator, according to Sillén's view.

The major buffering system may be represented by an idealized equation (Eqn. 4-7).

$$3Al_2Si_2O_5(OH)_{4(s)} + 4SiO_{2(s)} + 2K^+ + 2Ca^{2+} + 9H_2O$$

$$\rightleftarrows \quad 2KCaAl_3Si_5O_{16}(H_2O)_{6(s)} + 6H^+ \quad (4-7)$$

The pH dependence is indicated by the corresponding equilibrium expression (Eqn. 4-8).

$$\log K = 6 \log[H^+] - 2 \log[K^+] - 2 \log[Ca^{2+}] \quad (4-8)$$

Sillén[1] estimated the buffering capacity of the silicates is about 1 mole per liter or about 2000 times the buffering capacity of the carbonate system. There are at least four consequences of the buffering capacity of silicates.

1. The carbonate system really serves as a pH-sensitive indicator system, rather than a pH-controlling system (at least in the long-range sense). If there were no carbonate system, the indicator system would involve the next available acid-base pair, probably the boric acid–borate or maybe the silicic acid–silicate system.

2. Silicates have a long-term effect on pH. Suppose the amount of carbon dioxide in the atmosphere were increased to 0.10 mole per liter of sea water (about 2.5 times the

present value). This would cause a detectable decrease (possibly 0.2 units) in the pH of the surface layer of sea water. Ultimately the increased carbonic acid would be diluted by the bulk of the ocean. The decreased pH would cause calcium carbonate to dissolve and the increased calcium concentration would lead to a readjustment of the solution-silicate equilibria (Eqn. 4-8). The final pH of the ocean would not be significantly different because of the relative buffering capacity of the silicate and the carbonate systems (1.0 versus 0.003 mole per liter).

3. Silicate minerals (including those listed in Table 4-5) probably are a major control of the concentration of the silica in the sea. Mackenzie, Garrels, and co-workers[11] found that several common silicates rapidly released dissolved silica to silica-deficient sea water (dissolved concentration, 3ppm) and abstracted silica from silica-enriched water (dissolved silica concentration, 25 ppm). When the reaction with silicate minerals was complete, the dissolved silica concentrations were near the average value for the oceans. The 10-month period involved in the experiments is comparable to the average exposure of suspended materials which streams bring to the oceans.

4. The ion-exchange capacity of silicate minerals also seems to regulate the concentration of certain cations (Na^+, K^+,

Ca^{2+}, Mg^{2+}) in the present ocean. This regulation is based on the strength of binding of various cations in the silicate minerals. For example (see Holland[12] for a detailed treatment and pertinent references), fresh-water clay minerals rapidly (few tens of hours) undergo ion-exchange; calcium is exchanged for magnesium, sodium, and potassium. Unfortunately, we need more information about a true equilibrium system in which two silicate phases are in equilibrium with each other and with sea water (Eqn. 4-9).

$$1.5 \ Al_2Si_2O_5(OH)_{4(s)} + K^+ \ \rightleftarrows$$

$$KAl_3Si_3O_{10}(OH)_{2(s)} + 1.5 \ H_2O \qquad (4-9)$$

Hemley and co-workers[13] among others have studied such a system. The pertinent equilibrium constant (Eqn. 4-10) has been estimated at sea water temperature, using

$$K = [H^+]/[K^+] \qquad (4-10)$$

Hemley's data.[13a] The value for K, $10^{-6.0}$ to $10^{-6.5}$, is remarkably close to the observed $[H^+]/[K^+]$ value in sea water ($10^{-6.2}$). The sodium system (sodium montmorillonite instead of potassium mica) requires a risky extrapolation of the equilibrium ratio $[Na^+]/[H^+]$ (from 300 to 25°) but the estimated value $10^{7.0}$ agrees reasonably well with the sodium-hydrogen ion ratio in sea water.[12] Unfortunately, laboratory data for

magnesium and calcium are not available.

In summary, then, there are two buffering agents or

mechanisms operating in sea water: (1) the carbonate system,

the short-term mechanism, (2) the silicate system, the long-

term mechanism. The two systems differ with respect to

buffering capacities and with respect to the time scale in-

volved. The major point of controversy over the two systems

really centers on the actual time scale. For example,

Pytkowicz[14] presented good evidence that the role of sili-

cates is negligible for those problems for which the time scale

was less than 1,000 years. This might seem to be an ex-

cessively long period in view of other observations,[11] but

Pytkowicz's estimate is based on a careful analysis of the

amounts of weathering (Eqn. 4-1), of addition of silicates by

rivers (Eqn. 4-7) and of dissolved clays. It must be added, in

any case, that biological activity in isolated portions of the

marine ecosystem can cause **sizable** diurnal variations in

pH (0.4 units).[15]

At this point, with ten constituents in the model ocean,

we are able to rationalize some essential features of the real

ocean: the constancy of pH (though there is a disagreement

about the time scale), the buffering action, and the constancy

of the Na^+/Mg^{2+} ratio (because of ion-exchange with alumino silicates). The next constituent, iron as FeOOH, would have a small effect on the pH, perhaps 0.1 unit. This step deserves some consideration, however, because there are some paradoxical features.

4.4 The Iron Paradox

The iron paradox may be stated simply - we know the concentration of dissolved iron in sea water, but we are unable to account for most of it. Let us see how the problem arises.

First, we recognize that sea water is an oxidizing environment because of the presence of dissolved oxygen. As Step 11, 0.027 mole of oxygen is added to our system. Though most of the oxygen is in the gas phase, some dissolves (2×10^{-4} $\underline{M}$). The dissolved gas maintains an oxidation potential which is expressed in terms of electron activity and, more conveniently, as pE (Eqn. 4-11),

$$pE = -\log(e^-) = E^o/RTF^{-1}\ln 10 \qquad (4-11)$$

where $\underline{E}^o$ is the standard redox potential (e.g., $E^o_{H_2-H^+} = 0$ V), $\underline{R}$ is a constant (8,314 mV coulombs $deg^{-1}mole^{-1}$), $\underline{T}$ is the absolute temperature (^{o}K), $\underline{F}$ is Faraday's constant (96,500 coulombs $mole^{-1}$) and ln 10 is equal to 2.303. The factor $RTF^{-1}\ln 10$ has a value of 59.15 mV at 25^oC and 54.19 mV at 0^oC.

For example, the pE of the model system or sea water would be determined by the equilibrium (Eqn. 4-12).

$$\tfrac{1}{2}O_{2(g)} + 2H^+ + 2e^- \rightarrow H_2O; \log K_{eq} = 41.55 \qquad (4-12)$$

Using appropriate values ($25°C$, zero activity) the value of pE can be calculated (Eqn. 4-13).

$$\log K = \log(H_2O) - \tfrac{1}{2}\log P_{O_2} - 2\log(H) - 2\log(e^-) \qquad (4\text{-}13a)$$

$$41.55 = 0.0 \qquad - \tfrac{1}{2}\log(0.21) + ?pH + 2pE \qquad (4\text{-}13b)$$

$$41.55 = 0.0 \qquad + .34 + 2 \times 8.1 + 2pE \qquad (4\text{-}13c)$$

$$pE = \tfrac{1}{2}(25.0) = 12.5 \qquad (4\text{-}13d)$$

It is apparent (Eqn. 4-13) that an increase in pH would be accompanied by a corresponding decrease in pE, and that pE is less sensitive to the partial pressure of oxygen. However, pE can be considered as the master variable in an oxidation-reduction system (just as pH is the master variable in an acid-base system). The master variable plot for the ferrous-ferric ion system is a typical example (Fig. 4-2).

It might seem likely that pH or pE could govern the concentration of dissolved iron in the model ocean or in sea water, but this does not seem to be true. There are three pertinent equilibria (Eqn. 4-13, -14, -15).

$$FeOOH_{(s)} + H^+ \rightleftarrows Fe(OH)_2^+ + H_2O; \ \log K = -2.35 \qquad (4\text{-}14)$$

$$FeOOH + 3H^+ \rightleftarrows Fe^{3+} + 2H_2O; \quad \log K = 41.0 \qquad (4\text{-}15)$$

$$e^- + Fe^{3+} \rightleftarrows Fe^{2+}; \qquad \log K = 13.0 \qquad (4\text{-}16)$$

These would be involved as a consequence of Step 12 (the addition of 0.55 mole FeOOH). (In addition, rearrangement of silicate phases and a minor adjustment of pH might be expected.) Sillén[1] regarded the first process (Eqn. 4-14) as the most

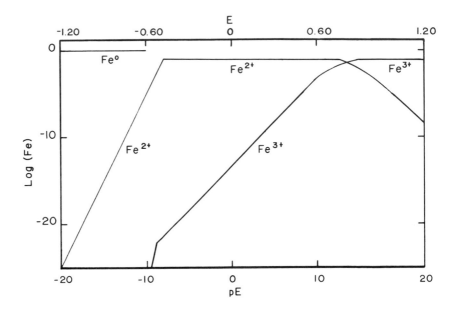

FIG. 4-2

Master variable plot for iron: log (Fe) as a function of pE.
Total concentration assumed to be $(Fe^{2+}) + (Fe^{3+}) = 0.1$ M,
except when in equilibrium with solid iron. (After Sillén[2])

important, since at the pH of sea water the concentration of
$Fe(OH)_2$ would be $10^{-10.45}$ M. In contrast, the average observed
concentration of dissolved iron is about $10^{-7.2}$ M. The equilibrium concentration of ferrous ion may be estimated from the
pertinent equilibrium equation and constant (Eqn. 4-17) obtained by combining Eqn. 4-15 and 4-16.

$$FeOOH_{(s)} + 3H^+ + e^- \quad Fe^{2+} + 2H_2O \qquad \log K = 17 \qquad (4-17)$$

Thus

$$\log (Fe^{2+}) = 17 - 3pH - pE = 17 - 24.3 - 12.5 = -20 \qquad (4-18)$$

Obviously, the equilibrium concentrations of Fe^{2+} and $Fe(OH)_2$ are too low to account for the observed dissolved iron concentration. In effect 99+% of the dissolved iron is present as unknown species. Typically, it is suggested that the iron is present as unknown species or complexes; this is reasonable because all of the metal ions probably exist in sea water as complexes of one type or another (Note 5). In this instance it is tempting to suggest that this is present in the form of a humate or iron salt of humic acid. These materials are the decomposition products of plant and animal matter found in the soil; specifically the acids comprise that fraction of soil that is alkali soluble, acid and alcohol insoluble. The main characteristics of the polyphenolic humic acids are structural complexity, a tendency to chelate or sequester trace metals (including iron), and an association with soil and, maybe, water fertility.[16] For example, it has been suggested that these materials are associated with blooms of dinoflagellates ("red tides"),[17] and it has been found that the growth rates of one dinoflagellate Gonyaulax tamarensis are enhanced in the presence of humic acid fractions.[18]

In summary, the nature of the iron complexes in sea water may be suggested, but these suggestions are, at present, speculative and are the subject of investigations in progress.

4.5 The Atmosphere

Up to this point little has been said about the composition of the atmosphere   (Table 4-6) which has two groups of constituents, nonvariable and variable. The composition of the nonvariable constituents is regarded as constant for most purposes, though there are reports of variability of oxygen composition (within 0.01%), for example and more seriously, the carbon dioxide concentration is evidently increasing. (The implications of this change will be considered in Chapter 8.) The composition of variable constituents (ozone, sulfur dioxide, nitrogen dioxide, ammonia, carbon monoxide, and sodium chloride, among others) depends upon the season and/or the location, depending upon the origin. There are in effect four main constituents of the atmosphere: nitrogen, oxygen, carbon dioxide, and argon.

Argon. This is perhaps the easiest gas to consider. Most (99.63%) of the argon exists in the form of ^{40}Ar with smaller amounts of ^{36}Ar (0.31%) and ^{38}Ar (0.06%). Argon-40 probably existed in the primordial earth as potassium-40 and has been formed by radioactive decay process (Eqn. 4-19) which is an extremely slow process.

$$^{40}K \rightarrow {}^{40}Ar + \beta^- \qquad\qquad (4\text{-}19)$$

Oxygen. It seems likely that the primordial atmosphere was essentially devoid of molecular oxygen and that all of the molecular oxygen in the contemporary atmosphere represents the

TABLE 4-6[19]

Present Average Composition of the Atmosphere

Constituent	% by Volume	ppm
A. "Nonvariable		
N_2	78.004±0.0004	
O_2	20.946±0.002	
CO_2	0.033±0.001	
Ar		18.18±0.04
He		5.24±0.004
Kr		1.14±0.01
Xe		0.087±0.0001
H_2		0.5
CH_4		2.0
B. "Variable"		
O_3^a		0-0.07 (summer)
		0.02 (winter)
SO_2^b		0-1
NO_2^b		0-0.02
NH_3^b		0-trace
CO^b		0-trace
$NaCl^c$		10^{-4} ppm

[a] From ultraviolet radiation.
[b] Industrial origin.
[c] Due to sea spray.

balance of five oxygen-producing and--consuming processes.

These are

1. Photochemical decomposition of water is an oxygen-
   producing process in which photons (hv) in the upper
   atmosphere effect decomposition (more) of water to
   oxygen and hydrogen (Eqn. 4-20), the latter being
   lost to outer space.

$$H_2O_{(g)} \xrightarrow{hv} H_{2(g)} + \tfrac{1}{2}O_{2(g)} \qquad (4\text{-}20)$$

2. Photosynthesis (Chapt. 9) leads to the production of
   molecular oxygen and organically bound carbon (Eqn.
   4-21).

$$CO_{2(g)} \xrightarrow{hv} C_{(org)} + O_2 \qquad (4\text{-}21)$$

3. Biological oxidation is, in effect, the reversal of
   Eqn. 4-21 and is an oxygen consuming process. Burial
   of the organically bound carbon or other withdrawal
   of photosynthesis products minimizes the oxidation
   process and leaves a net production of O_2.

4. Other oxidation processes that remove molecular
   oxygen from the atmosphere include oxidation of sulfide and ferrous minerals (cf. Fig. 3-6), oxidation
   of volcanic gases (especially $H_2)^{20}$ and oxidation due
   to industrial activity.

5. Sulfate-reducing bacteria use sulfate as a source of
   oxygen in the absence of molecular oxygen and when

organic compounds are present as an energy source.
The overall process, $SO_4^{2-} \rightarrow S^{2-} + 2O_2$, actually
consists of two steps, which occur in different environmental portions of the marine ecosystem: (1) sulfate reduction (Eqn. 4-22) occurs under anoxic
conditions (Note 6)

$$SO_4^{2-} + 2C_{(org)} \rightarrow 2CO_2 + S^{2-} \qquad (4\text{-}22)$$

and (2) photosynthesis (Eqn. 4-21) occurs near the
surface in the presence of light (hv).

The relative importance of these processes has varied
with geological history. In the primitive atmosphere, processes 1 and 2 must have been major oxygen-producing processes.
Now, the importance of photosynthesis (combined with burial or
removal of organically bound carbon) is evident. It appears
from estimates of the reduced and buried carbon (coal and
petroleum) in the earth's crust that photosynthesis has been
more than adequate to produce the present 21% by volume of
oxygen in the atmosphere. If so, why doesn't the atmosphere
contain more oxygen? Why does the oxygen content remain
constant, as it evidently does? In short, what are the oxygen-
regulating processes?

It seems likely that the regulatory process(es) must be
found in the sea. Conditions on land are less favorable for
producing any major changes in the molecular oxygen content of
the atmosphere because organically bound carbon is not easily

permanently entrapped (Note 7). Moreover any change in the dissolved oxygen content of the surface water will not remain permanently; the solubility of oxygen in a unit volume of sea water at the surface is one-twentieth that of a comparable volume of air. Thus, if any process resulted in an increase in dissolved oxygen at the sea surface, much of the increase would pass into the atmosphere. In effect, it may be more accurate to believe that the sea controls the oxygen composition of the atmosphere than to believe that the atmosphere controls the oxygen composition of the sea.

Granting this, what is the actual regulatory process? Redfield[21] suggested that the dissolved oxygen content in the sea (thus the atmosphere) may have been regulated by sulfate-reducing bacteria (process 5). At first glance, this might seem unlikely because most of the world ocean is well oxygenated and anoxic basins are rare (e.g., the Black Sea, the Cariaco Trench, and the Gulf of Cariaco in the Caribbean). there are, however, extensive areas of muds, marshes, and estuaries, that represent anoxic environments. There is good evidence that sulfate reduction occurs where anoxic environments exist in the sea.[19b] Presently, the oxygen produced by these processes may be little more than that required to balance the loss due to various oxidative processes (process 4).[21,22] At an earlier time in geologic history, anoxic conditions may have been more prevalent and the production of oxygen through sulfate reduction may have been more extensive.

At either time, the net production of oxygen would have been regulated by other portions of the sulfur biogeochemical cycle. Notably, these would include (1) removal of sulfides, e.g., by formation of unsoluble iron sulfides, or (2) the oxidation of sulfides by one of several processes.

Carbon dioxide. This gas will be the subject of a separate treatment (Chapter 8).

Nitrogen. In his first description of the model ocean, Sillén omitted nitrogen from consideration. One liter of the equilibrium model ocean should have about 0.10 mole of N_2, about 95-96% of which is present as molecular nitrogen gas. Nitrogen was omitted because this is a startling example of non-equilibrium. In effect there is a nitrogen problem: according to reasonable calculations there should be no molecular nitrogen in the atmosphere.

At present values of pH and pE in the ocean, nearly all of the nitrogen at equilibrium should exist as nitrate ion, NO_3^-. Moreover, an analysis of the present nitrogen budget would indicate that during the past 50 million years nearly all molecular nitrogen should have been converted to nitrate ion in the ocean. The calculations seem to be reasonable, as we shall see when we consider the nitrogen cycle (Chapter 7), but a process for reducing nitrate to N_2 seems to be missing. Possibly, more to the point, the organism or the portion of the nitrogen biogeochemical cycle that is responsible for the necessary process is missing.

An earlier atmosphere. Sillén[3] has described an imaginative experiment - reducing the equilibrium model ocean, i.e., assuming the pH of the ocean to be unchanged and checking the effects of a variation of pE. As the pE decreases to lower (more reducing) values, a number of changes would occur: (1) O_2 would disappear; (2) soluble forms of manganese would change from solid MnO_2 at pE = 7-8 to Mn^{2+} at pE = 3 or less; (3) iron would be reduced from the ferric to the ferrous state (4) sulfate would be converted to sulfides and be fixed in the form of insoluble minerals (pE<-5); (5) N_2 would change to NH_4^+ (pE < -5) and the latter would replace potassium ion in aluminosilicates; (6) inorganic carbon, as $CaCO_3$, would be converted to CH_4 (pE<-6).

Many have speculated that random reactions of organic compounds led to the formation of life in a primitive sea in contact with a reducing atmosphere. Some have mentioned the concentration of organic compounds (fatty acids, amino acids, carbohydrates, etc.) could have been as high as 10% by weight, which would have been a "protobiotic soup," more than an ocean. Sillén[3] has cast doubt on the likelihood of these high concentrations, and he has suggested that it is more

likely these concentrations would have been found in systems
isolated from the ocean (lagoons, shallow lakes, estuaries,
moist soil).

In summary, it appears reasonable to suppose from this
model that the early ocean might have had a composition generally comparable to the present one, though the atmosphere
may have contained mainly molecular nitrogen and some methane.

4.6 The Model Versus the Real Ocean

The remarkable feature of the equilibrium model system is
how closely it seems to approximate the chemical properties of
the real system. This does not imply that the two systems are
alike, because many components were omitted from the present
treatment and because it is recognized that the world ocean
does not truly exist in a state of equilibrium. The equilibrium model does show how a complex set of problems can be
broken down into a number of partial problems. It also reveals many unsolved problems in a different light. Finally,
it does indicate by virtue of its approximation of the real
system that if the real ocean is not in a state of equilibrium,
it has attained a steady state with respect to many properties.
It has been suggested that this is due to a combination of
mixing processes and biogeochemical cycles.

These cycles are entwined. For instance, the importance
of the sulfur biogeochemical cycle in the regulation of the
oxygen composition of the atmosphere has been considered

(Section 4-3). The sulfur cycle is associated with the phosphorus cycle (Fig. 3-6), which in turn is associated with the nitrogen and other cycles.

This relationship is indicated in Fig. 4-3 , which suggests a fundamental principle that the variation of phosphorus, nitrogen, and carbon is largely due to the synthesis or decomposition of organic matter.[21]

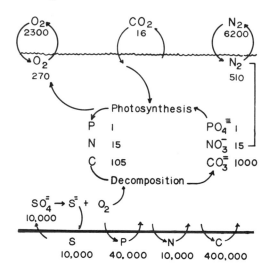

FIG. 4-3

Relative proportions and interaction of some major elements in the marine ecosystem. Ratios are based on the number of atoms per atom of phosphorus in sea water. (After Redfield[21]).

According to Liebig's "law of the minimum," the rate of growth is dependent upon that nutrient or condition (light, temperature, salinity) present in smallest quantity in terms of

need and availability. Thus, the limiting factor for growth
will be that constituent or condition present in the smallest
amount relative to the requirement. These requirements are
indicated by analyses of phytoplankton and changes in sea water
as a result of growth. The analysis of many samples of
phytoplankton provide the average values listed in Table 4-7.

TABLE 4-7[21]

Average Atomic Ratios of Elements Involved in a

Marine Ecosystem Biogeochemical Cycle

	P	N	C	O
Analyses of plankton	1	16	106	−276
Changes in sea water	1	15	105	−235
Available in sea water	1	15	1000	200−300

The oxidation of phytoplankton is estimated to require
about 276 atoms of oxygen. It is assumed that, on the average,
the oxidation state of carbon is that of carbohydrate (CH_2O),
the nitrogen is in the amino form ($-NH_2$, $-NHR$, $-NR_2$), and the
phosphorus is present in the maximum oxidation state. On the
average, organic matter might be formulated as $(CH_2O)_{106}(NH_3)_{16}$
H_3PO_4 for purposes of mass balance. This formula ignores all
trace elements and all deviations from the average analyses,
both of which may be significant.

Organic decomposition would involve (1) hydrolytic cleavage and release of NH_4^+ and $H_2PO_4^{2-}$ ions (Eqn. 4-23) and (2) concurrent biochemical oxidation of carbohydrate (Eqn. 4-24) and nitrogen (Eqn. 4-25). The sum of these (Eqn. 4-26) is the 276 atoms of oxygen per atom of phosphorus needed to produce complete oxidation.

$$(CH_2O)_{106}(NH_3)_{16}H_3PO_4 \rightarrow 106\ CH_2O + 16\ NH_3 + H_3PO_4 \qquad (4\text{-}23)$$

$$106\ CH_2O + 106\ O_2 \rightarrow 106\ CO_2 + 106\ H_2O \qquad (4\text{-}24)$$

$$16\ NH_3 + 32O_2 \rightarrow 16\ HNO_3 + 16\ H_2O \qquad (4\text{-}25)$$

$$(CH_2O)_{106}(NH_3)_{16}H_3PO_4 + 138\ O_2 \rightarrow 106\ CO_2 + 122\ H_2O$$
$$+ 16\ HNO_3 + H_3PO_4 \qquad (4\text{-}26)$$

On the other hand, as item 2 of Table 4-7 indicates, in many areas of the world ocean, nitrogen and phosphorus are used up simultaneously in constant proportion (15 atoms N: 1 atom P) by phytoplankton. As we shall see (Chapter 6), there are a good many exceptions, notably in surface or restricted waters. Nevertheless, the significance of the 15:1 ratio cannot be overlooked. It appears that phosphorus and nitrogen are commonly available in sea water (Table 4-7, item 3) in the proportions required for phytoplankton growth, though carbon is in great excess.

Considering these three items (analysis of phytoplankton, nutrient stripping, and availability), it would appear that phosphorus is a limiting or master element which controls the availability of the other elements. In turn, the limiting factor that controls the master element may be the solubility of calcium phosphate. It appears to some that the deeper waters are essentially saturated with $Ca_3(PO_4)_2$, and this could regulate phosphate concentration.[21]

The view of phosphorus as a master element provides a useful starting point for examining several important biogeochemical cycles in the coming chapters. It is necessarily a restricted view because it neglects the importance of other elements, such as silicon and iron, and the fact that these elements may be master elements in certain instances. Nevertheless, the view does emphasize the fundamental relationship between the environment, the organisms and the constituents of the marine ecosystem that has given the ocean and the atmosphere their present composition.

4.8 Summary

This chapter has been concerned with developing a model that helps rationalize the composition of the sea and the atmosphere. The utility of Sillén's equilibrium model is that it does this and points up areas for future study. The pH of the ocean, for instance, was explained by two mechanisms involving the carbonate or the silicate system as the major buffering agent; the silicate system appears to be responsible for the long-term constancy.

It appears that ocean composition has not changed substantially from early times, though the composition of the
atmosphere has. The processes that produce oxygen in the atmosphere include photochemical decomposition of water, photosynthesis, and the action of sulfate reducing bacteria. Processes that consume oxygen include biological oxidation and
various oxidative processes. There is reason to believe that
changes in oxygen content of the sea regulate the oxygen
content of the atmosphere and that the regulating processes
involve the association of the sulfur, phosphorus, and nitrogen biogeochemical cycles.

NOTES

1. It is estimated[3] that the amount of suspended solids
    carried to the sea during 100 million years[2] is in the
    range 250-640 kg/cm^2.

2. This equation might be interpreted in terms of an acid
    (volatiles)-base (igneous rock) titration. According to
    a current hypothesis ("dust-origin" or "cold earth"), the
    earth was formed by an aggregation of stony meteorite
    (chondritic) substance at low temperature about 4.5
    billion years ago. The temperature of the initially cold

earth increased due to heat liberated in radioactive disintegration. Volatiles would have distilled from the interior to the surface. This process would also be in
accord with a "hot-origin" hypothesis.

3. This view would clarify two mysteries: (1) generally no
sedimentary rock or sediment other than Jurassic (135-180
million years before present, B.P.) has been obtained from
the exposed ocean bottom; and (2) the layer of sediments
covering the earth's floor is too thin: it is the order of
hundreds of meters thick, instead of thousands of meters
as might be expected. On the other hand, Ewing and his
colleagues believe they have found evidence that indicates
the oldness rather than the youthfulness of the ocean
floor (Ref. 7, p. 238).

4. Illite is not used as a specific mineral name, but as a
designation of a group of clay mineral constituents of
argillaceous materials belonging to the mica group.

5. A complex or a coordination entity is formed when a metal
or a metal ion accepts a share in an electron pair provided by a donor atom.[17] This atom may be an ion or part
of a molecule, either of which are said to be ligands. A
chelate is a ligand that has two donor atoms bonded to a
metal.

6. The usage here follows that of Richards.[19] The term anoxic has been used to designate those conditions or environments that contain no dissolved oxygen, though other gases may be present. The adjective anerobic properly refers to organisms living in, or physiological processes occurring in, the absence of air. Commonly, the two words are used interchangeably.

7. Typically, soil is either eroded or well aerated and the organically bound carbon does not remain out of circulation for long. Oxygen-poor environments do exist in swamps, and here conditions are more favorable for permanent entrapment.

REFERENCES

1. L. G. Sillén, Oceanography, Publ. No. 67, AAAS, Washington, D. C., 1961, pp. 549-581.

2. L. G. Sillén, Adv. Chem. Ser., 67, 45, 57 (1967).

3. L. G. Sillén, Science, 156, 1189 (1967); Arkiv Kemi, 24, 431 (1965).

4. F. T. Mackenzie and R. M. Garrels, Am. J. Sci., 264, 507 (1966).

5. V. M. Goldschmidt, Fortschr. Mineral Krist. Petr., 17, 112 (1933).

6. M. K. Horn and J. A. S. Adams, Geochim. Cosmochim. Acta, 30, 279 (1966).

7. cf. H. Takeuchi, S. Uyeda, and H. Kanamori, Debate about the Earth, Freeman-Cooper, San Francisco, 1967.

8. J. T. Wilson, Continental Drift, Sci. Am., April, cf. p. 86; cf. E. Orowan, Sci. Am., November 1969, p. 103.

9. O. V. Shishkina, On the Salt Composition of Marine Interstitial Waters, Preprints, Int. Ocean Cong., pp. 977-980, AAAS, Washington, D. C., 1959.

10. W. M. Sackett and G. O. S. Arrhenius, Geochim. Cosmochim. Acta, 26, 155 (1962).

11. F. T. Mackenzie and R. M. Garrels, Science, 150, 57 (1965); F. T. Mackenzie, R. M. Garrels, O. P. Bricker, and F. Bickley, Science, 155, 1404 (1967).

12. H. D. Holland, Proc. Nat. Acad. Sci., U.S., 53, 1173 (1965).

13. J. J. Hemley, Amer. J. Sci., 257, 241 (1959); J. J. Hemley, C. Meyer, D. H. Richter, U.S. Geol. Surv. Profess. Paper 424-D (1961) p. 338.

14. R. M. Pytkowicz, Geochim. Cosmochim. Acta, 31, 63 (1967).

15. K. Park, D. W. Hood, and H. T. Odum, Publ. Inst. Mar. Sci., Univ. Tex., 5, 47 (1958).

16. C. Steelink, J. Chem. Educ., 40, 379 (1963).

17. cf. D. F. Martin, Adv. Chem. Ser., 67, 255 (1967).

18. A. Prakash and M. A. Rashid, Limnol. Oceanog., 13, 598 (1968).

19. (a) F. A. Richards in Chemical Oceanography (J. P. Riley and G. Skirrow, eds.) Vol. 1, Academic Press, New York, 1965, pp. 198-199; ibid., Chap. 13; (b) E. Gleuckauf in Compendium of Meteorology (T. F. Malone, ed.) American Meteorological Society, Boston, 1951, pp. 3-10.

20. H. D. Holland, Proc. Nat. Acad. Sci., 53, 1173 (1965).

21. A. C. Redfield, Am. Scientist, 46, 205 (1958).

22. W. F. Claussen, Science, 156, 1228 (1967).

5

THE SILICON CYCLE

5.1 Introduction

The importance of biogeochemical cycles in regulating the concentration of many constituents of the marine ecosystem has been emphasized in the preceding chapter. As noted earlier, the sulfur biogeochemical cycle may be responsible for regulating the constancy of the oxygen content of the atmosphere. Moreover, this cycle is associated with the biogeochemical cycles of carbon, nitrogen, phosphorus, and silicon. In this and succeeding chapters these cycles will be considered in reverse order. This order seems to be a logical one in terms of increasing complexity of the oxidation states and the number of forms of a given element.

The silicon cycle is a useful starting point because combined silicon exists in only one oxidation state and because silicates seem to be involved in the regulation of the ocean pH on a long-term basis.

The major processes of the silicon biogeochemical cycle are represented schematically in Fig. 5-1. Weathering of igneous rock (1) leads to the removal of silicon in the form of clays and dissolved silica which are transported to the sea via

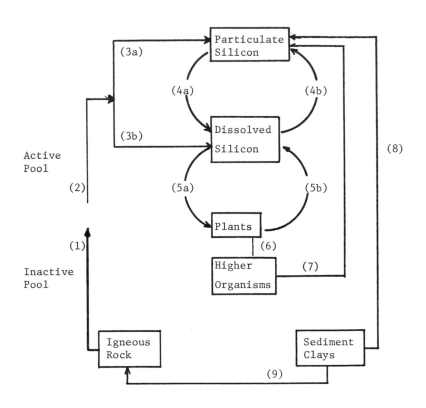

FIG. 5-1

Portions of the silicon cycle.
(See text for explanation of numbers.)

streams and rivers (2). Interaction occurs and silicon is present in the ocean as reconstituted clays (3a) or as dissolved silicon (3b). It appears that further process of interaction can occur,[1] as silicates typical of those suspended in streams release dissolved silica to the sea (4a) or take up

dissolved silica from silica-enriched sea water (4b). Dissolved silicon is used by lower organisms in primary productivity (5a); these organisms may die and release silica (5b) or
they may be ingested by higher organisms (6). The organisms
release silicon either upon excretion or death (7). Particulate silicon (as clays, dead organisms, or other forms) sinks
to the ocean bottom (8). Ultimately, the sediment and sea
water are entrapped and converted to igneous rock (process 9;
cf. Notes 2 and 3, Chapter 4). This would complete the cycle.

It is evident (Fig. 5-1) that silicon exists in the marine
ecosystem as dissolved and particulate silicon. An understanding of the nature and properties of these forms (Sections
5.2, 5.3) is the key to understanding the cycle. With this information, analysis of the processes of the cycle (Section 5.4)
should be more meaningful and should lead to a better understanding of the variation of silicon in the ecosystem
(Section 5.5).

5.2 Dissolved Silicon

The dissolved forms exist largely as orthosilicic acid,
$Si(OH)_4$. There is a small fraction (about 5% at pH 8.1)
that exists as dissociated forms, as indicated by the values of
3.90×10^{-10} and 1.95×10^{-13} for the first and second dissociation constants, respectively (cf. Sillén[2]). There is a difference of opinion about the existence of polymerized forms.
It seems likely that in sea water silicon exists as monomeric

Si(OH)$_4$ rather than as a colloidal form.[2,3] How much silicon

exists in the form of oligomeric silicic acid (molecules con-

taining up to six condensed SiO$_4$$^{4-}$ tetrahedra) is open to ques-

tion[4] because there is reason to believe that sea water favors

depolymerization.[3] Probably much of the disagreement and un-

certainty is due to: (1) the solubility of silica in sea water;

and (2) the significance of the colorimetric method used for

silicon analysis.

The solubility of silica in sea water has been the subject of

study and the results have been summarized by Stöber,[4]

Krauskopf,[5] and Siever[6] (cf. Table 5-1). The factors involved

in the solubility include the following:

1.   Polymorphic form. Different silica polymorphs (quartz,

     amorphous silica, etc.) have different solubilities. For

     example, quartz samples did not show measurable solution

     in distilled water at 25°, even after three years.[6]

     Amorphous silica may be artificial (hydrated and dehy-

     drated silica gel) or skeletal remains of silica-secreting

     organisms (diatoms, radiolaria, and siliceous sponges).

     Under comparable conditions, various samples of amorphous

     silica have about the same solubility at 25°C (120-240

     ppm), but solubilities of diatom frustules vary markedly

     from diatom to diatom.

TABLE 5-1

Solubility Data for Silicon[5,6]

Form	Conditions	$t^{\circ}C$	Solubility, ppm
Amorphous	distilled	0	60–80
Gel	water	25	132–148
		90	300–380
Gel	artificial sea water	25	132–5, 145
Gel	brine, 30,000– 50,000 ppm	25	138–142
Gel	EDTA + distilled water	25	130,148
Quartz	distilled water	25	10^a
	washed, 2–5µ distilled H_2O	125	94–104
	same	140	125–132

[a]Extrapolated value; $\log SiO_2 (ppm) = 4.829 - 1.132 \times 10^3/T^{\circ}K$

2. _Particle size_. This is not a critical factor in determining the solubility of amorphous silica, unless the particle diameters are less than 50 mµ.

3. Surface area.[4] Once surface irregularities of silica
   particles were removed by etching with sodium hydroxide,
   the dissolution curves (dissolved silica as a function of
   times) were very reproducible. The curves depend upon the
   total surface exposed, the volume of the solution, and the
   composition of the solution. If the surface is not etched
   the initial dissolution may be enhanced, probably because
   of fine particles adhering to certain regions of the surface. Also, silicic acid may be adsorbed on the surface
   in time and form a coating that inhibits dissolution.

4. Ionic strength. The solubility of amorphous silica gel in
   distilled water and in sea water is approximately equal,
   according to Siever.[6] The dissolution rate of crystalline
   silica was enhanced in an aqueous solution of 0.9% NaCl
   and 0.1% $NaHCO_3$; chloride ions reportedly have a catalytic
   effect via the hydrolysis of Si-O-Si bonds.[4] The bicarbonate was supposed to prevent the pH from attaining low
   values.

5. pH. The solubility of amorphous silica gel increases with
   pH above pH 9;the solubility is little affected by changes
   of pH in the range 1-9.[4,5]

6. Temperature.[6] The solubility of amorphous silica and
   quartz increase with temperature and probably are nearly
   equal at a temperature greater than 200°. If a sediment
   contained both quartz and amorphous silica, the water at

the solid-liquid interface should become saturated with respect to amorphous silica, not quartz; this is not always true and factors other than relative rates of dissolution and precipitation (as measured in the laboratory) may be involved. The importance of organic materials or trace metal ions that complex silica deserves emphasis, as indicated by the following observations.

7. Chelating agents. The solubility of amorphous silica is greatly reduced in humic acid solutions, possibly because of adsorption of organic compounds on the free silica gel surface. Siever[6] found that adding EDTA (ethylenediaminetetraacetic acid), an effective chelating agent, had no effect on the solubility of silica (Table 5-1). Presumably the EDTA would have sequestered any trace metal impurities that might have interacted with silicic acid. On the other hand, chelating agents do seem to minimize the retardation of diatom cell dissolution.[7]

8. Trace metals. Certain trace metals (aluminum, beryllium, iron, among others) can retard the dissolution of diatoms in sea water at pH 8, and there appears to be incorporation of small amounts of aluminum or iron in the siliceous material of diatoms.[7,8] These and related observations are considered in more detail (Section 5.4).

Analysis of silicon. The interpretation of these observations depends upon the significance of the colorimetric (molybdate)

151

method used for the analysis of dissolved silica (Vol. 1, Chapter 15). It is generally conceded that the molybdate method measures "reactive" silica as opposed to total dissolved silica. Silicic acid (1-6 units) can polymerize at the pH of the sea water to give oligomeric silicic acid. It appears that monomeric silicic acid reacts with molybdate in about 75 seconds, though dimeric and other oligomeric silicic acids require 10 minutes or more.[9] In contrast, one determination[10] of total silica consisted of causing depolymerization (by heating the sample which had been made very alkaline) then analyzing a neutralized sample.

Thus, the colorimetric method may not measure all of the soluble silicate, but the values have been regarded as useful. For example, Lewin[11] found that all the silicon determined by the colorimetric method could be utilized by some diatoms. The reactive silicon is not necessarily a measure of "significant" silicon, i.e., the amount available to growing cells. For instance, Golterman[12] described the use of ethyl orthosilicate $[Si(OC_2H_5)_4]$ as a silicon source for diatoms. Thus silicate hydrolyzes in water to produce colloidal silica which is available for diatoms but unreactive to molybdate. In general, though, the "reactive" silicon is a useful approximation of the significant silicon if, as has been suggested,[2] the amount of colloidal or unreactive silica in sea water is limited.

5.3 Particulate Silicon

The importance of suspended or particulate silicon minerals in affecting the pH of the sea water has been discussed (Section 4.3). There are several additional features that deserve comment here.

1. Amount. The amount of suspended material, even in clear pelagic water, varies significantly in a given body of water. Jacobs and Ewing[13] report the results of the three-year study of distribution of particulate matter in major oceans (Table 5-2). Most samples from clear pelagic water were in the range 0-10 mg/200 liters, and the next largest number of samples were in the range of 10-20 mg/200 liters. The reported concentrations were much lower than those reported by other workers[13] (cf. Armstrong[3] and Table 5-2). No explanation for the variance was offered.[13] It must be noted though that the possibilities of contamination, the chief source of error in this determination, are ever present and difficult to overcome.

2. Horizontal distribution. It is evident[13] from the mean values for clear ocean water that the order of concentration in major ocean bodies is: South Pacific < North Pacific < North Atlantic < South Atlantic < Indian Ocean. The concentrations of suspended matter increase toward the continental shelf.

TABLE 5-2

Suspended Particulate Matter in the Major Oceans

Water Bodies	Concentration, mg/200 liters	
	Range	Mean
N. Atlantic	0.1-49.5	9.8
S. Atlantic	0.3-39.4	10.2
N. Pacific	0.1-30.5	7.5
S. Pacific	0.9-17.3	5.9
Indian	1.8-35.4	14.3
	100-200[a]	

[a]Lisitzin data.[14]

3. Vertical distribution. There is a critical variation below the surface layer according to some workers, though
not according to others. Hobson,[15] for example, found no
variation in particle size with depth in the N. E. Pacific,
which he interpreted as indicating that the chemical composition did not change with residence time below 250 m.
Moreover, vertical as well as horizontal distributions
appeared to be controlled mainly by advection. Jacobs
and Ewing[13] reported that where a thick accumulation of
pelagic sediment occurs there is a nephelinic layer ex-
tending upward for several hundred meters. It appears

that oceanic deposition occurs in this layer, and evidently particles in this layer have been transported long distances before settling on the bottom.

4. Silicon content. The suspended matter seems to have an appreciable silicon content which varies with location and depth.[3] For example, the SiO_2 content of particulate matter in the eastern North Atlantic was reported to be in the range 8-80%. At the surface, the amount of suspended silicon evidently exceeded the amount of dissolved silicon; below 100 m, the suspended silicon was 2-10% of the dissolved silicon. This trend is probably real, though the actual values are suspect in view of other findings.[13]

5. Types of particulate silicon.[16] Two types of particulate silicon are involved, biogenic (such as diatom frustules) and nonbiogenic. About 60% of the nonbiogenic phase of pelagic deposits is composed of particles less than 2μ in size (Table 5-3). The clay-size fraction of the sediments is essentially represented by four clay minerals: illite, montmorillonite, chlorite, and kaolinite. The distribution of these minerals in the sediments of the world ocean has been analyzed by Griffin, Windom, and Goldberg.[16] In general terms: (1) chlorite is characterized as a high-latitude mineral because it is found in

TABLE 5-3

Clay-Size Particle Contents of Carbonate-Free Sediments[16]

Sediment Type	Area	Percentage by Wt. < 2 μ Fraction
Suspended river	33 U.S. rivers	37
Continental shelf	U.S., Atlantic coast	2
	Gulf of California	19
	Gulf of Mexico	27
	Australia (N.W.), Sahul shelf	72
Pelagic	Atlantic	58
	Indian	64
	Pacific	61

greatest abundance in the polar regions; (2) montmorillonite is indicative of a <u>volcanic</u> regime, though some comes
directly from the continents; (3) kaolinite is characterized as a <u>low-latitude</u> mineral; (4) illite concentrations
tend to indicate the contribution of <u>riverborne</u> <u>solids</u> to
the sediments, though airborne input of illite is significant in the northeast Atlantic.[16]

6. <u>Modes of entry of particulate silicon.</u>[16] The relative
amounts of clay-size particles in the sea and the sediment
their rate of accumulation,·, and the mineral type in the
sediment depend upon (1) the source, (2) the mode of entry

from land to the sea (by atmospheric winds, by glaciers, by rivers), and (3) the topography of the sea floor. These factors have been considered in detail for several oceanic provinces.[16]

The modes of entry and the rates of accumulation for the Atlantic Ocean are summarized in Table 5-4. Five zones have been suggested.[16] In two polar zones (1, 5: > $50°N$ or > $50°S$), glacial movements represent the major transport mechanism, though there are appreciable contributions of airborne material (chiefly montmorillonite). The lowest rate of accumulation is in zone 4 (for the Atlantic or the Pacific), presumably because there is less land area per unit of ocean area. Granting this, there should be higher rates of accumulation in the northern hemisphere (zone 2), as seems to be the case. The high rates seem to be due to high input of airborne materials because the highest concentration of illite was found in the northeast Atlantic where the river contribution was not significant. Input of illite from the air and from rivers both seem to be significant in the third zone. Two areas (mid-Atlantic Ridge Valley vs. the area from the continents to the flanks of the ridge) exist within zones 2-4. The two areas have substantially different rates of sedimentation which is attributable to the topography factor. The rates in the ridge valleys represent the

TABLE 5-4

Modes of Entry and Rates of Accumulation

of Sediments in the Atlantic Ocean[16]

Ocean	Zone	Mode of Entry	Rate of Accumulation (mm/1000 years)
Atlantic 1,	50°N	Glacial from Arctic Polar easterlies, Jet stream	–
2,	15°N-50°N	Jet stream,	$0.3-0.5^a$
		St. Lawrence River	$2-7^b$
3,	15°S-15°N	Trade Winds	$0.7-0.8^a$
		South American,	
		African rivers	$1-8^b$
4,	50°S-15°S	Jet stream	$0.2-0.4^a$
			$2-6^b$
5,	50°S	Glacial from Antarctic Polar easterlies, Jet stream	2

^{a}Mid-Atlantic Ridge Valley.

^{b}Continents to flanks of Ridge.

limit of input due to windborne (eolian) transport. The valleys are protected by topography and remoteness from input by riverborne solids.

In summary, the concentration of suspended silicon is probably less than has been estimated in the past. The concentration in the northern hemisphere is greater than in the southern because of the greater land area per unit ocean area. The distribution of clay-sized particles and the mineral types is a useful indication of the origin and mode of entry of non-biogenic particulate silicon.

5.4   Some Processes of the Silicon Cycle

Some factors involved in changes in the concentration of silicon in the marine environment include - river transport, transformation of clay minerals, incorporation into organisms, dissolution of plants, and physical properties.

River Transport. Input of particulate silicon by river transport is only one of three modes of entry, but it deserves special consideration. River transport represents a significant contribution to the clay-sized fraction of the sediments near the shelf, and more information is available concerning this mode of entry than for the other two.

The effect of river transport on silicon distribution requires an estimate of the rate of chemical denudation (Note 1) of the continents. This estimate requires, in turn, an estimate of the area of the land surface, the runoff of various rivers, and the analysis of the constituents of those rivers. The data in Tables 5-5 and 5-6 summarize this information. There are obvious limitations in the use of these data particularly because of the paucity of analysis of certain major areas, notably Africa. Though the data in these tables might

159

TABLE 5-5

River Discharge Data[17]

Region	Area, 10^3 miles^2	Runoff 10^3 ft^3/sec	Chemical Denudation
North America	8,172	5,510	85[a]
South America	7,551	8,962	73
Europe	4,211	2,796	110
Asia	17,985	12,431	83
Africa	11,500	6,604	63
Australia	2,970	354	6

[a]Metric tons of substances removed each year per square mile of total land surface.

not be as accurate as might be wished, they do serve to indicate several points of major interest.

1. The <u>amount</u> of chemical denudation is impressive. According to one estimate, rivers introduce 8.3 billion tons of suspended solids into the sea each year.[18] The amount of dissolved solids introduced annually is about 3.9 billion tons. It appears that if denudation is equated with erosion, the continental United States is being lowered 1-3 inches per thousand years.[19]

2. The <u>range</u> of chemical denudation is also impressive. Europe has the highest rate of chemical denudation, though the actual value might be reduced when data become

TABLE 5-6

Mean Composition of Rivers of the World[17]

Region	Mean Composition, ppm								Total[a]
	Cl	Na	SO_4	Mg	Ca	K	HCO_3^-	SiO_2	
Sea	19.353	10.76	2.712	1.294	0.413	0.387	0.142		35
North America	8	9	20	5	21	1.4	68	9	142
South America	4.9	4	4.8	1.5	7.2	2	31	11.9	69
Europe	6.9	5.4	24	5.6	31.1	1.7	95	7.5	182
Asia	8.7	b	8.4	5.6	18.4	b	79	11.7	142
Africa	12.1	11	13.5	3.8	12.5	-	43	23.2	121
Australia	10	2.9	2.6	2	3.9	1.4	31.6	3.5	59
World	7.8	6.3	11.2	4.1	15	2.3	58.4	13.1	120

[a]Mean total dissolved solids, ppm.

[b]$_{Na}$ + K = 9.3.

available for Mediterranean Europe. Livingstone[17] suggests
that two factors may contribute to the high rate, the
moist European climate and the existence of large areas of
fine-grained Pleistocene deposits (Note 2). The rate for
Asia is impressively great if one remembers that there
are extensive areas of desert that contribute nothing to
the rate. Finally, Australia has the lowest rate.
Roughly one-third of the continent has no rivers flowing
to the sea; the remainder has perennial rivers that are
very dilute despite abundant rainfall. Evidently, the
rocks present are very resistant to weathering and most
have been leached for a considerable time.

3. The data indicate that rivers are rich in calcium and
potassium relative to the oceans. Moreover, only about
10% of the potassium now carried to the sea remains in
solution and this must be explained in terms of the reactions of dissolved solids.

Transformation of Clay Minerals.

Reactions of suspended solids. At least four reactions
occur when suspended solids in rivers come in contact with sea
water.[1,20] These are the following:

1. Base exchange is the replacement of calcium in riverborne
clays by sodium, potassium, and magnesium. This reaction

162

occurs in a few tens of hours, which is short with respect to the residence time of the clays. This process obviously changes the weight percentage of calcium in the clays, and, to a lesser extent, alters the weight percentage of silicon. The process has other consequences because presently, clay minerals are removing more sodium and magnesium than potassium from the ocean. Obviously, there must be potassium-extracting processes operating; reconstitution is one such process.

2. Reconstitution of degraded illites and chlorites involves an increase in the percentage of potassium and magnesium, respectively, to give typical illite and chlorite. This, too, is apparently initiated rapidly. Many consider the extraction of potassium by the reconstitution and formation of illite to be one of the more important processes operative in the sea. It also has been suggested that a major portion of the potassium brought to the ocean is removed by entrapment in interstitial water in marine and delta muds; then after deep burial this potassium may be fixed in the illite lattice.[21]

3. Uptake and loss of silicon by clay minerals in contact with silicon-rich or silicon-poor ocean waters, respectively, may be an important silicon-regulating process. Mackenzie and Garrels and co-workers[1] have demonstrated

that clay minerals typical of those suspended in streams release silica to silica-deficient sea water or remove silica from silica-rich sea water (Table 5-7). In their experiments, silica-poor systems ultimately had silica concentrations typical of sea water (dissolved silica about 6 ppm). The silicon-rich systems ultimately had silica concentrations somewhat higher than typical silica

TABLE 5-7

Uptake and Release of Silica from Sea Water
by Some Clay Minerals[1]

Mineral[a]	Silica-Poor System[b]		Silica-Rich System[c]	
	ΔSiO_2, ppm	pH, final	ΔSiO_2, ppm	pH, final
Chlorite	+4.2	7.85	-8.8	7.91
Glauconite	+3.6	6.61	-17.7	6.77
Kaolinite A	+3.8	7.91	-7.5	7.75
Montmorillonite	7.8	7.92	-10.2	7.83
Illite	5.7	7.79	-7.0	7.80

[a]One-gram mineral samples (< 62μ) in 200 ml of sea water at room temperature.

[b]Initially: SiO_2 = 0.33 ppm, pH = 8.18; reaction time = 8850 hr.

[c]Initially: SiO_2 = 25 ppm, pH = 8.10; reaction time = 7050 hr.

concentrations. Evidently, the release of silica depends upon the formation of a degraded and ill-defined aluminosilicate or a hydrated aluminum oxide, but the uptake of silica is governed by the formation of other siliceous substances.

4. Formation of new clay minerals in the marine environment (authigenesis) has been the subject of much consideration.[3,16] The four major clay minerals considered (illite, montomorillonite, chlorite, and kaolinite) have continental sources, but only montmorillonite is formed in the marine environment in significant amounts.[16] This mineral is evidently produced in the marine ecosystem by the degradation of volcanic materials. The input of these materials is largely eolian, as noted earlier. Other authigenic clay minerals are found to a lesser extent in the marine ecosystem, and in certain locations the process may be very significant. For example, Swindale and Fan[22] have demonstrated that gibbsite, $Al(OH)_3$, is transformed to the clay mineral chlorite in Waimea Bay of Kauai, Hawaii. Gibbsite, which occurs in the soils and weathered rocks of Hawaii, is eroded and deposited in the sea where the transformation to clay minerals occurs rapidly. Chlorite is evidently favored in the environment of Waimea Bay.

165

Many examples of authigenic minerals might be expected.
The concentrations of silicic acid, magnesium, potassium,
and hydrogen ions in sea water are only slightly greater
than those required for the stability of many layer silicates (kaolin, mica, chlorite), according to one suggestion.[23] Authigenic montmorillonite, chlorite, and probably a few others (glauconite, phillipsite, illite) have
been found.[3] Why not more? Probably the answer is that
it is difficult to distinguish authigenic minerals from
those that are not.

Incorporation into Organisms. Silicon is undersaturated in the
sea. The expected solubility is about 140 ppm (Table 5-1); the
observed average value is about 6 ppm. There are probably two
reasons for this. First, a hydroxylated magnesium silicate
precipitates from sea water when the silica concentration exceeds 26 ppm and the pH is 8.1.[1] The second reason is biological activity or incorporation of silica into organisms,
which is responsible for an additional reduction of the amount
of dissolved silica in sea water.

The factors that are involved in the uptake and loss of
silicon from organisms are of great interest but there are at
least two major experimental difficulties involved in studying
these factors: (1) contact with glass must be avoided and (2)
the organisms must be grown in nontoxic transparent containers. These problems have been overcome, and the experimental

observations of Jorgensen[24] and Lewin[11,25] may be summarized as follows:

1. Growth rate vs. silicon concentration. The growth rates of selected diatoms (e.g., Nitzschia palea, fresh water) is proportional to the silicate concentration of the medium. A minimum concentration (30-40 µg Si/liter) of silicate seems to be needed below which growth rates decrease, even though other nutrients are added.

2. Silicate inhibition. Assimilation of silicate is inhibited in late stages of growth, in a static or a flowing medium. Silicon assimilation (Navicula pelliculosa) is associated with aerobic respiration, and silicon uptake is inhibited by respiratory inhibitors.

3. Effects of trace metals. Cadmium inhibits uptake of silicon by Navicula pelliculosa, though cadmium is not a respiratory inhibitor. The effect of cadmium ion may be related to its ability to reduce the sulfur (as sulfate or sulfide) concentration because the sulfide or sulfate ions increased the uptake rate of washed cells.

Dissolution of Organisms. It is believed that this process would significantly alter the silicon concentration of surface waters or of shallow seas, but not of deep waters. The suspended matter of deep water has a low silicon content (Section 5-3) and dissolution would cause little alteration of the silicon concentration in the deep water. In contrast, the silicon content of suspended matter is greater in surface water, and living or recently dead diatom frustules represent a significant fraction of the suspended matter there.

Despite the obvious importance of the process, direct evidence for dissolution of diatoms seems to be scarce.[3] Laboratory experiments indicate the solubility of diatom frustules in sea water varies with the species, the state, and the age of the organism. These points have been discussed by Cooper[26] and Armstrong,[3] who summarize many of the apparently contradictory findings. Many observations can be understood if Cooper's modified postulate is accepted[26]: the silica in diatom frustules is similar to hydrated silica dispersed in water, but is protected with a coating or constituent which retards dissolution. Examples of laboratory and field studies are available.

A laboratory study was conducted by Lewin,[7] who investigated dissolution of silica from frustules of Navicula pelliculosa. Living or killed cells or cleaned frustules were pretreated in various ways, then allowed to dissolve for several days under controlled conditions (pH 9-9.3, 19°C). The rate of solution was determined by measuring the dissolved silica in the supernatant liquid (after the cells had been removed by centrifugation). Solubility equilibrium limits (40-50 mg Si/liter) were reached rather than complete dissolution.

Very little silicon dissolved from the walls of living cells during a several-week period of darkness. Any treatment that killed cells (heat, protein-denaturing agents, organic solvents, breakage) was accompanied by an increase in the rate of silica dissolution; treatment with hot concentrated nitric acid was most effective.

An inorganic constituent, rather than an organic coating, seemed to retard dissolution of dead cells (though there may be an additional mechanism of stabilizing the walls of living cells). The retarding factor could be removed or the effects minimized by treatment with a chelating agent such as EDTA, which should remove a multivalent cation, but not organic coating. Also, the protective factor could be dissolved in hot nitric acid, but not decomposed by the treatment, which may eliminate the possibility of an organic coating. The nitric acid extract was evaporated to dryness and the residue was dissolved in water to give a solution which could be used to treat cleaned cells and reduce their solubility.

Certain metal ions under specific conditions affected the rate of dissolution of diatoms. Acid-washed cell walls were treated with solutions of various metal ions. Lanthanum, chromium, calcium, magnesium, and molybdate pretreatments had no significant effect on the solubility of the cell walls. Aluminum, beryllium, iron, gallium, gadolinium, and yttrium pretreatment retarded the rates of dissolution of the treated cells to varying degrees. Pretreatment with aluminum ion was effective in retarding dissolution, both with the dead but intact cells and the acid-washed cells.

The effect of certain adsorbed inorganic cations in retarding the rate of dissolution is probably an important factor in the insolubility or persistence of diatomaceous ooze in the marine environment. This is true even though the effective concentrations of most of the metal ions used by Lewin[7] are considerably greater than those present in sea water. The iron or aluminum that may be present within the living cell may be enough to have a retarding effect. For example, Rogall[8] reported that silica valves (which may be transmitted from cell to cell) adsorbed about 1.0% aluminum (or 2% Al_2O_3).

These results may be correlated with those of Berger,[27] who studied the solution of radiolarian (Note 3) skeletons suspended at various depths in the central Pacific. Siliceous Radiolaria from planktonic samples evidently dissolved eight times faster than those from sediment. This observation is consistent with (1) the observed effect of an organic coating on "fresh," not older shells:or (2) the effect of adsorbed inorganic cations. The percent of solution (of siliceous radiolaria from Recent sediments) decreased with depth, and was consistent with (1) observed decrease in temperatures and (2) increase in dissolved silica with depth. Presumably, the solubility of siliceous skeletons would be reduced in silica-rich (deeper) waters, other factors being equal.

Physical Properties. At least two physical properties probably have a major influence on the variation of silicon concentration in the sea: temperature and solubility of certain minerals. The variation of silica solubility with temperature (Table 5-1) is striking but is not an explanation of the under-saturation of silicon in the sea. The amount of dissolved silica in sea water is only about 5-10% of the expected value. The incorporation of silica in organisms is regarded as being responsible for much of the undersaturation.[6]

Possibly, a very important factor in the undersaturation of silica is the insolubility of hydroxylated magnesium silicate, as noted earlier.[1] The solubility of this material limited the dissolved silica in actual sea water (pH 8.1) to about 26 ppm, though Siever[6] reported much greater solubilities in artificial sea water. Possibly, the artificial sea water did not adequately reflect the properties of real sea water.

In summary, it seems that there are many processes of the silicon cycle that cause the variation of silica content of

sea water. Two major factors are probably responsible for the
undersaturation of silica in sea water: (1) biological activity and uptake of silica into organisms;and (2) the insolubility of a material believed to be a hydroxylated magnesium
silicate.[1]

5.5 Variation of Silicon in the Marine Ecosystem

Armstrong[3] has written an excellent review of the variation of silicon concentrations in the marine ecosystem. This
summary and subsequent work indicate that the two major ecosystems, coastal waters and major oceans, need to be considered
separately.

Coastal Waters. The coastal waters are characterized by a
high silicon content, due to land drainage, and a large
seasonal variation in silicon content, due to variation of
biological activity and variation in physical properties
(river runoff, upwelling, development of a thermocline, etc.).
There are three examples:

1.   Influence of silicon-rich rivers. Voipio (cf. Armstrong[3])
      found a major decrease in the silicon content of surface
      waters going from the silicon-rich rivers (Si, 14-28 mg
      Si/liter),which entered the Gulf of Bothnia (8.40-16.80
      mg Si/liter),which adjoins the Bothnia Sea (5.60-8.40 mg
      Si/liter) which empties into the Baltic Sea (2.8-5.8 mg
      Si/liter). Bottom samples (100 m) contained about twice

the concentration of silicon as surface samples in the
Baltic, but the concentration was uniform in the water
column in the northern Gulf of Bothnia. The silicon
content was a linear function of the chlorinity, though
the slope was less than that calculated for simple mixing
of silicon-rich river water and silicon-poor sea water.
The reduced slope was ascribed to the influence of biological activity. Similar, though more extensive, observations[28,29] have been made for the mixing of the
Columbia River and the North Pacific.

2. Seasonal variations. Regular observations have been made
at Station E.1 about 22 miles from Plymouth (Note 4).
There are coastal influences here: the concentration of
silicate increases rapidly toward Plymouth and there are
considerable gradients in the area around Station E.1.
The seasonable patterns are evident. In general, seasonal
changes in the silicate concentration resemble changes in
the phosphate concentration, though the changes in silicate tend to be greater and less regular (Fig. 5-2).[30]
A cycle begins with a winter maximum. This is followed
by a rapid decrease in April and May, as silicon and
phosphorus are utilized in phytoplankton blooms. Some regeneration occurs during summer months as the phytoplankton growth diminishes. A secondary phytoplankton bloom

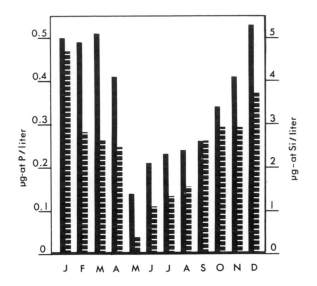

FIG. 5-2

Integral mean concentrations in water column at
International Hydrographic Station E.1 in 1954.
Orthophosphate, solid bar; silicate, dashed bar
(cf . Armstrong and Butler[30]).

in late summer or early fall may deplete silicon and

phosphorus slightly. The cycle is completed with a re-

generation phase in late fall and winter. The variation

of silicate and phosphate within the water column (Fig.

5-2) is a significant feature of the cycle. The decrease

for February was ascribed to the influx of another body of

water, not diatom growth, because there was not a corre-

sponding decrease in phosphate. The pronounced differ-

ences in values at 10 and 50 m are due to two effects:

(1) growth of diatoms which removed silicate and phosphate and (2) development of a stable thermocline (cf. Section 2.6) at 30 m in May which limited vertical mixing until the breakdown in September.[31]

3. Other factors. Duxbury and McGary[29] studied time-dependent influences of the Columbia River on changes of salinity and nutrients at sea. The data collected at three anchor stations demonstrate that routine measurements from single hydrocasts can give rise to misleading assessments. As noted earlier the river supply and biological utilization may vary and affect silicate concentrations. Other factors include upwelling, tidal and wind-induced currents, and small variations in station locations. Some adjustment must be made for the short-term variations produced by these factors.

    In general, silicate concentration seems to be a good indication of what processes are occurring in coastal waters, provided it is coupled with salinity and compared with mixture curves as Voipio,[3] Duxbury and McGary,[29] and others[3] have done.

Major Oceans. The distribution of silicon in major oceans has been reviewed by Armstrong.[3] There are several features which may be recognized:

1. Variation with depth. There seem to be three categories based on the variation of silicate with depth (Table 5-8)

TABLE 5-8
Types of Silicon Distribution in Major Oceans

Type	Variation with Depth	Silicate at Bottom General	mg Si/liter	Example
I	Small positive gradient, little variation	low	1-2	N. Atlantic
II	Marked positive gradient to mud depth then no change	high	4-5	N. Pacific N. Indian S. Atlantic
III	Marked positive gradient, several breaks, complex, no minimum value	medium-high	3-5	S. Atlantic S. Indian S. Pacific

and the concentration of silicate in bottom waters. The category of the South Atlantic is uncertain.

2. Surface waters. In general, concentrations of silicate in the upper 100 m are adequate for phytoplankton growth with two exceptions - in several areas of the Atlantic (the Antilles arc, the Sargasso Sea, the Woods Hole-Bermuda area) and the Antarctic. In these regions, it may be reasonable to conclude that the low silicate concentrations have limited plant growth.

3. High silicate concentrations (5 mg Si/liter) are characteristic of the deep waters of the North Pacific, the North Indian, and the Antarctic Oceans.

The concentration differences between the Pacific-Indian

and the Atlantic Oceans (Type II, III vs. Type I) have
been ascribed to the restricted exchange of bottom water
at the equator in contrast to the ease of movement and
greater dispersion which is prevalent in the Atlantic.
A modified view has been suggested by Yasuo and
Saruhashi,[32] who have analyzed geochemical cycles of silicon, phosphorus, and nitrogen in the oceans. These
workers conclude that the cause of the concentration differences, Atlantic vs. Indian-Pacific Oceans, is mainly
due to differences in residence time in deep layers of
these oceans. The estimate of the nutrient residence
times is 160-270 years vs. 90-130 years for the
Indian-Pacific and Atlantic Oceans, respectively.

5.6 <u>Summary</u>

We have considered the major forms of silicon in the
marine ecosystem, dissolved and particulate, as well as the
problems of analysis of silicon, and the factors affecting the
solubility of dissolved silica. Several processes of the silicon biogeochemical cycle lead to changes of the concentration
of silicon in the marine ecosystem. The processes considered
were river transport, incorporation into organisms, decomposition of organisms, transformation of clay minerals, and
physical processes. Silica is undersaturated in the sea,

probably because of the combined effects of biological activity and the unsolubility of a hydroxylated magnesium silicate
(Note 5, Fig. 5-3). The major trends in variations of silicon
in coastal and oceanic waters were summarized.

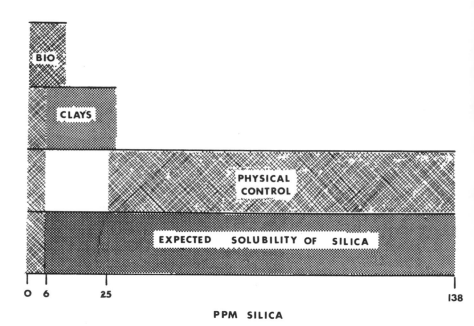

FIG. 5-3

Schematic representation of major factors that
control the solubility of silica in sea water.
Expected (138 ppm) and observed (0-10 ppm) solubilities are compared with physical control
(removal by formation of a hydroxylated magnesium silicate, 138-25 ppm), with control by
clays (25-6 ppm), and with control by biological
activity (10-0 ppm).

NOTES

1. Evidently the term denudation has no rigorous definition,
    at least as it has been applied in a geological sense.
    It has been used commonly as a synonym for erosion and
    does imply lowering of the earth's surface. It can be
    estimated for a major area by measuring the amount of
    eroded material being transported from within the limits
    of that area. Most studies involve the implicit
    assumptions that the eroded material comes equally from
    all portions of the region, and considering the hetero-
    geneity of most small regions this is obviously an un-
    warranted assumption. The review by Ritter[19] provides a
    useful summary of the problems of denudation.

2. Pleistocene, 1-10 million years B.P.

3. Radiolaria are small protozoans that have siliceous
    shells and live in the plankton of the open sea.

4. This is the International Hydrographic Station E.1 (lat.
    $50^{\circ}02'N.$, long. $4^{\circ}22'W$). A series of observations were
    made at this station during the period 1950-1965, and
    observations in the area are available as early as 1922.
    Armstrong and Butler[30] list pertinent references.

5. Fanning and Schink[33] have considered the interaction of
    marine sediments with dissolved silica. They conclude,

"It seems impossible that adsorption on clays is the prime agent for the extraction of silica from the present oceans."

REFERENCES

1. F. T. Mackenzie, R. M. Garrels, O. P. Bricker, and F. Bickley, Science, 155, 1404 (1967).

2. L. G. Sillén, Oceanography, Publ. No. 67, AAAS, Washington D. C., 1961, pp. 549-581.

3. F. A. J. Armstrong in Chemical Oceanography (J. P. Riley and G. Skirrow, eds.), Vol. 1, Academic Press, New York, 1965, Chapt. 10.

4. W. Stöber, Adv. Chem. Ser., 67, 161 (1967).

5. K. B. Krauskopf, Geochim. Cosmochim. Acta, 10, 1 (1956).

6. R. Siever, J. Geol., 70, 127 (1962).

7. J. C. Lewin, Geochim. Cosmochim. Acta, 21, 162 (1961).

8. E. Rogall, Planta, 29, 279 (1939).

9. G. B. Alexander, W. M. Heston, and R. K. Iler, J. Phys. Chem., 58, 453 (1954).

10. D. E. White, W. W. Brannock, and K. J. Murta, Geochim. Cosmochim. Acta, 10, 27 (1956).

11. J. C. Lewin, J. Gen. Physiol., 39, 1 (1955).

12. H. L. Golterman in Chemical Environment in the Aquatic Habitat (H. L. Golterman and R. S. Clymo, eds.), Proc. I. B. P. Symp., Amsterdam, 1967, pp. 56-62; Oceanogr. Abstr., 15, A393 (1968).

13. M. B. Jacobs and M. Ewing, Science, 163, 380 (1969).

14. A. P. Lisitzin, Oceanogr. Res., 2, 71 (1960).

15. L. A. Hobson, Limnol. Oceanog., 12, 642 (1967).

16. J. J. Griffin, H. Windom, and E. D. Goldberg, Deep-Sea Res., 15, 433 (1968).

17. D. A. Livingstone, U.S. Geol. Surv. Profess. Paper 440-G (1963).

18. F. T. Mackenzie and R. M. Garrels, Am. J. Sci., 264, 507 (1966).

19. cf. D. F. Ritter, J. Geol. Educ., 15, 154 (1967).

20. H. D. Holland, Proc. Nat. Acad. Sci. U.S., 53, 1173 (1965).

21. C. E. Weaver, Geochim. Cosmochim. Acta, 31, 2181 (1967).

22. L. D. Swindale and P.-F. Fan, Science, 157, 799 (1967).

23. R. M. Garrels and C. L. Christ, Solutions, Minerals and Equilibria, Harper and Row, New York, 1965, pp. 359-361.

24. E. G. Jorgensen, Dansk. bot. Ark., 18, 1 (1957), and other papers in the series.

25. J. C. Lewin, J. Gen. Physiol., 37, 589 (1954); 39, 1 (1955); cf., J. C. Lewin and C.-H. Chen, J. Phycol. 4, 161 (1968).

26. L. H. N. Cooper, J. Mar. Biol. Ass. U.K., 30, 511 (1952).

27. W. H. Berger, Science, 159, 1237 (1968).

28. U. Stefansson and F. A. Richards, Limnol. Oceanog., 8, 394 (1963).

29. A. C. Duxbury and N. B. McGary, Limnol. Oceanog., 13, 626 (1968).

30. F. A. J. Armstrong and E. I. Butler, J. Mar. Biol. Ass. U.K., 48, 153 (1968).

31. F. A. J. Armstrong, J. Mar. Biol. Ass. U.K., 34, 223 (1955).

32. M. Yasuo and K. Saruhashi, Pap. Met. Geophys., Tokyo, 18, 89 (1967); Oceanogr. Abstr., 15, A406 (1968).

33. K. A. Fanning and D. R. Schink, Limnol. Oceanog., 14, 59 (1969).

THE PHOSPHORUS CYCLE

6.1 Introduction

If any element in the marine ecosystem can be said to be a
master element it is phosphorus. At first glance, this might
seem surprising in view of the evidently low concentration.
The _average_ concentration of phosphorus in sea water is about
73 μg P/liter or $10^{-5.6}$ M, though in the upper 100 m the amount
usually is much less because of intense biological activity.[1]

The apparent paucity of phosphorus may be misleading and
we should consider the relative amounts of various elements, as
Redfield[1] has (Table 6-1). A listing of the number of atoms of
various elements relative to the number of atoms of phosphorus
in the world ocean indicates the validity of regarding phosphorus as a limiting element, if not a master element. For instance, in sea water every atom of phosphorus is matched by

15 atoms of nitrogen (as NO_3^-). In addition, there is a reserve
of 510 atoms of nitrogen (as N_2) which could be used by nitrogen-fixing organisms, and there is a considerable atmospheric
reserve of molecular nitrogen. Similarly, it is clear that the
carbon, sulfur, and oxygen supplies are adequate to maintain the
the intensely active biochemical cycle.

TABLE 6-1

Proportions of Elements at the Earth's Surface[1]

Element	Relative Proportion[a] in			
	Ocean	Atmosphere	Earth's Crust Sedimentary Rocks	Coal and Petroleum
P	1[a]		40,000	
N			10,000	
as NO_3^-	15			
as N_2	510	62,000		
C	1,000	16	400,000	160,000
S	10,000		10,000	
O	270	23,000		

[a]Atoms of element relative to atoms of phosphorus in world ocean.

    The role of phosphorus in a massive biogeochemical cycle incolving carbon, nitrogen, and oxygen was described earlier (Section 4.6). It seems appropriate here to consider the phosphorus cycle in detail.

    The major processes of the phosphorus biogeochemical cycle may be represented schematically (Fig. 6-1). The processes of the cycle fall into three categories (indicated by the symbols A, B, and C): A, addition of phosphorus to the active pool (by

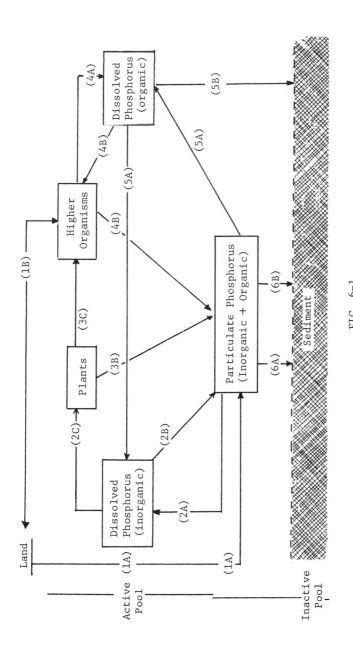

FIG. 6-1

The phosphorus biogeochemical cycle.
(See text for explanation of numbers).

input, regeneration, decomposition, dissolution, or turbulent action, such as upwelling); B, removal of phosphorus from the active pool (by precipitation or physical removal); and C, uptake or concentration of phosphorus by living organisms (consumers or destroyers).

In summary, the processes of the phosphorus cycle involve the following:

1. Annual delivery of phosphorus (about 14 million metric tons, cf. Table 7-2) to the sea because of erosion and agricultural fertilization (1A). Largely, this is a unidirectional process because only about 0.01 million metric tons of phosphorus (mostly as guano from marine birds) are returned to the land (1B).

2. The reserve of dissolved phosphorus in the sea is about 120,000,000 million metric tons. This amount is maintained by (2A) dissolution of particulate inorganic phosphate or the hydrolysis of organic phosphorus compounds (cf. 7A), (2B) the precipitation of insoluble phosphate or (2C) the uptake by plants (annual phytoplankton requirements are about 1,200 million metric tons of phosphorus).

3. Plants are consumed by higher organisms (3C) or upon death become particulate phosphorus (3B) and phosphorus is removed temporarily; ultimately dissolved phosphorus is produced (2A).

4. Organisms other than plants may excrete soluble organic
    phosphorus compounds (4A). Bacteria take up these com-
    pounds (4C) and release other phosphoric compounds (4A).
    Finally, the death of these organisms produces particu-
    late phosphorus as organic detritus (4B).

5. Dissolved organic phosphorus compounds may also be formed
    by the decomposition of the organic detritus (5A) or may
    be removed by burial in muds (5B).

6. Finally, particulate phosphorus settles to the bottom (6B)
    or is brought from the nephelotic layer to the active pool
    by turbulence (6A). In addition, inorganic phosphate may
    be released (2A) as part of the sulfur biogeochemical
    cycle (cf. Fig. 3-3) or by dissolution of particulate
    phosphorus. This completes the cycle.

Following the pattern used with silicon, let us consider
the two major forms of phosphorus, dissolved and particulate
(Sections 6.2 and 6.3), analyze some of the processes of the
cycle (Section 6.4), and see how these processes effect the
variation of phosphorus in the ecosystem (Section 6.5).

6.2 Dissolved Phosphorus

Dissolved phosphate exists as soluble inorganic phosphate and as soluble organic phosphorus compounds. Soluble inorganic phosphate has been regarded as being present exclusively as orthophosphate or $H_2PO_4^-$ and HPO_4^{2-} with negligible

amounts of PO_4^{3-} or H_3PO_4 (Note 1). In addition, phosphoric acid can undergo condensation to form isopolyacids as anions of

$$2H_3PO_4 \rightarrow H_4P_2O_7 + H_2O \rightarrow [2H_3PO_3] + H_2O \rightarrow (HPO_3)_n \qquad (6-1)$$

pyrophosphoric acid, $H_4P_2O_7$, or as anions of polymetaphosphoric acid $(HPO_3)_n$, linear polymers where $\underline{n}$ is 3-70 per chain. There has been no evidence of the presence of dissolved polyphosphates in sea water until recently. This was due in part to limitations of the analytical method and in part to natural processes. Polyphosphates are not readily hydrolyzed to orthophosphate ions, using the conditions of a standard method. Thus, typically the phosphates would appear as part of the "total phosphorus" or as "organic phosphorus" (a method is now available that permits detection of inorganic polyphosphate[3]). Accumulation of soluble polyphosphate probably is unlikely, except in polluted estuaries and harbors, because such compounds as might be formed by marine phytoplankton are soon used by other plants or by bacteria.[3] It has been suggested, though, that the amount of polyphosphate in certain estuaries might be a useful index of pollution.[3]

Dissolved organic phosphorus compounds represent an important fraction of soluble phosphorus. The nature of these compounds is uncertain, though nucleic acid material, phospholipids,and many decomposition products would be expected.[2,3] Little of the organic phosphorus material seems to be present as "enzyme" hydrolyzable phosphate esters but may be mainly nucleic acid material.[3]

Analytical considerations are particularly significant in the phosphorus cycle because the phosphorus concentration is slight and the limitations of the commonly used method are great, though it may be the only one available. There are three analytical methods available: the Dénigès or molybdenum blue method, atomic absorption spectrophotometry, and radiotracer analysis. These may be compared as follows:

1. The molybdenum blue method (cf. Vol. 1, Chapt. 9) has been used exclusively in one modification or another to determine orthophosphate in fresh or sea water. The sample is treated with molybdate, the compound(s) which result are reduced, and the absorbance of the blue product is related to the concentration of phosphorus. There are several disadvantages and limitations of the method, including (1) the empirical nature of the determination, (2) the low sensitivity, (3) the interferences by arsenic and silicate, and (4) slowness of the determination. These limitations have been mitigated by, respectively, (1) standardizing the conditions and the operations, (2) extracting the blue compound(s) into organic solvents and increasing the sensitivity, (3) extracting only specific phosphomolybdates, or correcting for arsenic, (4) making the operation automatic as with a Technicon AutoAnalyzer.

One major limitation remains - the validity of the method. Evidently the molybdenum blue method does not accurately measure the concentration of orthophosphate in certain lakes and possibly elsewhere. Rigler's results[4] indicate that the molybdenum blue method gives higher values than a radiotracer method. He postulated that the source of error was the hydrolysis of organic phosphorus compounds. This seems reasonable. Unfortunately, the error would not be constant and would depend on the amount and kind of organic phosphorus compounds present, as well as the length of time required for the determination.

2. <u>Atomic absorption spectroscopy</u> involves a modification of the preceding method. A specific compound, phospho-12-molybdic acid, $H_3(PO_4)Mo_{12}O_{36}$ (formed by the interaction of orthophosphate and an excess of ammonium molybdate in 1 $\underline{M}$ hydrochloric acid) is extracted into isobutylacetate.[5] The concentration of molybdenum (and thus phosphorus) in the organic extract is determined with an atomic absorption spectrophotometer. The sensitivity of the method (12μg PO_4-P/liter) at present is not adequate to permit determination of phosphorus in sea water,[6] though the method may be applicable when the sensitivity of the spectrophotometer is improved. Certainly the method is attractive in the ease, rapidity, avoidance of the reduction step, and lack of interference from silicate.

3. The radiophosphorus method has been used to trace the
    flux of phosphorus in an ecosystem, to measure exchange
    rates, and to test the accuracy of the molybdenum blue
    method (or some particular modification of it).
    Radiophosphorus (as $^{32}PO_4^{3-}$) would not be used for routine
    analysis because of time required and because of the ex-
    pense; this isotope has a half-life of 13 days. An iso-
    topic dilution technique could be used. This would con-
    sist of adding radiophosphate to a water sample containing
    ordinary orthophosphate, collecting all of the ortho-
    phosphate, and measuring the specific activity (disinte-
    grations per minute per gram). The specific activity of
    the total orthophosphate is compared with the specific
    activity of the added sample; the extent of dilution in-
    dicates the amount of inactive orthophosphate in the water
    sample. The specific activity would be reduced 50%, for
    example, if the radiophosphate were mixed with an equal
    weight of ordinary orthophosphate. The radiophosphorus
    method has been used by Rigler[4] to test the validity of
    the molybdenum blue method under specific conditions and
    by Pomeroy[7] to measure the turnover of phosphorus in
    marine environments.

In summary, the molybdenum blue method has some serious
limitations, most of which can be overcome or allowed for; the
most serious limitation, validity under a given set of typical

191

conditions, needs to be checked using the radiophosphorus
method. The use of atomic absorption spectroscopy will be
attractive if phosphate levels are high or if the sensitivity
of the instrument is improved.

6.3 Particulate Phosphate

There are two forms of particulate phosphorus: inorganic
compounds and combined organic phosphorus in organic detritus.
[Technically, the latter form might also include living
organisms, but this inclusion has not been made in the biogeochemical cycle (Fig. 6-1).]

Processes involving both forms significantly affect concentration of orthophosphate ion in the sea. For example, decomposition of organic detritus (process 2B, Fig. 6-1) occurs
slowly as organisms sink to the bottom,and this process
coupled with the physical process is probably responsible for
the "phosphorus paradox" and the phosphorus mid-depth maximum
(Section 6.5). Processes involving inorganic particulate phosphorus, however, may be more significant in controlling the
concentration of orthophosphate ion.

It appears to many that the availability of orthophosphate
ion is controlled by the solubility of an inorganic phosphorus
compound (or maybe compounds).

This physical property, the solubility of a unique substance, would be essentially unaltered under conditions of
constant temperature and pressure (differences in salinity

would affect the activity coefficients of component ions). As noted earlier (Section 4.6), the phosphorus, nitrogen, carbon, and sulfur biogeochemicals are intimately involved. This view leads to the suggestion[1] that an essentially invariant property, the solubility of an inorganic phosphorus compound, is basically responsible for the long-term constancy of nutrient supplies in the sea and the oxygen concentration of the atmosphere. This suggestion is intriguing but it raises the obvious question: What inorganic phosphorus compounds are involved?

Probably, one compound is some form of calcium phosphate. Dietz et al.[8] suggested that sea water (below an upper layer of a few hundred meters) is essentially saturated with $Ca_3(PO_4)_2$. This is not easy to confirm because the literature data on the solubility of calcium phosphates do not agree very well. There are two major reasons: (1) difficulties in achieving a true state of equilibrium and (2) difficulties in identifying the phases. The available data[9] do suggest that the order of solubility is $CaHPO_4 > Ca_3(PO_4)_2 > Ca_5(PO_4)_3(OH)$ (hydroxyapatite) where the solubility product constants are $10^{-7.0}$, $10^{-26.0}$, and $10^{-55.9}$, respectively.

Both $CaHPO_4$ and $Ca_3(PO_4)_2$ may be in equilibrium with hydroxyapatite (Eqs. 6-2, 6-3). The equilibrium constants for these processes have been estimated by Sillén[9] (Note 2).

$$3\ CaHPO_4(s) + 2\ Ca^{++} + H_2O \rightleftarrows Ca_5(PO_4)_3OH(s) + 4\ H^+,$$

$$\log K = -16 \qquad\qquad (6\text{-}2)$$

193

$$3\ Ca_3(PO_4)_2(s) + Ca^{++} + 2\ H_2O \rightleftarrows 2\ Ca_5(PO_4)_3OH(s) + 2\ H^+,$$

$$\log K = 6 \qquad (6-3)$$

Once equilibrium was established between each pair of calcium phosphate phases, the following relationships would apply

$$4\ \log(H^+) - 2\ \log(Ca^{2+}) = \log K = -16 \qquad (6-2a)$$

$$\text{or}\quad 2\ \log(H^+) - \log(Ca^{2+}) = \log K = -8 \qquad (6-2a')$$

$$\text{and}\quad 2\ \log(H^+) - \log(Ca^{2+}) = \log K = 6 \qquad (6-3a)$$

(where Eqns. 6-2a and 6-3a are obtained from Eqns. 6-2 and 6-3, respectively, using the usual assumption of unit activity of solid phases). In sea water, the value of $2\ \log(H^+) - \log(Ca^{2+})$ would be equal to $(-16.2 + 2.8)$ or -13.4. In short, both reactions (Eqns. 6-2, 6-3) should proceed to completion; hydroxyapatite should be the stable calcium phosphate phase.

The next point of interest is the estimation[9] of the amount of orthophosphate (as HPO_4^{2-}) that would be expected. The pertinent equilibrium is

$$Ca_5(PO_4)_3OH(s) + 4H^+ \rightleftarrows 5\ Ca^{2+} + 3HPO_4^{2-} + H_2O,$$

$$\log K = -5.0 \qquad (6-4)$$

In sea water, pH = 8.0 and $\log[Ca^{2+}] = -2.0$ or $\log(Ca^{2+}) = -2.8$. This leads[9] to an estimated value of $[HPO_4^{2-}]$ of $10^{-7.0}$. As Sillén[9] notes, this estimate does not consider the effect of temperature and is an order-of-magnitude calculation. Nevertheless, the value is consistent with the observed range of orthophosphate, $10^{-6} - 10^{-8}$ $\underline{M}$, and is in accord with the suggestion that the solubility of some inorganic compound controls the orthophosphate levels in the major portion of the ocean.

By way of summary, several observations can be made concerning particulate phosphorus in the marine ecosystem.[1,9,10,11]

1. Loss to sediments. Of the annual input of phosphorus

    (about 14 million metric tons), most (13 million metric

    tons) is lost to formation of sediments (cf. Table 7-2).

2. Two types of marine phosphates, both of which are authi-

    genic, are found: phosphatic nodules and stratified

    phosphates associated with shales or limestones. Thick

    beds of phosphorite or phosphate rock consist of nearly

    pure sedimentary apatite. These beds are not common but

    where found (southeastern and northwestern United States

    and North Africa, among other locations) are extensive,

    puzzlingly so (cf. item 3). Apatite is really a col-

    lection of minerals that range from hydroxyapatite to

    $Ca_5(PO_4)_3F$. Hydroxyapatite is slowly converted to fluoro-

    apatite, e.g., newly buried bones have low fluorine

    content and older buried ones have more fluorine. In

    addition, widespread deposits of francolite, Ca_5F-

    $(PO_4,CO_3)_3$, are found in shallow low-latitude areas. The

    solubility of francolite can be drastically reduced in the

    presence of zirconium and rare earth metal ions which sub-

    stitute for calcium.

3. <u>Two modes of precipitation</u> of phosphorite minerals are
    recognized: (1) calcium phosphate minerals, calcium phos-
    phate hydroxyapatite, are precipitated and undergo con-
    version to other minerals fluoroapatite, francolite; or
    (2) limestone deposits react with orthophosphate ion
    (possibly from guano) and are converted to less soluble
    phosphorite minerals. The latter process seems to ex-
    plain the extensively reworked phosphorite deposits in the
    southeastern United States. Direct precipitation, how-
    ever, seems to rationalize the well-preserved structures
    of the phosphoria formation in the northwestern United
    States. It seems likely that both processes can occur,
    though local conditions determine which process dominates.

4. <u>The role of organisms in phosphorite deposition</u> is largely
    indirect, according to the view of many. Phosphorus has
    not been introduced in sediments by extensive entrapment
    of organic matter, as evidenced by the high phosphorus-
    nitrogen ratio (4:1) relative to that typical of phyto-
    plankton (1:15). There are, however, deposits of apatite
    areas of high productivity which suggests that these de-
    posits were formed under reducing conditions (see item 5).
    It has also been established that no precipitation of
    phosphorite occurs on the deep-ocean floor through the
    hydrolysis of organic matter.

Direct involvement of organisms in phosphorite deposition would occur if the phosphorus from organic matter from organisms accumulates rapidly. Then the phosphorus could be extensively converted to apatite before it is entirely consumed by scavengers. This process is responsible for accumulation of skeletal apatite in the form of bone, teeth, and shell fragments.

The indirect involvement of organisms is indicated for those areas of high productivity due to upwelling. In these areas, conditions are favorable for both the rapid growth of phytoplankton and for direct precipitation of calcium phosphate. As the colder phosphate-rich water is brought from the depths to the surface, it tends to move into an area of increasing pH. This increase in pH occurs when dissolved carbon dioxide is lost because of increased temperature, decreased pressure, and increased photosynthetic activity. The conditions of higher pH and warmer water favor direct precipitation of calcium phosphate, which should deposit at a lower pH than calcium carbonate, according to solubility calculations. Thus, under certain rather narrowly defined conditions, calcium phosphate would be the sole deposit, without the involvement of organisms. With an increase of pH or temperature, concurrent deposition of carbonate would occur and phosphate would be a minor or greater constituent of limy mud.

5. The environment of deposition has been mentioned (item 4) in connection with areas of high organic productivity. Widespread deposits of marine phosphorite occur in tropical waters and in the absence of conditions of high organic productivity. The deposition of aragonite may occur under an oxidizing or a reducing environment. The oxidizing environment is indicated by the absence of organic compounds and low uranium content (the prevaling hexavalent uranium ion does not substitute for calcium ion). A reducing environment is indicated by the presence of organic compounds and the presence of uranium (which in the reduced tetravalent state readily substitutes for calcium). The deposition of phosphorite, thus, seems to be insensitive to the pE value of the marine ecosystem because deposition occurs under a range of oxidizing and reducing conditions. The composition of the deposit is, however, sensitive to pE because of the effects of substitution by trace elements such as uranium.

6. The favored form of phosphorite is unsettled. Calculations summarized in this section show that two simple forms of calcium phosphate should be readily converted to hydroxyapatite. Unfortunately, enough solubility data are not available to permit a broader assessment. It does appear from measured solubility products, for example, that

hydroxyapatite should be converted to fluoroapatite
(Note 2), as has been observed for buried bones.

6.4 Origins of Variations

It may be useful to consider the possible short-term
causes of variations of phosphorus distribution before looking
at the actual variations. Obviously, this is historically
backwards, though it is useful in rationalizing the observed
variations. It has been a commonly held view that the phosphate distribution had a strong, if not controlling, distribution on annual productivity. Seasonal changes in phosphate
seem to be less erratic than in silicate (Section 5.5). The
regularity has been interpreted as indicating that there is a
regular long-term cycle which consists of a period of regeneration of phosphorus and a period of uptake by phytoplankton.
The rapid turnover of orthophosphate and other forms of phosphorus has been discovered more recently by means of radiophosphorus studies. Now it is evident that naturally
occurring forms of phosphorus are involved in a dynamic steady
state condition. The seasonal changes seem to be the consequence of shifts in the rates of processes controlling the
steady state.[7] Thus, the long-term events seem to be deli-
cately balanced on short-term events.

Some of the short-term events include the following.

River runoff. Data for annual river input of phosphorus are available, but these data do not indicate the wide range of contribution of phosphorus. Tampa Bay waters, for example, tend to be fairly rich in phosphorus because of the nature of the tributaries.[12] Of these, the Alafia, Little Manatee, and Manatee River drainage areas contain Hawthorne (Miocene) phosphate deposits, and the Hillsborough River drainage area contains the less extensive Alachua (Pliocene) phosphate formation (Fig. 6-2). The data in Table 6-2 indicate that the phosphorus concentrations vary substantially during the year and from river to river. Typically, the phosphate represented about 77-95% of the total phosphorus. These data indicate the influence of underlying phosphate deposits (e.g., Hillsborough versus Alafia and other rivers). Also maximum concentrations of phosphate in the Alafia were observed during the rainy season (June-October) at the time of maximum discharge. The organic phosphate tends to be low because peat and muck soils tend to be scattered patches rather than extensive areas in the Tampa Bay drainage basin.

Changes related to biological activity represent a category that encompasses the following observations:

1. Light intensity. Increased duration and intensity of
    light causes enhanced growth of plants (process 2C) and

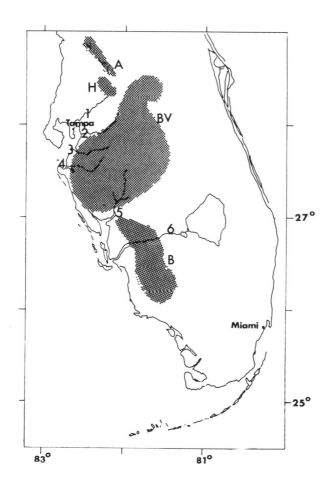

FIG. 6-2

Location of surface phosphate-bearing formations in
south Florida. Rivers: 1, Hillsborough; 2, Alafia; 3,
Little Manatee; 4, Manatee; 5, Peace; 6, Caloosahatchee.
Formations: A, Alachua; H, Hawthorne; BV, Bone Valley;
B, Buckingham Marl. (After Dragovich and May[12])

TABLE 6-2

Total Phosphorus and Inorganic Phosphate (μg-at./liter)

at Selected Stations in Tampa Bay Tributaries[a]

October 1958 - December 1959[12]

River	Total PO_4-P			Inorganic PO_4-P		
	Min.	Max.	Mean	Min.	Max.	Mean
Hillsborough	2.5	13.9	6.1	2.7	7.4	4.7
Alafia	25.0	58.1	39.7	20.2	46.0	34.9
Little Manatee	8.2	19.8	13.0	6.9	18.6	13.2
Manatee	4.7	13.0	10.1	5.9	10.9	8.4

[a]Data refer to surface samples.

reduces the concentration of phosphate in the water column. This assumes vertical mixing of the water column by the action of waves and winds. The period of maximum phosphorus utilization will vary with location and even in, say, temperate waters, the period does vary.

2. Stable layering, due to the establishment of a seasonal thermocline (Section 2.6), restricts the vertical mixing of the water column. Consequently, vigorous plant growth occurs above the thermocline until the orthophosphate is depleted. Some distance below the thermocline plant

growth is minimal because of lack of light, and orthophosphate concentrations increase as plants die (processes
4A, 5A). Because of stable layering, the differences in
orthophosphate concentration above and below are substantial. The example given (Fig. 6-3) is for a location
where the seasonal thermocline is found at about 30 m.[13]
A similar pattern has been observed for silicate ion
(Section 5.5).[13]

3. <u>Diurnal changes</u> associated with biological activity have
been noted (cf. Armstrong[2]). For example, in Chesapeake
Bay orthophosphate concentration in surface waters is
relatively high prior to sunrise, diminishes during the
day until a minimum is reached, then increases and a
maximum is attained at night (Fig. 6-4).[14] In shallow
tropical and semitropical bays, a similar pattern may be
observed,though the maximum and minimum concentrations
tend to differ less in the deeper temperate bays. Total
and particulate phosphorus concentrations seem to show
little diurnal variation.

4. <u>Bacterial action</u> can result in consumption or production
of dissolved phosphorus depending upon the circumstances.
Bacterial decomposition of bottom muds near the Great
Barrier Reef seemed to be responsible for a constant

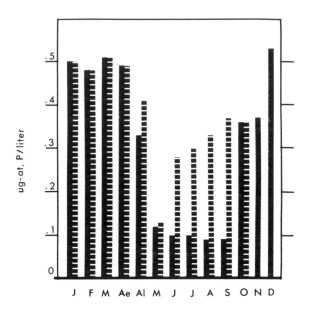

FIG. 6-3

Orthophosphate (µg-at. P/liter) at 10 and 50 m at
International Hydrographic Station E.1 during 1954.
Phosphate at 10 m, black bar; at 50 m, dashed bar;
Ae, Al, early and late April. (After Armstrong.[13])

supply of phosphate in overlying water; no seasonal vari-

ation was noted and phosphate concentration was negli-

gible in a nearby river.[15] Heron[16] noted the reduction

in phosphate concentration when lake water was stored in

untreated polyethylene bottles; he attributed the reduc-

tion to the activity of a film of bacteria on the walls

of a container. Finally, Pomeroy[7] points out that there

is evidence bacteria have a significant influence on the

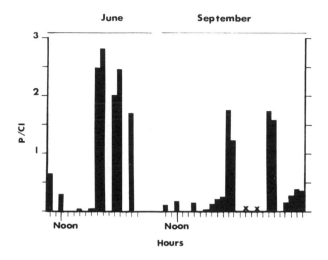

FIG. 6-4

Variation of phosphate (as μg PO_4-P/kg/Cl^o/oo) in Chesapeake Bay in June and September.[14]

turnover of phosphate; the influence in marine waters varies greatly, possibly with the size or character of the bacterial flora.

5.   Zooplankton regeneration. The relative importance of zooplankton versus bacterial regeneration of orthophosphate (processes 4B+2A or 5A) is not clear. Hargrave and Green[17] found the bacteria in their experiments accumulated phosphorus, and they concluded the regeneration of orthophosphate by zooplankton was "of considerable, if not of prime, importance," at least in their study areas.

Again, the conclusion of Pomeroy[7] (item 4) seems applicable.

6. Blocking chemicals. The addition of trace amounts of blocking agents (cyanide ion, 3×10^{-4} $\underline{M}$, and methylene blue, 5×10^{-5} $\underline{M}$) to natural waters inhibits the short-term uptake of radiophosphate.[7] The effect of methylene blue on the release of phosphate could not be determined because the reagent interferes with the phosphate analysis; cyanide inhibited both release and uptake. These experiments and others suggest that the short-term turnover of phosphorus is due to the involvement of 80-90% of the phosphate in some biochemical process, which may be phosphorylation (Note 3).[7] Here, about 10-20% of the phosphate could be involved in sorption reactions, but this amount would not be statistically significant in replicated experiments.

Other factors or processes are indicated by these and other experiments. These factors include:

1. Sorption and desorption by particulate phosphorus probably account for some 10-20% of the total phosphorus turnover in the marine environment, though these processes may be more significant in certain areas where the biochemical activity is less. Uptake of phosphate by suspended sediments is evidently reversible and removal is

favored by increased pH, which suggest the process is significant at river-estuary interaction regions. De-sorption may not need to be extensive to be significant because some estuarine muds tend to be rich in phosphorus; in some cases, the phosphate concentration in muds is 100,000 times that of the overlying water.

2. <u>Physical mixing processes</u> such as near-bottom turbulence and upwelling alter phosphate concentrations significantly. For example, high phosphate concentrations off the Malabar coast during the monsoon seasons have been ascribed to stirring up of bottom muds; though enhanced river outflow might be very influential. Upwelling (Section 2.6) also contributes to the enrichment of phosphate in surface waters off the west coasts of continents in equatorial regions.

In summary, many short-term and long-term events affect the concentration of phosphorus and other nutrients in the marine environment. In this connection, Yasuo and Saruhaski (Section 5) introduced the concept of a "Biological Activity Index," β (Eqn. 6-5), which is characteristic of a nutrient in a given environment.

$$\beta = \frac{\text{Biological decomposition}}{\text{Input}} \div \frac{\text{Content in euphotic zone}}{\text{Biological uptake}} \tag{6-5}$$

The index takes into consideration the marine concentration of
a nutrient (in various forms), input from rivers and streams,
biological production and decomposition, removal to the sea
bottom, and transfer between deep and surface layers. These
workers estimate that in the marine ecosystem, β is 180
for phosphorus. Other values of β are 0.015 (carbon),
60 (silicon), and 330 (nitrogen).

6.5 Variations of Phosphorus in the Marine Ecosystem

The variations described in the preceding section seem
to fall into two patterns: short-term events and long-term
events. Many now believe that the long-term variations, such
as seasonal changes, are a consequence of changes in the rates
of processes controlling the dynamic steady state of phosphorus
in the marine environment. It seems appropriate to consider
what variations are observed in the long-term events. Four
types of variations will be reviewed here: seasonal, vertical,
horizontal, and changes in the nitrogen-phosphorus ratio. A
more extensive review is given by Armstrong.[2]

Seasonal variations are best documented in coastal waters,
where more intensive and extensive observations are available.
The seasonal pattern of the upper 50-100 m of open ocean in
temperate latitudes should follow the pattern of coastal
waters.

1. Variations of the seasonal pattern. The seasonal pattern
   of phosphate is well established at International Hydrographic Station E.1, near Dover, where a long run of
   analyses is available. The general pattern of events has
   been described earlier (Section 6.4): a period of regeneration, followed by a period of uptake by phytoplankton.
   The events do not follow the pattern closely: the time of
   maximum utilization of phosphorus varies, the time of
   maximum regeneration varies, and even the fertility of
   the waters seems to change.

   For example, data assembled by Cooper[18] and others,[19] indicate that the phosphorus winter maximum changes over a
   period of years (Fig. 6.5). The phosphorus maximum has
   been related to the potential production for the following
   spring and summer.[18] In this instance, the change in
   phosphorus maximum was ascribed to changes in circulation.
   These changes may be due to essentially random or to cyclic fluctuations. Generally, phosphorus-poor waters
   (as characterized by the winter maximum) tended to be
   characterized by the scarcity of most holoplanktonic
   organisms (Note 4) and by poor production of the offspring
   of summer spawning fish.

2. Significance of the phosphorus minima. At times, the concentration of phosphate above the thermocline is less than
   the sensitivity of the analytical method ($<10^{-9}$ M).[20]

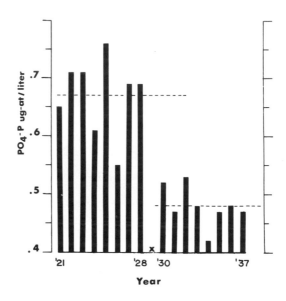

FIG. 6-5

Winter maxima for phosphate in the English Channel
(at Station E.1) for the period 1921-1938.[18] Mean
values for 1923-1929 (0.67) and 1930-1938 (0.48)
indicated by dashed lines.

This condition alone cannot be taken as evidence that

phosphate is limiting population growth or primary pro-

duction for two reasons, based on studies of phosphorus

uptake by Phaeodactylum tricornutum (sometimes called

Nitzschia closterium forma minutissma). First, this

organism (and evidently many others) can accumulate phos-

phorus (30 times) in excess of the amount required for

cell division; phosphorus-rich cells could continue to

divide in suitable illumination even in "phosphorus-deficient" media. Secondly, this organism and other phytoplankton can remove phosphorus below the analytical detection limit ($<7.2 \times 10^{-10}$ $\underline{M}$), using the radiophosphorus method.[20] The phosphate minima in the English Channel are typical of relatively shallow coastal waters, which are largely unaffected by upwelling processes. In contrast, the phosphate _minima_ in the San Juan Channel (northwest Washington,U.S.) are greater than the maxima of the English Channel. The situation in the San Juan Channel shows the affect of upwelling of nutrient-rich waters.[2]

3. Phosphorus limitation in the sea. The effects of micronutrient deficiencies are more likely to be observed in lakes than in the sea. A mathematical model for nutrient limitation in the sea has been devised by Dugdale.[21] Nutrient limitation theory is significant for the sea but primarily in terms of phytoplankton competition and succession.

4. Orthophosphate versus organic phosphorus concentration
The comparison of these two parameters is a little difficult because many analyses of organic phosphorus have not been corrected for errors due to the presence of arsenite ion, and most have not been corrected for the presence of

polyphosphate ions (cf. Section 6.2). Both ions appear as "organic phosphorus." These problems have been overcome by Armstrong and Tibbitts,[22] who developed a photochemical combustion technique of analysis. Their data (Table 6-3) evidently provide the first demonstration of the presence of organic polyphosphates in sea water. These data also indicate, as has been demonstrated previously, that the fraction of organic phosphorus can be substantial, approaching 50%.

TABLE 6-3

Phosphorus Fractions at Various Stations

English Channel, April 1967[22]

Station		Phosphorus, μg-at P/liter		
No.	Type	Ortho-phosphate	Total Organic	Organic Poly-phosphate
2	English coastal 50°00'N, 4°55'W	0.31	0.21	0.02
16	English coastal; 50°10'N, 4°40'W	0.42	0.33	0.03
13	Western; 49°10'N, 6°10'W	0.44	0.26	0.03
9	French coastal; 48°30'N, 5°10'W	0.40	0.21	0.02

<u>Vertical distribution</u> patterns fall into two general categories (1) patterns typical of coastal waters or the upper 50-100 m of pelagic waters; (2) patterns typical of oceanic waters.

1. <u>Shallow coastal waters</u>. Data indicating the vertical dis-
    tribution of phosphate and the monthly variation are
    available for a long and extended period (cf. Armstrong
    2,13,18). The general pattern is indicated in Fig. 6-2.
    More specific data are given in Table 6-4 for April, July,
    and August (1957) at Station E.1. These data show the
    variation with depth of salinity, phosphate and silicate

TABLE 6-4

Observations at Station E.1, 1957[19b]

Depth	Salinity, o/oo			Orthophosphate µg-at P/liter			Silicate µg-at Si/liter		
m	April[a]	July	August	April	July	August	April	July	August
0	35.19			0.20			1.5		
0.5		35.13	35.12		0.11	0.11		1.2	1.6
5	35.13	35.16	35.10	0.19	0.15	0.09	1.5	1.3	1.4
10	35.14	35.17	35.08	0.20	0.14	0.10	1.4	1.3	1.4
15		35.18			0.36			1.7	
20	35.16	35.20	35.16	0.21	0.34	0.12	1.8	2.0	0.2
25			35.16			0.14			0.3
50	35.29	35.20	35.17	0.17	0.33	0.43	0.8	2.0	3.2
70	35.30	35.21	35.18	0.25	0.34	0.42	0.8	2.0	3.3

[a]24 April, 16 July, 21 August 1967.

before (April) and after (July and August) the establishment of a seasonal thermocline at 15-20 m. Phosphate and
silicate levels had been reduced from the winter maxima
(0.47 and 3.47 µg-at/liter, respectively) by the onset
of spring phytoplankton blooms, but stable layering had
not occurred. Sometime between July and August, a significant decrease in salinity occurred in the upper 10 m,
the phosphate decreased,and silicate increased slightly.
These changes in the upper 10 m were thought to be due to
a replacement of water with water of differing chemical
properties. Otherwise, the data for July and August are
in accord with the typical regeneration of nutrients.

2.   Vertical distribution in the oceans. This distribution
     in the oceans seems to be characterized by a four-layer
     pattern (Table 6-5). Specific details have been sum-
     marized by Armstrong.[2] The nature of the individual
     layers will be considered in the next section. It may be
     sufficient here to emphasize the pattern, and to note
     that the phosphate content of the Pacific and Indian
     Oceans tends to follow a closely similar pattern and to
     be greater than that of the Atlantic.

Horizontal distributions[2,23] may also be compared using the
pattern summarized in Table 6-5 because the vertical distribution below the surface is due to (1) the characteristics of
horizontal flow of various strata of water masses and (2) the

TABLE 6-5

Vertical Distribution of Phosphorus

in Oceanic Waters

Layer	Feature	Relative Phosphate Concentration
Surface	thin, relatively low gradient	low
Transition	high, positive concentration gradient	higher
Maximum phosphate	layer corresponds to oxygen-minimum layer	maximum
Intermediate to bottom	zero or slight negative concentration gradient	lower

properties the sea water masses acquired at the time they were

near the sea surface.

1.   The thickness of the surface layer varies widely, and it

is mainly in this layer that biological processes modify

phosphate concentrations. In equatorial regions, where

there is an optimum utilization of phosphate plankton, the

surface layer is likely to be much deeper on the average

than in temperate zones. In higher latitudes, the surface

zone becomes very thin (particularly if this layer is in

contact with a layer which is relatively rich in phos-

phate). The surface layer tends to disappear effectively

in Arctic waters during the polar night when phytoplankton

activity is minimal. The surface layer may also disap-

pear during periods of turbulence.

2.   The transition layer in the Atlantic represents the ef-
      fects of interaction between subsurface waters and water
      in the intermediate layer (2,000-3,000 m, σ_t = 27.0-27.5).
      About half of the concentration of orthophosphate in the
      intermediate layer is "preformed" i.e., present as such at
      the time the water sank from the surface, and about half
      is of oxidative origin, i.e., regenerated after the time
      the water sank. The concentration of preformed phosphate
      generally decreases moving northward from the subantarc-
      tic and disappears at 15°N. In the equatorial region,
      the subsurface (200 m) and intermediate levels are sepa-
      rated by layers collectively termed the North and South
      Atlantic central water masses. Interaction between the
      phosphate-impoverished subsurface water and the rich
      intermediate layer depends upon the circulation of the
      central water masses. Consequently, a variation in the
      general decrease of phosphate toward the surface is noted.

3.   The phosphate maximum layer is complex in origin. It
      seems to be due to (1) the transport of phosphate in the
      intermediate layer water from the subantarctic area of
      origin, and (2) local regeneration of phosphate in tropi-
      cal and subtropical regions. The oxygen minimum layer is
      somewhat above the phosphorus maximum layer because the
      maximum local regeneration occurs somewhat above the

maximum concentration of preformed phosphate. The phosphate concentration should have a positive gradient from the surface to the thermocline because phosphate-rich dead organisms gradually sink to the thermocline. On occasion, the upper 5-10 m tend to be richer in total phosphate than underlying water and this situation may be termed a "phosphate paradox." This paradox might be due to intrusion of phosphate-rich waters, but there is a more likely explanation: The situation could arise when bubbles are formed in breaking waves and are pushed to a depth of at least 10 m, where surface active organic phosphates could be adsorbed on the bubble and brought to the surface. The difference in the distribution of phosphate in the Pacific and Atlantic Oceans is related to the pattern of deep-water circulation and to the presence of the oxygen minimum layer at 3,500 m (north of 40°S) in the Pacific. In the Pacific and Indian Oceans, very little deep water flows southward. The surface water does flow southward and this is replaced by the intrusion of phosphate-rich water drawn from the south.

The phosphorus-nitrogen ratio.[2] Harvey noted in 1926 the interesting and remarkable fact that phytoplankton simultaneously accumulated phosphate and nitrate in constant proportions in the English Channel. Redfield demonstrated in 1934 that the phosphorus-nitrogen atomic ratio is 1:15 in a number of oceans at most depths and that about the same ratio was valid for phytoplankton. Cooper (1937,1938) showed that the constancy of the N:P ratio had significant exceptions (in coastal surface and restricted waters) and Fleming in 1940 obtained more extensive data. The carbon-nitrogen-phosphorus ratios for phytoplankton are 103:16.5:1; for zooplankton they are 108:15.5:1; on the average, the values would be 106:16:1.

The constancy of the phosphorus-nitrogen ratio is due to constituents that are present generally in limited amounts.[1] The constancy would not be observed if trace metals or other constituents were generally limiting, though there are instances in which trace metals, such as iron, are present in limiting amounts.

The exceptions to the P:N constancy are interesting because these occur in what might be collectively termed "restricted waters." These might be surface waters (during periods of intense biological activity and restricted circulation) or in physically restricted waters.

1.   Coastal waters. Ratios (N:P) that have been observed are

0 to 8 (Long Island Sound), 0 to 5-10 (summer and winter, respectively, in New England coastal surface waters) 19 and 10.5 (summer and winter, respectively, in the English Channel).

2.   Restricted waters. Anomalously high (N:P) ratios have
been found in the Mediterranean which is probably the
most impoverished body of water known because of the
presence of a fairly shallow sill (300 m) which restricts
the intrusion of Atlantic water. Several workers have
compared the ratio of N:P utilized with that normally
present in a given location. Subtracting the phosphate
summer minimum (integral) concentration from the winter
maximum gives the amount of inorganic phosphate used.
At Station E.1, N:P utilization ratios as high as 24 have
been observed, though other workers have found ratios of
about 15 or 16.[19] When the utilization ratios exceed the
normal N:P ratio, nitrogen would seem to be a limiting
factor and phosphate would be left behind.

6.6   Summary

The prime difficulties in studying phosphorus are two-
fold: (1) measuring the concentrations of orthophosphate
accurately at low levels and measuring the concentrations of
different forms of phosphorus accurately; and (2) measuring the
ratios of phosphorus uptake and release in the surface waters
of the marine ecosystem. It appears that there are two major
groups of processes, physical and biological, that affect the
concentration of phosphate in the sea. Physical processes include the solubility of calcium phosphate compounds (possibly

hydroxyapatite), which seems to regulate the amount of phosphate in deep water, in conjunction with the effects of deep-
water currents. The concentration of phosphates in surface
waters seems to be involved in a dynamic steady state and the
concentration of, say, orthophosphate is affected by biological
activity or more generally by short-term events. Examples of
some short-term events were given. Vertical distribution is
characterized by a four-layer pattern (surface, transition,
phosphorus maximum, and intermediate-deep layers). The nitrogen-phosphorus ratio (properly nitrate-phosphate) is about 15,
though many exceptions are found in surface and restricted
waters and in the utilization by organisms.

NOTES

1. The dissociation constants of H_3PO_4, $H_2PO_4^-$, and HPO_4^{2-}
   are approximately $10^{-2.1}$, $10^{-7.2}$, and $10^{-12.4}$,
   respectively.[10]

2. Pertinent references to the data are given by Armstrong[2]
   and Sillén.[9] Calcium phosphate solubility equilibria
   were used by Sillén to derive other equilibria constants
   (Eqs. 6-2, 6-3).

$$CaHPO_4(s) \rightleftarrows Ca^{2+} + HPO_4^{2-}; \log K = -7.0$$

$$Ca_3(PO_4)_2(s) \rightleftarrows 3Ca^{2+} + 2PO_4^{3-}; \log K = -26.0$$

$$Ca_5(PO_4)_3OH(s) \rightleftarrows 5Ca^{2+} + 3PO_4^{3-} + OH^-; \log K = -55.9$$

These three equations are combined with the acid-base equations

$$HPO_4^{2-} \rightleftarrows H^+ + PO_4^{3-}; \log K = -12.3$$

$$H_2O \rightleftarrows H^+ + OH^-; \log K = -14.0$$

Calculations are based on the assumption of $25^\circ C$ and zero activities, unless otherwise noted.

Krauskopf[10] reports that solubility product constants for hydroxy- and fluoro-apatite are $10^{-57.8}$ and $10^{-60.4}$. The former differs from other values.[9]

3. Phosphorylation reactions involve the incorporation of orthophosphate ion into organic phosphorus compounds, such as creatine phosphate and adenosine triphosphate (ATP). Cleavage phosphate bonds in these compounds afford relatively large amounts of free energy.

4. The definition of this and other terms of plankton terminology will be found in Appendix A.

REFERENCES

1. A. C. Redfield, Am. Scientist, 46, 205 (1958).

2. F. A. J. Armstrong in Chemical Oceanography (J. P. Riley and G. Skirrow, eds.), Vol. 1, Academic Press, New York, 1965, Chapt. 8.

3. L. Solórzano and J. D. H. Strickland, Limnol. Oceanog., 13, 515 (1968).

4. F. H. Rigler, Limnol. Oceanog., $\underline{13}$, 7 (1968).

5. G. F. Kirkbright, A. M. Smith, and T. S. West, Analyst, $\underline{92}$, 411 (1967).

6. D. Dyrssen, B. Johansson, and K. Arén, Report on Chemistry of Sea Water, VI, Dept. of Anal. Chem., Univ. of Göteborg, Sweden, Nov. 5, 1968

7. L. R. Pomeroy in Radioecology (V. Schultz and A. W. Klement, Jr., eds.), Reinhold, New York, 1963, pp. 163-166.

8. R. W. Dietz. K. O. Emery, and F. P. Shepard, Bull. Geol. Soc. Am., $\underline{53}$, 815 (1942).

9. L. G. Sillén in Oceanography (M. Sears, ed.), Publ. No. 67, AAAS, Washington, D. C., 1961, pp. 549-581.

10. K. B. Krauskopf, Introduction of Geochemistry, McGraw-Hill, New York, 1967, pp. 88-93.

11. G. Arrhenius in The Sea (M. N. Hill, ed.), Vol. 3, Interscience, New York, 1963, Chapt. 25.

12. A. Dragovich and B. Z. May, Fish. Bull., $\underline{62}$, 163 (1962).

13. F. A. J. Armstrong, J. Mar. Biol. Ass. U. K., $\underline{34}$, 223 (1955).

14. C. L. Newcombe and H. F. Brust, J. Mar. Res., $\underline{3}$, 76 (1940).

15. A. P. Orr, Great Barrier Reef Expedition Reports, 1928-9, No. 2(3), London, 1933; cited by Armstrong.[2]

16. J. Heron, Limnol. Oceanog., $\underline{7}$, 316 (1962).

17. B. T. Hargrave and G. H. Geen, Limnol. Oceanog., $\underline{13}$, 332 (1968).

18. L. H. N. Cooper, J. Mar. Biol. Ass. U. K., $\underline{23}$, 181 (1935).

19. F. A. J. Armstrong and E. I. Butler, J. Mar. Biol. Ass. U. K., $\underline{48}$, 153 (1968); $\underline{38}$, 41 (1959).

20. E. J. Kuenzler and B. H. Ketchum, Biol. Bull., $\underline{123}$, 134 (1962).

21. R. C. Dugdale, Limnol. Oceanog., 12, 685 (1967).

22. F. A. J. Armstrong and S. Tibbitts, J. Mar. Biol. Ass. U. K., 48, 143 (1968).

23. A. C. Redfield, B. H. Ketchum, and F. A. Richards in The Sea (M. N. Hill, ed.), Interscience, New York, 1963, Chapt. 2.

7

THE NITROGEN CYCLE

7.1 Introduction

In trying to understand the nitrogen cycle, we are con-
fronted with many of the features of the silicon and phosphorus
cycles, as well as many unique features. First, as with silicon and phosphorus, the compounds of nitrogen may be divided
into two groups, dissolved and particulate. Secondly, as with
phosphorus, though not silicon, each of the two groups may be
divided into two subcategories, inorganic and organic.
Finally, many of the processes of the nitrogen cycle have
counterparts in the silicon and phosphorus cycles (assimilation, regeneration, and dissolution of particulate matter).

The nitrogen cycle also has several unique or complicating
features.

1. Nitrogen exists in nine oxidation states all of which have
significant roles in the marine environment. These oxidation states are listed in Table 7-1, together with examples of each state. The sea contains about 450 mg of
nitrogen per cubic meter of water. Most of the nitrogen
is present as molecular nitrogen (roughly 95%). Of the

TABLE 7-1

Oxidation States of Nitrogen

Oxidation Number	Examples
5+	$NO_3^- N_2O_5$
4+	NO_2
3+	$HONO,$[a] NO_2^-, N_2O_3
2+	$HONNOH,$[b] $HO_2N_2^-$, $N_2O_2^{2-}$, N_2O
1+	N_2
0	H_2NOH, HN_3, N_3^-
1-	H_2NOH, HN_3, N_3^-
2-	H_2NNH_2
3-	RNH_2, $NH_3,$[c] NH_4^+ [d]

[a] $\log K_A = -3.35$;

[b] $\log K_{A1} = -7.05$, $\log K_{A2} = -11.0$;

[c] $\log K_B = 4.75$;

[d] $\log K_A = -9.48$.

combined soluble nitrogen, 65% is present as nitrate-
nitrite (Note 1).

2. Additional processes are involved in the nitrogen cycle
    because of the multiplicity of oxidation states of the
    element. These processes include fixation, nitrification,
    and denitrification.

3. The nitrogen budget of the sea of the world is apparently unbalanced. According to available estimates (cf. Tables 7-2, 7-3), the silicon and phosphorus budgets seem to be balanced (Section 7-2).

4. Calculations involving a model ocean system (such as that described in Chapter 4) indicate that in geological time all of the earth's molecular nitrogen should have been converted to nitrate ion in the sea.[1] That this is not the case is obvious and is one of the mysteries of the nitrogen cycle.

These four observations will be discussed in the following sections as an aid to understanding the known distributions of various species of the nitrogen cycle.

7.2 The Nitrogen Budget

The nutrient budget of the oceans, as summarized in Table 7-2, is based on estimates made by Emery, Orr, and Rittenberg.[2] Allowing for the uncertainties in the available data, we can see that the budgets for phosphorus and silicon in the ocean are balanced. That is, the input from the land balances the phosphorus and silicon lost to the sediments, as would be the case if the ocean had reached a steady state (Chapter 4). In contrast, the nitrogen budget shows an interesting unbalance. There is an annual excess input of about 70 million metric tons (input vs. loss to sediments).

TABLE 7-2

Nutrient Budget of the Oceans[2]

	Nitrogen	Phosphorus	Silicon
Reserve in ocean	920,000[a]	120,000	4,000,000
Annual use by phytoplankton	9,600	1,300	—
Annual contribution by:			
Rivers (dissolved)	19	2	150
Rivers (suspended)	0	12	4,150
Rain	59	0	0
Annual loss to sediments	9	13	3,800

[a]Units, million metric tons.

Features of interest in the nitrogen budget include the following:

1. A steady-state condition probably exists for nitrogen, as it does for silicon and phosphorus.

2. The available nitrogen reserve in the ocean corresponds to about 100 times the annual requirement for phytoplankton.

3. About 13,000 years would be required to renew the oceanic reserve of available nitrogen.

4. The most significant observation is that the nitrogen budget does not balance. The annual contribution is

about 78 million metric tons; the annual loss to sediments is about 9 million metric tons; there is an annual
excess input of about 70 million metric tons of nitrogen.

5. Nitrogen must escape from the sea in some way. If it
does not, the annual deposition of nitrogen in sediments
should cause the molecular nitrogen in the atmosphere to
be depleted in 400 million years (Note 2; cf. Table 7-3).

TABLE 7-3

Nitrogen Budget of the Earth[3,7]

	Nitrogen (billions of metric tons)
Global distribution	
Atmosphere	3,860,000
Sedimentary rock	77,000
Hydrosphere	23,000
	3,960,000
Oceanic reserves	
Molecular (N_2)	22,000
Combined as	(920)
Nitrate	570
Ammonia + Nitrite	10
Dissolved organic	340
	22,920
Present as standing crop of organisms	1
Annual oceanic requirement (18% of 150g $C/m^2/yr$)	10
Annual contribution by:	
Rivers	0.019
Rain	0.059
Annual loss to sediments	0.009

229

This period of time is less than 20% of the estimated age of the oceans.

6. The budget cannot be balanced by postulating that nitrogen in the sediments is denitrified (i.e., reduced from nitrate or nitrite to the 0 or 2+ oxidation states). A maximum of 8.6 million metric tons per year might be accounted for (Note 3) by this process and this value is about 10% of the inbalance.

7. At the pH and pE of the ocean, molecular nitrogen should be irreversibly converted to nitrate ion, on the basis of Sillen's calculations[1] for the model ocean system (Fig. 7-1). Accordingly, the atmospheric nitrogen would be depleted.

Obviously, there is a need to rationalize the unbalance of the nitrogen budget (fourth observation), and it has been postulated[2,3] that denitrification is the mechanism for escape of nitrogen from the sea. The difficulty with this postulation might be described as the eighth observation, i.e., the calculated effect seems to be too low.

Several answers to the quandary have been suggested.[3]

1. The data used to estimate the nitrogen budget could have been exceedingly inaccurate, though there is no reason to believe that this is so. On the contrary, Eriksson[4] estimated a value of 100 million metric tons as the annual

230

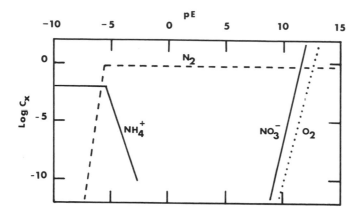

FIG. 7-1

Redox diagram for some species of the nitrogen cycle:
logarithm of species concentration (log C_x, solid lines)
or partial pressure (log p, broken lines, for gases) as
a function of pE. (After Sillén[1])

excess input. This is a comparable estimate, and espe-

cially significant because a different approach was used

to calculate the nitrogen balance.

2. Anoxic or oxygen-poor microenvironments might exist with-

    in the water column. This may be tested through mass

    spectrometric measurement of the nitrogen-isotopic ratios

    ($^{29}N_2/^{28}N_2$) or the nitrogen-argon ratios in sea water.

    The former ratios are markedly different in nitrogen of

    biogenic origin from those of atmospheric nitrogen (cf.

    Richards and Benson[5]). Also, the nitrogen-argon ratio is

of interest in more precise estimates of the amount of biogenic nitrogen; the ratio is larger if biogenic nitrogen is present than if only atmospheric nitrogen were present. For example, Richards and Benson[5] did establish through mass spectrometric measurements that denitrification is an active process in the anoxic environment of the Cariaco Trench (Caribbean Sea).

3. Eriksson[4] suggested, "There are organisms that can carry out denitrification inside their bodies. It may be possible that at least in some species denitrification occurs as a by-product in the normal reduction of nitrate to ammonia which has to be carried out in the assimilation of nitrate by plants."

4. There might be bacteria that denitrify in the presence of oxygen. This suggestion and the preceding one make sense to the marine chemist or microbiologist. Rittenberg[3] noted that both suggestions might be regarded as heresy by a modern biochemist who believes in comparative biochemistry and who respects the precision of nature in performing biosynthesis.

In summary, we have an excess of nitrogen input in the nutrient budget of the sea that seems to be based on valid estimates. We have one rationalization (denitrification) to compensate for the excess input, and we have a tool to study denitrification (nitrogen-isotopic or nitrogen-argon ratios).

Finally, we have two heresies to account for the means of denitrification.

7.3 The Nitrogen Cycle

The nitrogen biogeochemical cycle has been pictured in
two ways: (1) in terms of the circulation of nitrogen between
the components of the marine ecosystem with special emphasis
on the physiological origins of the various forms of nitrogen;
or (2) in terms of the energy-increasing and -decreasing steps.

The latter type (Fig. 7-2) indicates that there are two
kinds of steps: (1) energy-requiring steps by which energy from
sunlight in organic matter is used to convert nitrate (or
higher energy forms) to protoplasm; and (2) energy producing
steps by which energy is released to decompose organisms. In
both cases, the high-energy forms are at the top of the diagram. The hump on the right of Fig. 7-2 indicates the sizeable
energy barrier involved in the nitrogen-fixing step. This
representation is useful for depicting the energy flow involving nitrogen in the marine ecosystem.

The other representation (Fig. 7-3) complements the energy
flow representation. The complementary roles of bacteria,
plants, animals, and physical processes are summarized in
Fig. 7-3 and are identified by numerals. Letters are used to
indicate the origin of various forms of nitrogen.

The complexities of the nitrogen cycle are evident from
this condensed version (Fig. 7-3). Also, evidently various

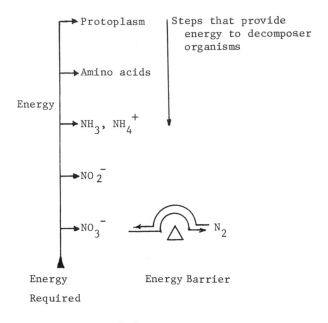

FIG. 7-2

Energy-increasing and -decreasing steps
of the nitrogen cycle (after Odum[6]).

bacteria effect a large variety of reactions in the cycle and
have an important role in regenerating forms of nitrogen,
particularly molecular nitrogen. The active role of plants,
especially phytoplankton, has been emphasized in preceding
chapters. The ability of plants to fix nitrogen (i.e., convert molecular nitrogen to compounds)has not been emphasized,
but it provides a further unbalance of the nitrogen budget.
Finally, the contribution of animals is relatively limited to
the two important processes of grazing and excretion.

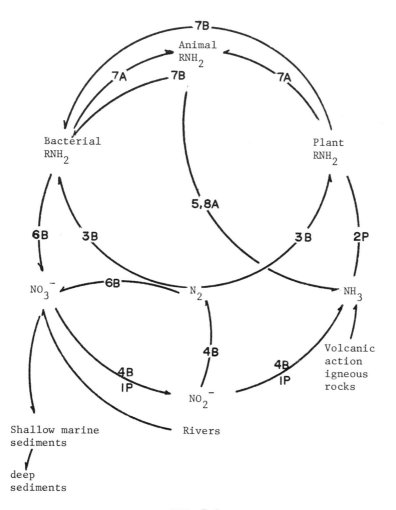

FIG. 7-3

Origins of various forms of nitrogen
in the sea (after Vaccaro[7]).

Key: Origins: Animal, A; Bacterial, B; Plant, P;

Processes: Reduction, 1; Assimilation, 2; Fixation, 3;
Denitrification, 4; Regeneration, 5; Nitrification, 6;
Grazing, 7; Excretion, 8.

It is also evident that both representations are highly qualitative. In large part this is due to the same analysis problems described for phosphorus. Sea water contains 0.1-20 µg-atoms of organic nitrogen per liter, which is too small to be determined by micro-Kjeldahl techniques, though more sensitive techniques, such as gas chromatography, seem promising.

Even though the representation (Fig. 7-3) of the nitrogen biogeochemical cycle is highly qualitative, it is useful as a guide to the processes involved and serves to indicate the areas of uncertainty and debate. The processes fall into two categories.

1. Input-removal processes. Essentially, three major processes bring nitrogen to the sea: (1) volcanic activity; (2) atmospheric precipitation; and (3) continental drainage (admittedly there is overlap in the first two processes). Three processes remove nitrogen from the sea: (1) loss to deep marine sediments; (2) migrations of marine animals; and (3) loss of nitrogen to the atmosphere.

2. Intramarine processes. These processes involve changes in the nitrogen content of various volumes of the sea. The general scheme might begin with ammonia, which is the first inorganic product in the regeneration of nitrogen. Liberation of ammonia can occur under anoxic or under

oxygen-rich conditions and the process is independent of pE. Ammonia may be assimilated by organisms or nitrified by other organisms to lower energy forms of nitrogen (Fig. 7-2). Combined nitrogen may also be produced by nitrogen fixation. The low-energy forms may be denitrified (to nitrous oxide or molecular nitrogen) or assimilated, which completes the cycle.

In the two sections that follow, the salient features of the two categories will be considered.

7.4 Input-Removal Processes

Volcanic activity. As noted earlier (Section 4.1), heating associated with radioactivity in the primitive earth presumably was responsible for the distillation of nitrogen (as N_2 and NH_3) into the hydrosphere. During this time ($<5 \times 10^9$ years B.P.) and subsequently, most of the juvenile nitrogen had reached the atmosphere as a result of volcanic activity or volcanism. (Other sources of juvenile nitrogen include weathering and meteorites.)

Reducing conditions must have prevailed in the primitive ocean and concentrations of ammonium ion and the reduced forms of nitrogen must have been present in much greater concentration than in the modern ocean. How much greater is difficult to assess, though Bada and Miller[8] have suggested limits of 10^{-1} M (maximum) and 10^{-3} M (minimum). If clay minerals regulated cations in the primitive ocean as they evidently do in the modern ocean, the pH should have been comparable. The

ammonium and potassium ion concentrations should have been the

same, about 0.1 $\underline{M}$. The two ions are similar in their clay

mineral ion-exchange equilibria. The estimate of minimum

ammonium ion concentration was based on the reversible

deamination of aspartic acid and it was assumed this acid was

necessary for the origin of life. Highest concentrations of

ammonia-ammonium in the English Channel seem to be about

$2 \times 10^{-6} \underline{M}$.[7]

Atmospheric input. Inorganic nitrogen enters the sea from the

atmosphere, mainly, in two ways: as dissolved molecular

nitrogen and as atmospheric precipitation.

1.   The distribution of dissolved molecular nitrogen in the

world ocean is known only generally and somewhat impre-

cisely. This will improve as gas chromatographic tech-

niques are applied more extensively; other methods suffer

from the difficulty of separating the inert gases from

nitrogen. The equilibrium solubility of nitrogen in sea

water follows Henry's law (Eqn. 7-1) where $\underline{p}$ and $\underline{P}$ are

the partial pressures in the gas phase and in solution

$$p = P, \quad c = \alpha\, p \qquad\qquad (7-1)$$

respectively, at equilibrium; c is equilibrium concentra-

tion of nitrogen in solution and α is the solubility coef-

ficient which varies with the temperature and the salinity

of the sea water sample. Equilibrium solubilities have been determined in the laboratory by equilibrating sea-water samples with air and measuring the solubility. Thus, the equilibrium solubility of nitrogen in sea water (Cl^o/oo, 19) is 12.78 (5^oC), 11.56 (10^oC), 10.53 (15^oC), 9.65 (20^oC) and 10.08 (20^oC; Cl^o/oo, 15) ml (at STP) per liter of sea water from a normal atmosphere of 760 mm.[9] It appears that sea water is normally saturated with molecular nitrogen and that this form of nitrogen behaves conservatively.

The situation in selected portions of the marine ecosystem may be different, particularly when molecular nitrogen is consumed or produced. Specifically, the extent to which these processes affect the distribution of two stable nitrogen isotopes (^{15}N, ^{14}N) is a matter of some interest. Does the rule of mass effect (selective removal of the lighter isotope during biological assimilation) apply? Some evidence for slight ^{15}N-enrichment in certain seaweeds, clams, grains, fish, plants, and lake waters is available, though no measurable isotope effect in nitrogen fixation by _Azotobacter_ was detected (cf. Vaccaro[7]). Fractionation of nitrogen isotopes seems to be a consequence of denitrification, and Richards and Benson[5] observed a higher $^{15}N^{14}N$ to $^{14}N_2$ ratio in anoxic

waters than was prevalent in atmospheric nitrogen or
ordinary sea water. As noted earlier, this secondary effect is a guide to the extent of denitrification. The
extent to which biological systems influence the separation of nitrogen isotopes remains uncertain in most processes, including the critical ones of ammonification
and nitrification.

2. The other major source of atmospheric input is in the
form of oceanic rain. Evidence is available which indicates the importance of contributions of inorganic compounds from rain versus those from intramarine processes.
Available data indicate a wide variation in the nitrate
and ammonia contents of rain water. Moreover, in at least
one instance, a positive correlation was obtained between
the ammonia content of surface water (near Bermuda) and
the ammonia in a five-day accumulation of rain (nitrate
data were not available).[7]

In view of the importance of ammonia and nitrate contributions from rain, what is the origin of these combined
forms of nitrogen? Evidently, most of the nitrate in the
atmosphere is the result of oxidation of ammonia not from
the oxidation of nitric oxide, which might have been
produced electrically (Eqs. 7-2, -3) in the atmosphere.

$$\Delta + N_2 + O_2 \quad \xrightarrow{\text{lightning}} \quad 2NO \qquad (7\text{-}2)$$

$$NO + O_2 \rightarrow 2NO_2; \quad 3NO_2 + H_2O \rightarrow 2HNO_3 + NO \qquad (7-3)$$

This assessment was made by Hutchinson,[10] who suggested the source of ammonia is the decomposition of organic matter, mainly adsorbed on dust particles. This assessment was confirmed by Hoering,[11] who quantitatively isolated ammonia and nitrate in rainwater (using ion-exchange resins) and measured the nitrogen-isotope ratio in each component. What if the source of nitrate had been electrically fixed nitrogen (Eqs. 7-2, 7-3) and the ammonia could have been produced by reduction of this nitrate? Were this the case, ammonia should have been depleted in ^{15}N (because ^{14}N would react faster due to the mass effect); the opposite was observed.

Continental drainage. The reported (cf. Table 5-6) mean composition of river waters of the world is about 1 ppm nitrate, though the range is considerable: from 0.05 ppm (Australia) to 3.7 ppm (Europe). The world mean is thought to be of the correct order of magnitude, but range is probably not significant for several reasons. The annual total water flow from land surfaces into the sea is 0.20 geograms (Gg = 10^{20}g),[10] from which an estimated river input of nitrogen might be computed.

The annual input of nitrogen from continental drainage is about one-third that provided by oceanic rain (Table 7-3). Together these sources provide only about eight percent of the annual nitrogen requirements for primary production. This is based on a nitrogen requirement equivalent to 18% of 150 g of carbon per square meter of surface.

Loss to sediments. The extent to which regeneration of nitrogen and other nutrients occurs in upper sediment layers of semienclosed basins in the sea is a matter of considerable interest for two major reasons. First, a study of the interrelations and time-dependent concentrations of ammonia, nitrite, and nitrate in upper portions of basin sediments may provide the means of predicting the resupply of nutrients to the productive layers in the overlying water. (This will be considered in connection with the intramarine processes.) The second reason is related to the first, that this information may indicate the extent to which nutrients are being lost from the nitrogen cycle either temporarily or essentially permanently.

Ocean basins are logical sources of burial and nutrient regeneration. Basins are great depressions in the lithosphere where the depth is somewhat uniform and within a range of 3-6 km (1500-3000 fm). This encompasses about 80% of the ocean bottom. Probably less than one per cent of the ocean bottom is a deep (depth greater than 6 km). Moreover, many enclosed

or semienclosed basins are characterized by varying periods
and regions of stagnation because the utilization of oxygen by
decaying organic matter exceeds the dissolved oxygen supply,
and the pE may vary considerably. The influx of new water
over the sill depth typically prevents permanent stagnation
(though this may be insufficient, as in the Black Sea or the
Cariaco Trench).

Regeneration of nutrients in sediments of marine basins
near Southern California has been investigated by Rittenberg,
Emery, and Orr.[12] These workers were able to correlate some
regeneration processes with the biological, physical, and
chemical environments. Three types of sediment environments
were examined: (1) reducing environment (Santa Barbara which
had a negative pE, little free oxygen in a depth of 2 ml);
(2) oxidizing (Santa Monica, slightly positive to slightly
negative pE, no hydrogen sulfide, some free oxygen); and (3)
mixed (Catalina, positive pE in top to 1 m, negative pE at
lower depth). The sediment thickness approaches 3,000 m. The
sediments in the top 100 cm were deposited during a 475-year
period; those in the 300-400-cm zone correspond to 700 years.
The following features may be noted.

1.   Biological activity seems to be dominant in regeneration
     of nitrogen. In all environments, the amount of organic
     nitrogen decreased with depth of burial, but the ammonia
     content increased.

2. The amount of organic nitrogen disappearing is greater
    than the amount of inorganic nitrogen accumulating, and
    some nitrogen is escaping to the overlying water. This
    escapes as ammonia from sediments of Type 1 and in several
    forms (NH_3, N_2, NO_2^-, NO_3^-) from sediments of Type 3.

3. Inorganic nitrogen, regenerated in the sediments, is
    brought to the overlying water by diffusion (which results
    in a marked concentration gradient) or by channeling or
    churning of sediments.

4. The amount of nitrogen returned from sediment to over-
    lying water is about 0.4% of the amount required annually
    by indigenous phytoplankton. (Comparably low values
    were noted for silicon and phosphorus.)

Thus, nitrogen becomes lost to marine sediments by a combination of burial of organic nitrogenous matter and low rate
of decomposition, particularly at depths below the zone of
major bacterial activity. Nitrogen may be lost to the sediments in other ways, including the following: Some small amount
of ammonium ion is involved in cation exchange with clays.
Calcium carbonate shells contain amino acids and proteins
(6-40 micromoles per gram, $1 \, \mu \, \underline{M}/g = 100$ ppm) which are protected from bacterial action and seem to be present in water-
insoluble layers.[13]

Marine animal migrations. Nitrogen is brought from the sea by
marine birds in the form of ammonium oxalate and waste in

guano. The guano deposits have been exploited commercially for fertilizer. Hutchinson[10] has provided figures that indicate the relative amount of nitrogen brought to land. About 54×10^{12} g of nitrogen were present as soda niter ($NaNO_3$) in Chilean deserts. The total nitrate-nitrogen present in surface deposits of the earth was estimated as 10^{14} g and the nitrogen in guano deposits as about 10^{11} g.

The Chilean deposits of sodium niter probably arose from transportation of nitrates in ground water followed by evaporation. The source of nitrate is controversial and may have been from (1) guano, (2) bacterial fixation of nitrogen from vegetation, or (3) volcanism, which is the most probable.

Loss to the atmosphere. Nitrogen must be lost to the atmosphere largely (Note 4) through the process of denitrification, which may be defined as "biological reduction of nitrate or nitrite to either nitrous oxide or free nitrogen." This is of course an intramarine process, but is considered here because it also falls into the input-loss category. It is, in fact, the missing item of the nitrogen budget, as noted earlier (Section 7.2).

The organisms that effect denitrification are of two types: (1) heterotropes use organic compounds as an energy source and (2) autotropes use inorganic compounds as an energy source. The free energy change is favorable (cf. Section 3.5) if the hydrogen needed for the reduction comes from an organic compound such as methane (Eqn. 7-4) or a sugar (Eqn. 7-5). On

the other hand, if the hydrogen comes from an inorganic com-

pound (H_2, H_2S), the free-energy change is favorable only in an

$$4\ NO_3^- + 3OH_4 \rightarrow 2N_2 + 3CO_2 + 6H_2O, \ \Delta G^o = -475 \text{ kcal} \qquad (7-4)$$

$$8\ NO_3^- + C_6H_{12}O_6 \rightarrow 4N_2 + 4CO_3^{2-} + 2CO_2 + 6H_2O, \ \Delta G^o = -728 \text{ kcal} \qquad (7-5)$$

oxygen-poor environment (as indicated by Eqn. 7-6).

$$2\ NO_3^- + 2H^+ \rightarrow N_2O + O_2 + H_2O, \ \Delta G^o = +21 \text{ kcal} \qquad (7-6)$$

The oxygen-poor or anoxic environment would most logically

be in a sediment with a low (or negative) pE and a high organic

content. As noted earlier, though, the estimated area and

volume of appropriate sediments seem too small to account for

more than ten percent of the estimated loss to the atmosphere.

Obviously, another locality is involved, i.e., within the

water column. The most likely possibilities are in anoxic

environments, in ocean basins where intermittent stagnation

occurs, and in intermediate depths of the ocean where the

oxygen minimum layer is found. These represent progressively

larger areas of denitrification activity.

1.   Anoxic environments.[5]   The Black Sea, the Cariaco Trench,

and certain Norwegian fjords are anoxic environments that

have been studied intensively. These are also areas of

active denitrification. Nitrite and nitrate (typically)

are absent or present in trace amounts, oxygen is absent,

and sulfur is present as sulfides. The amount of molecular nitrogen expected from denitrification can be computed in two ways. First, it can be computed from the
apparent oxygen utilization, AOU (Eqn. 7-7), using the
oxygen-consumed to phosphorus-released ratio, for anoxic

$$AOU:C:N:P = 270:106:15:1 \qquad (7\text{-}7)$$

waters, of 235 instead of 270, and knowing the phosphate
concentration. Alternatively, other relationships may be
used (Eqn. 7-8, -9, -10). Where concentrations are
expressed as µg-at element/liter (Note 4). In addition,
the amount of nitrogen in excess of that expected from

$$N_2^{B(P)} = 15[PO_4]^{3-} - [NH_3]-[NO_2^-]-[NO_3^-] \qquad (7\text{-}8)$$

$$N_2^{B(O)aerobic} = 0.056(AOU)-[NH_3]-[NO_2^-]-[NO_3^-] \qquad (7\text{-}9)$$

$$N_2^{B(O)anoxic} = 0.064(AOU+[S^{2-}])-[NH_3]+[NO_2^-]+[NO_3^-] \qquad (7\text{-}10)$$

the atmosphere (ΔN_2) can be computed (Eqn. 7-11).

$$\Delta N_2 = \left[\frac{N_2}{Ar} - \frac{N_2'}{Ar'} \right] Ar_o \qquad (7\text{-}11)$$

Here N_2/Ar is the observed volumetric nitrogen-argon ratio
in the dissolved gas from a water sample; N_2'/Ar' is the
ratio of the solubilities of the two gases in water (at
the same temperature and salinity) equilibrated with air;
and Ar_o is the absolute concentration of argon in the
sample. (The approximation that $Ar_o = Ar'$ has been used
with little resulting error.)

The variation of these parameters with depth is indicated

in Table 7-4. Within the limits of experimental error,

the increase in biogenic nitrogen is constant with depth

in the anoxic zone, the negative values are not signifi-

cant, and the agreement between ΔN_2 and N_2^B is good.

Richards and Benson[5] were able to show also that the bio-

genic nitrogen was most probably produced by denitrifi-

cation and that oxidation of amino groups by sulfate ion

was not a major concomitant process.

2.   Intermittently stagnant basins. The Gotland Basin is in

the central Baltic, east of the island of Gotland.[14] The

sill and maximum depths are 60 and 250 m, respectively.

During January-August 1966, a period of negative O_2 budget

occurred at the 245-m level. This was characterized by

decrease in nitrate (7 to 0 µg-at /liter) and nitrite

(11 to 0 µg-at /liter) and a parallel increase in ammonium

nitrogen (0-11 µg-at/liter). A progressive loss of nitro-

gen from the water column seems to have been observed,

which might be ascribed to the loss of molecular nitrogen.

This point would need to be checked with one of the tools

described above.

The extent of loss of nitrogen is critical in the Gotland

Basin because the surface waters of the Baltic normally

seem to be nutrient depleted. Periodically, following

periods of stagnation, the nutrients that have accumulated

TABLE 7-4

Vertical Distribution of ΔN_2, $N_2^{B(P)}$, and

$N_2^{B(O)}$ (as µg-at /liter) in the Cariaco Trench[5]

Depth, m	ΔN_2	$N_2^{B(P)}$	$N_2^{B(O)}$
Surface zone			
5	-4.0	-0.8	-2.7
50	-1.0	-0.4	-0.7
100	0.8	-0.3	0.6
Transition zone			
300	19.6	27.6	21.2
Anoxic zone			
400	23.8	30.2	27.3
775	20.6	25.7	25.6
915	18.6	25.1	25.7
1208	22.5	23.8	25.6
mean	20.7	25.6	25.3
	±1.8	±2.2	±1.3

are lifted to the surface and phytoplankton blooms and
fish population increase. Gupta[14] has suggested that
maybe only these periodic stagnation-regeneration cycles
permit fishing to flourish in the Baltic. Intensive loss
of nitrogen could diminish this fertility.

3. Oxygen-minimum layer areas. Over broad expanses of the
tropical Pacific and Indian Oceans, the dissolved oxygen

concentration is nil at depths of about 150-800 m. The low-oxygen waters are often characterized by a lower concentration of nitrate and a secondary nitrite maximum (below the thermocline). The decreased concentration of nitrate has not been matched by a corresponding increase in nitrite, and this has been taken as an indication of denitrification.

Goering[15] has provided direct evidence by measuring the rates of denitrification (using a ^{15}N-tracer technique). Nitrite and molecular nitrogen are produced concurrently from $^{15}NO_3^-$ added to nitrite-rich and oxygen-poor water samples taken from below the thermocline in the tropical eastern Pacific. The ratio of molecular nitrogen produced to nitrate-nitrogen lost varied (0.1-0.8). The rate of denitrification was sensitive to the oxygen concentration and decreased 58% when the oxygen concentration changed from 0.02 ml O_2/liter (ca. 0.4% saturation with O_2) to 0.19 ml O_2/liter (3.5% saturation).

These are the three types of environments in which denitrification and loss of nitrogen to the atmosphere are occurring. It would seem that the most promising location of denitrification would be the enormous areas of the tropical Pacific and Indian Oceans. Granting this, several questions need to be considered.

1. How extensive are the active regions of denitrification? Goering and Dugdale,[16] for example, did not detect denitrification in a likely site (high-nitrite and low-oxygen waters near Peru). Was the active zone missed or did the reduction of nitrate stop at nitrite?

2. What concentrations of O_2 limit denitrification? The limits are uncertain but seem to be of the order of 0.n ml O_2/liter, and the limit probably depends upon the kind and the population of denitrifiers, as well as the amount of nitrate present. Obviously, laboratory studies with precisely defined conditions will be helpful.

3. What are the rates of denitrification? Some reported rates of denitrification (6-10 µg N liter^{-1}hr^{-1}) for tropical waters are probably unusually high because of experimental conditions.[15] During incubation time (7.5 days), large increases in denitrifying bacterial cells occur, and conditions for denitrification become more favorable when samples are stored for a week in glass bottles. The need for obtaining rates that are realistic in terms of the marine ecosystem is obviously great, but the experimental difficulties of obtaining in situ measurements are also great.

4. What organisms are responsible for denitrification? About half of the marine bacterial species can reduce nitrate to

nitrite in the presence of adequate amounts of organic
substrate, but less than five percent can reduce nitrate
or nitrite to N_2 or ammonia.[17] Denitrifying organisms
seem to belong mainly to the genera Erwina and Pseudomona,
and, to a lesser extent, Vibrio. Some 30 species of
nitrate-reducing bacteria seem to function at deep-sea
pressures, though the activity is reduced and more
rapidly at low temperatures (2°C) than at higher temperatures ($10,21,30^{o}$C).[18] Apparently, hydrostatic pressure
is not a limiting factor for nitrate reduction.

Available evidence suggests the denitrification process
is extensive and active, but whether the rate and amount of
denitrification are sufficient to balance the nitrogen budget
is uncertain and will be answered only by in situ studies.

7.5 Intramarine Processes

These processes include liberation of ammonia, nitrification, fixation, denitrification, and assimilation. Vaccaro[7]
has provided an excellent review of the subject, which may be
consulted for additional details.

Liberation of Ammonia

This arises from several sources - from the atmosphere,
by decomposition of protoplasm and nitrogenous organic matter
(bacterial proteolysis), zooplankton excretion, as well as by
reduction of nitrate, nitrite, and other inorganic nitrogen
compounds.

Proteolytic marine bacteria convert protoplasm and animal excretions into carbon dioxide, hydrogen sulfide, ammonia, and other basic chemicals. This is an immensely significant aspect of the carbon cycle and those compounds that are resistant to bacterial attack are kept in low concentration.

The ecological significance of zooplankton excretion has been the subject of much discussion, and it appears that the contribution to the ammonia content may be very significant (up to 50% in some instances).[7] The contribution must vary markedly with location and season. In Narragansett Bay (Rhode Island), for instance, zooplankton provide only about 2.5% of the phytoplankton's daily requirement during the periods of abundance (late April to late June), but an average 180% of the requirement during periods of relative scarcity (late August to late November).[19] Nitrogen contribution tended to be a maximum when phytoplankton were abundant and vice versa possibly owing to a greater utilization of protein as an energy source during periods of phytoplankton scarcity.[19]

The contributions of ammonia from rain and by reduction of nitrate-nitrite nitrogen have been considered in the preceding section.

Nitrification. The biological oxidation of ammonia to nitrite or nitrate (nitrification) has been the subject of much study. In soil, two physiological groups of autotrophic bacteria are responsible for the oxidation. Ammonia-oxidizing bacteria (e.g.,<u>Nitrosomonas</u>) derive energy for growth and cell synthesis from the oxidation of ammonia to nitrite (Eqn. 7-12)

$$NH_4^+ + OH^- + 1.5O_2 \rightarrow 2H^+ + NO_2^- + 2H_2O, \quad \Delta G^o = -59 \text{ kcal} \quad (7-12)$$

at an optimum pH of 7.5-8.8. A second group (e.g.,<u>Nitrobacter</u>) derives energy from the oxidation of nitrite to nitrate (Eqn. 7-13).

$$NO_2^- + 0.5O_2 \rightarrow NO_3^-, \quad \Delta G^o = -18 \text{ kcal} \quad (7-13)$$

Aleem and Nason[20] and Vaccaro[7] have provided excellent reviews of the metabolic pathways involved in the overall process (Eqs. 7-12, 7-13), on land and sea, respectively. It is generally conceded that the oxidation proceeds through several intermediate stages (Eqn. 7-14); the extent to which pathway <u>B</u> occurs is uncertain. Presumably there should be marine

$$NH_3 \rightarrow H_2NOH \rightarrow HONNOH \overset{(A)}{\rightarrow} NO_2^- \quad (7-14)$$

$$(3-) \qquad (1-) \qquad (1+) \qquad (3+)$$

$$\Big\downarrow (B)$$

$$N_2 \longleftarrow \longrightarrow N_2O$$

$$(0) \qquad (1+)$$

analogs of <u>Nitrosomonas</u> and <u>Nitrobacter</u>.

The first known ammonia-oxidizing pelagic bacterium <u>Nitrosocystis</u> <u>oceanus</u> Watson was isolated by Watson in 1962.[21] This autotrophic organism grows optimally at $30^o C$ and in ammonia concentrations of 5-240 mg-at NH_3-N/liter, and has been

isolated from depths of 1,000 m. Watson estimates the standing
crop to be less than one bacterium per milliliter and that the
0.07 μg-at NO_2-N/liter/year would be produced in the upper
100 m of tropical waters. Nitrosocystis oceanus and other
marine (though not terrestrial) ammonia-oxidizing bacteria
(thus far isolated) seem to be characterized by a unique
sculptured outer-wall layer.[22] The wall was thought to be a
macro-coordination entity composed of structural protein
linked together with metal ions (as metal-oxygen linkages).[22]

A major problem emerged from the work of Carlucci and
Strickland,[23] who isolated and purified Nitrosocystis and a
nitrite-oxidizing bacterium in connection with a kinetic study
of nitrification. These workers conclude that the predicted
rates of nitrite-nitrate productions are too high and that
other organisms and/or mechanisms must be involved unless
nitrifying bacteria and substrates are greatly concentrated in
microenvironments in the sea.

Again, the ultimate problem seems to be the need to demonstrate the rate and extent of nitrification in situ.

Nitrogen Fixation. The conversion of molecular nitrogen to
combined nitrogen (fixation) is probably one of the two most
important metabolic processes needed to maintain the productivity of the earth, the other being photosynthesis. Nitrogen
fixation in the marine ecosystem has received comparatively
little attention and accurate values of the fixation rates are

needed badly. To the extent that fixation occurs, it represents a further imbalance in the nitrogen cycle that must be compensated by denitrification or other processes. Nitrogen fixation has been reviewed by Vaccaro[7] and by Stewart.[24]

Tropical and subtropical surface waters are logical areas of nitrogen fixation because of the presence of large amounts of nitrogen-fixing algae. Blooms of the blue-green alga Trichodesmium cover hundreds of square km of the Arabian Sea, the Indian Ocean, and the Sargasso Sea, and it has been demonstrated[25] that these blooms assimilate $^{15}N_2$ (Note 6). Other likely nitrogen-fixing genera are Nostoc (though the marine forms need to be tested), Calothrix (Note 7), Tolypothrix, and Rivularia. The nitrogen fixed by these plants is rapidly assimilated, according to Stewart.[24]

The biochemical aspects of nitrogen fixation have been summarized by Stewart.[24] Of related interest is the ability of coordination compounds of cobalt to fix nitrogen (Eqn. 7-15). Many believe that compounds of this type are

$$[CoH_3(PPh_3)_3] + N_2 \rightarrow [CoH(N_2)(PPh_3)_3] + H_2 \quad Ph = C_6H_5 \qquad (7-15)$$

important in nitrogen fixing, maybe, as a reducing agent and, maybe, as a protection of the nitrogen activating sites (presumably a transition-metal ion).[25] In any case, activity in both areas will be helpful in understanding nitrogen fixation in the marine ecosystem.

Denitrification. This process has been considered in some detail in the preceding section.

Assimilation. Several significant features of nitrogen assimilation by marine phytoplankton may be reviewed here.

1. The assimilation ratio of carbon, nitrogen, and phosphorus is reasonably constant (C:N:P = 106:16:2; Section 6.5) because at this level organic synthesis is highly selective and relatively simple in terms of the composition of cellular amino acids.

2. For any extended period, primary nitrogen assimilation requires light and the process is limited to the upper 150 m (photic zone) of the sea.

3. In general, most common forms of marine algae evidently do not utilize organic nitrogen in significant amounts, though there may be exceptions among heterotropes in polluted estuaries. Those that utilize inorganic nitrogen obtain comparable growth rates with nitrate, nitrite, or ammonia. If all three are available, ammonia may be used preferentially because (1) it may be the major form available in the photic layer sometimes or (2) it may have a toxic effect on reduction of nitrate by enzymes or (3) because of a "short-circuiting" effect: a free energy increase is required to reduce nitrate and/or nitrite to ammonia; and more nitrogen can be assimilated for the same energy increase if ammonia is used.

257

4. Four stages seem to be involved in the utilization of nitrate; these are represented by Eqn. 7-16a-d.

$$NO_3^- + 2H^+ + 2e^- \rightarrow NO_2^- + H_2O \qquad (7\text{-}16a)$$

$$2NO_2^- + 5H^+ + 4e^- \rightarrow HN_2O_2^- + 2H_2O \qquad (7\text{-}16b)$$

$$HN_2O_2^- + 6H^+ + 4e^- \rightarrow 2NH_2OH \qquad (7\text{-}16c)$$

$$NH_2OH + 2H^+ + 2e^- \rightarrow NH_3 + H_2O \qquad (7\text{-}16d)$$

5. Reduction of nitrate in the dark and the light has different stoichiometries (7-17, 7-18).

$$\text{"dark"}: 2(CH_2O) + NO_3^- + 2H^+ \quad NH_4^+ + 2CO_2 + H_2O \qquad (7\text{-}17)$$

$$\text{"light"}: NO_3^- + 2H_2O \quad NH_3 + OH^- + 2O_2 \qquad (7\text{-}18)$$

6. MacIssac and Dugdale[26] have found (using a nitrogen-15-tracer technique) that the uptake of nitrate and ammonia by natural populations of marine phytoplankton[26] follows the Michaelis-Menton kinetic expression (Eqn. 7-19).

$$V = \frac{V_{max}S}{K_t + S} \qquad (7\text{-}19)$$

Here, V is the uptake rate in units of nitrogen per unit time and V_{max} is the maximum uptake rate; S is the concentration of the nutrient (substrate); K_t is that nutrient concentration at which $V = 0.5 V_{max}$.

Phytoplankton populations of tropical oligotrophic regions are adapted to low ambient nitrate concentrations and are able to remove nutrients at a greater rate than those of corresponding eutrophic regions (Note 8). This is indicated by the values of $K_t(NO_3^-)$ in the two regions (<0.2 and >1.0 µg-at/liter, respectively) because the value of K_t is related to the nutrient and productivity characteristic of the region. The values of K_t for ammonia do correlate with regional productivity, but the variation is much less probable because of the relative constancy of ammonia distribution.

The uptake experiments can indicate the possibility that ambient nitrate (or ammonia) concentrations limit the phytoplankton growth or uptake rates. (The situation is indicated in Fig. 7-4.) If the ambient nutrient concentration is not limiting, the rate (V) determined for that concentration will be a point on the plateau of the hyperbola; if the ambient nutrient concentration is limiting, the rate will be a point on the slope.

7.6 Distribution of Nitrogen in the Sea[7]

The problem of describing the distribution of the various forms of nitrogen is a formidable one because of the large number of forms and because of the intense involvement of these forms with the nitrogen and other biogeochemical cycles. Vaccaro[7] has provided a good summary of the distribution. It may be sufficient here to sketch some of the salient features.

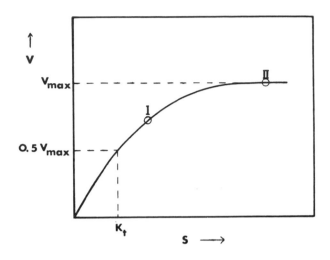

FIG. 7-4

Response curve (rate as a function of substrate concentration), showing characteristics of Michaelis-Menton kinetics, and showing examples when nutrient concentration is (I) and is not (II) limiting.

Two areas of interest may be considered: coastal areas within broad or within narrow continental shelves and the deep ocean.

Coastal Waters. Differences are found for broad and narrow continental shelves. Examples of the former in temperate waters include stations of the English Channel and the northeast coast of the United States. Variations in nitrate may be ascribed to seasonal variations, following the pattern described for silicon and phosphorus (cf. Table 7-5). A profoundly different pattern is observed in northwest coasts with narrow shelves where upwelling is prevalent. Nitrate is uniformly

TABLE 7-5

Nitrate Variations in Coastal Waters above

Broad Continental Shelf

Stage	Time	Effect	Vertical Distribution	Concentration
1	Summer	solar heating, bloom	quantitatively removed high positive gradient	above thermocline, very low, below 70-210 µg/liter
2	Winter	surface cooling, mixing	relatively uniform to 50 m	
3	January	homo-geneous density	homogeneous	140 µg/liter to 100 m
4	Spring	bloom	return to Stage 1	

high and does not have profound seasonal variations, as, for example, in the northeast Pacific (San Juan Channel), where the mean nitrite-nitrogen concentrations are 210 and 350 mg/liter for summer and winter, respectively.

The concentration of nitrite is generally small with respect to nitrate and is somewhat less than the ammonia concentration. Ammonia contents in surface and near-bottom layers may reflect significant contributions to the total nitrogen and be due to zooplankton excretion and regeneration, respectively.

These processes are also significant in productivity because of the short-circuiting effect of ammonia. Because of interaction of three processes (assimilation, excretion, and regeneration) the vertical variation of ammonia is difficult to categorize. The Deep Ocean. The relative variation of nitrate-nitrite-ammonia nitrogen has been used as a guide to the sites of nitrification and denitrification in the ocean. A nitrite maximum is typically found between 75-125 m and may be related to the compensation depth (the depth at which plant respiration is equal to photosynthesis during a 24-hour period). Above this maximum, the concentrations of nitrite appear to be uniform, low but detectable. Below this maximum, two patterns are observed. In the Atlantic, nitrate becomes the major form of nitrogen. In the tropical Pacific and Indian waters, a second nitrite maximum is observed near the oxygen minimum layer and below the thermocline at depths of 100-800 m (Section 7-3).The second nitrite maximum has been ascribed to denitrification.

7.7 Summary

The unique or complicating features of the nitrogen cycle include the multiplicity of forms and oxidation states, additional processes (fixation, nitrification, and denitrification), and the most significant: the nitrogen budget is not balanced. Strictly speaking, an item in the budget must be added to account for the fact that there seems to be an excess annual input of about 70 million metric tons of nitrogen.

The rationalization of this and other odd features led to
a consideration of the two types of processes of the nitrogen
biochemical cycle. Input-removal processes include: volcanic
activity, atmospheric precipitation, and continental drainage
(input); and loss of deep marine sediments, migration of marine
animals, and loss of nitrogen to the atmosphere, chiefly by denitrification. Intramarine processes include: liberation of
ammonia, fixation, denitrification, and assimilation.

Denitrification has been used to rationalize the evident
unbalance or missing term of the nitrogen budget. Ample evidence is available which indicates active denitrification in
vast areas; the existence of denitrifying organisms has been
demonstrated. Unfortunately, the in situ rates and the extent
of denitrification have yet to be evaluated accurately.

NOTES

1. Oxidation state. The oxidation number or state of an
    element is the number that element would have if its
    electrons were assigned following a certain convention.
    This represents the number of electrons effectively
    gained (from a less electronegative element) or effec-
    tively lost (to a more electronegative element). The
    algebraic sum of the positive and negative oxidation
    numbers must equal the charge on the species. Oxygen as

O^{2-} has a 2- oxidation number and hydrogen typically has an oxidation number of 1+. The oxidation state of nitrogen in NO_3 is 5+ $[(5+) + 3(2-) = 1-]$, the oxidation state of nitrogen in $ONNO^{2-}$ is 1+ because we recognize that the electrons in the N-N bond are shared equally.

2. This assumes all fixation of nitrogen is terrigenous or atmospheric, that all combined nitrogen enters the sea as rainfall or river runoff, and that in situ fixation of nitrogen does not represent a significant contribution.

3. This assumes that denitrification is an exclusively anaerobic process (Sterman and Mackal, 1957)[3] and that the process most likely occurs in sediments with high organic content (neritic basins, estuaries).

4. Nitrous oxide may also be produced by the decomposition of hyponitrous acid, an unstable compound, which is produced during the course of the oxidation of ammonia to nitrite. The contribution, relative to denitrification, must be slight, but the actual extent is unknown.

5. The superscript B refers to biogenic nitrogen. The superscripts (P) and (O) refer to calculations based on phosphate and oxygen (AOU), respectively. The value of 0.056 for aerobic waters comes from 15/270; the value of 0.064 for anoxic waters comes from 15/235.

6. Technically, the ^{15}N uptake by now-purified samples does not distinguish between uptake by Trichodesmium and by

associated microorganisms[24]; the <u>bloom</u> does fix nitrogen.

7. Stewart[24] notes that <u>Calothrix</u>, which is found in high-tide areas of inshore temperate waters, can fix 2.5 g of nitrogen per square meter. This is about 10% of the fixing value for a good leguminous crop on land.

8. Oligotrophic refers to bodies of water containing nutrient matter; eutrophic refers to waters that contain <u>abundant</u> nutrient matter.

REFERENCES

1. L. G. Sillén, Science, <u>156</u>, 1189 (1967).

2. K. O. Emery, W. L. Orr, and S. C. Rittenberg, Nutrient budgets in the Ocean <u>in</u> Essays in the Natural Sciences in Honor of Captain Allan Hancock, University of Southern California Press, Los Angeles, 1955, p. 299-309.

3. S. C. Rittenberg <u>in</u> Marine Microbiology (C. H. Oppenheimer ed.), C. C. Thomas, Springfield, Illinois, 1963, Chapt. 5.

4. E. Eriksson <u>in</u> The Atmosphere and Sea in Motion (Rossby Memorial Volume, B. Bolin, ed.), Oxford University Press, Rockefeller Institute Press, New York, 1959, p. 147.

5. F. A. Richards and B. B. Benson, Deep-Sea Res., <u>7</u>, 254 (1961).

6. E. P. Odum, Fundamentals of Ecology, 2nd ed., Saunders, Philadelphia, 1959.

7. R. F. Vaccaro in Chemical Oceanography (J. P. Riley and G. Skirrow, eds.), Academic Press, New York, 1965, Chapt. 9.

8. J. L. Bada and S. L. Miller, Science, <u>159</u>, 423 (1968).

9. N. W. Rakestraw and E. V. M. Emmel, J. Phys. Chem., <u>ew</u>, 1211 (1938).

10. G. E. Hutchinson in The Earth as a Planet (G. P. Kuiper, ed.), Vol. II, Univ. of Chicago Press, Chicago, 1954, Chapt. 8.

11. T. Hoering, Geochim. Cosmochim. Acta, 12, 97 (1957).

12. S. C. Rittenberg, K. O. Emery, and W. L. Orr, Deep-Sea Res., 3, 23 (1955).

13. P. H. Abelson in Researches in Geochemistry (P. H. Abelson, ed.), Wiley, New York, 1959, pp. 91-95.

14. R. S. Gupta, Science, 160, 854 (1968).

15. J. J. Goering, Deep-Sea Res., 15, 157 (1969).

16. J. J. Goering and R. C. Dugdale, Science, 154, 505 (1966).

17. C. E. Zobell, Marine Microbiology, Chronica Botanica Co., Waltham, Mass., 1946.

18. C. E. Zobell and K. M. Budge, Limnol. Oceanog., 10, 207 (1965).

19. J. H. Martin, Limnol. Oceanog., 13, 63 (1968).

20. M. I. H. Aleem and N. Nason in Marine Microbiology, (C. H. Oppenheimer, ed.), C. C. Thomas, Springfield, Illinois. 1963, Chapt. 37.

21. S. W. Watson, Limnol. Oceanog., 10 (Redfield Vol. Supply to 10), R 274 (1965).

22. S. W. Watson and C. C. Remsen, Science, 163, 685 (1969).

23. A. F. Carlucci and J. D. H. Strickland, J. Exp. Mar. Biol. Ecol., 2, 156 (1968).

24. W. D. P. Stewart, Science, 158, 1426 (1967).

25. J. Chatt, Science, 160, 728 (1968).

26. J. J. MacIssac and R. C. Dugdale, Deep-Sea Res., 16, 45 (1969).

THE CARBON CYCLES

8.1 Introduction

Apart from the component elements of water, carbon is possibly the most significant element we can consider for several reasons.

1. Carbon is the basic element of all living matter. Carbon has the unique property of catenation or self-linkage which produces a series of chain- or ring-like molecules in a variety of structures and forms the basis of life forms.

2. Carbon dioxide is a gaseous substance in contrast with the congener compound silicon dioxide, which is solid. As a consequence, when carbon dioxide is used in primary production, it can be replaced immediately through gaseous diffusion.

3. The properties of many life substances are based on asymmetric carbon compounds, i.e., certain molecules that occur in two configurations which are mirror images of each other. The two forms of such molecules are said to be optical enantiomers or antipodes and differ in two important respects: (1) the ability to rotate the plane

of plane-polarized light to the left (levo form) or to
the right (dextro form), by which they may be distinguished; and (2) the rate of interaction with other
optically active substances. For example, the system of
fermentation responds only to one form. Our bodies can
assimilate only one form of amino acids, and nearly all
naturally occurring amino acids are of the left-handed
form. The source of optical activity is commonly an
asymmetric carbon atom, i.e., one to which four different
groups are attached. The simplest example is alanine
(Fig. 8-1).

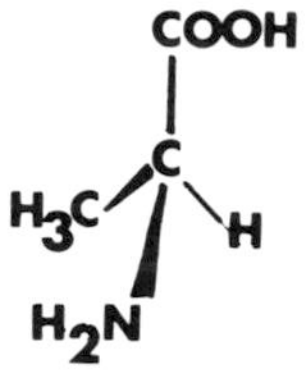

$$H_3C \diagdown \underset{\underset{H_2N}{|}}{\overset{\overset{COOH}{|}}{C}} \diagup H$$

FIG. 8-1

Structure of L-alanine.

4.   The carbonate-bicarbonate system is probably the short-
term or regulating system of the sea. Also, carbonate
and bicarborate ions form important ion-pair complexes
(Section 8.4).

268

5. The utilization of inorganic carbon compounds in primary
   production is of supreme importance because it forms the
   basis of the whole marine food chain (or pyramid) and
   energy flow in the marine ecosystem.

The importance of carbon compounds in the chemistry of
sea water and marine organisms is beyond question. The nature
of the carbon budget and the characteristics of the carbon
cycle are obviously matters of great interest.

8.2 The Carbon Budget

The carbon budget is based on nine major carbon deposits
or natural-exchange reservoirs (Table 8-1). There are several
pertinent comments about these.

1. The estimates given here are not necessarily the best
   available, but they are consistent with most estimates
   and do not differ by more than a few percent.

2. The estimates for the carbon content of humus and the
   land or marine biosphere (0.19, 0.06, 0.002 g/cm^2, respectively) have not been included because these values are
   less precisely known.

3. It is useful to divide the sea into two reservoirs
   (item 2); one is an upper layer 75-100-m deep which interacts and exchanges very slowly with the second lower
   layer. Some authors prefer a multi-reservoir model of the
   sea.

TABLE 8-1

Carbon Content of Natural Deposits[1,2]

Carbon Reservoir	Carbon Content, g/cm^2 of Earth's Surface
1. Atmosphere	0.125
2. Oceanic	
Dissolved organic carbon	0.533
Inorganic carbon (above thermocline)	0.20
Inorganic carbon (below thermocline)	7.25
3. Plants	0.053
4. Animals	0.00071
5. Sediments, as elemental C	633.00
6. Carbonates and sediments as $CO_3^{2-} - C$	2,340.00
7. Crystalline slate (total C)	1,960.00
8. Palingenic igneous rocks (total C)	567.00
9. Juvenile rocks	33.00
Total	5,541.00

4. Most of the carbon is stored as carbonate rock and as fossil fuel; comparatively little carbon is stored in oceanic or atmospheric reservoirs. Presumably, however, much of the carbon in the major carbon reservoirs must have been present in the atmosphere at some time.

8.3 The Carbon Cycles[3]

In addition to the nine carbon reservoirs, the carbon budget of 5,541 (with units of g C/cm^2 of earth's surface) is dependent upon three major cycles (biological, geological, combined), which may be represented schematically (Fig. 8-2).

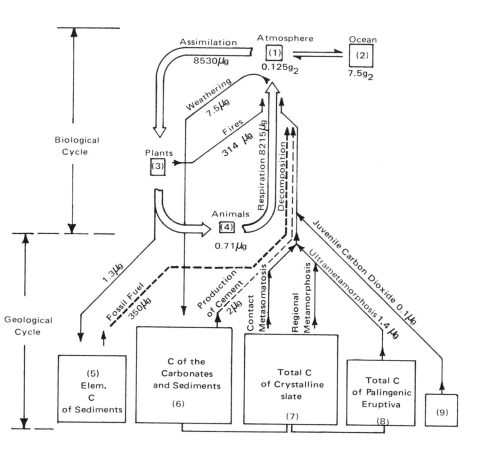

FIG. 8-2

The carbon cycles (after Dietrich[3]).

The biological cycle is a short but intense and obviously immensely significant cycle. Briefly, the cycle includes assimilation of 8.5 mg CO_2-C from the atmosphere by plants followed by return to the atmosphere directly through the action of fires or indirectly after consumption of plants by animals and respiration. Nearly all of the assimilated CO_2-C is returned to the atmosphere and the cycle is essentially a closed one.

The geological cycle is a major, balanced cycle which consists of the following steps: Atmospheric (7.5 µg C) CO_2-C from respiration participates in the weathering of carbonates and sediments and is incorporated as total carbon first of crystalline slate then of palingenic igneous rocks. Carbon dioxide is released to the atmosphere through four processes: artificial production of cement (2 µg C), contact metasomatism (0.16 µg C), regional metasomatism (6.04 µg C), and ultra metasomatism (1.4 µg C; see Note 1). If the first process (artificial production of cement) is excluded, the cycle is balanced.

A combined biological-geological-economic cycle is completely unbalanced. During the biological cycle (specifically, during the process of assimilation of CO_2-C from the atmosphere by plants and animals) a small amount of the carbon (1.3 µg) is not returned to the atmosphere. This carbon is incorporated

as elementary carbon in sediments. Approximately 350 μg of
carbon comes from the elemental carbon of sediments through
the production of fossil fuels,and decomposition of these
fuels should result in a massive return of CO_2-C to the
atmosphere.

There appears to be an increase in atmospheric carbon
dioxide over the last century. The change is progressively
increasing, and the increase from 1860 to 1959 is about
14-16%.[1]

There are three reasons for the increase in atmospheric
carbon dioxide. First, much of the increase is due to fossil-
fuel combustion, and it has been estimated that over the decade
1970-1979 carbon dioxide produced from such combustion might be
as much as 20% of the present atmospheric total.[4] This would
correspond to a 30% increase of atmospheric carbon dioxide
over the period 1860-1979 due to fossil-fuel combustion.
Secondly, deforestation and increased conversion of land to
agricultural use have accelerated over the past century.
Hutchinson[5] estimates that these two effects have reduced the
carbon dioxide content of the soil by an amount corresponding
to four per cent of the present atmospheric carbon dioxide
content. Thirdly, there are other phenomena that cause
negligible increases in the atmospheric carbon dioxide concentration. For example, the increase in mean sea water

temperature during the past century was estimated to be less than $0.05^{\circ}C$, which would cause a significant increase in P_{CO_2}, the partial pressure of carbon dioxide.[4] Also, it seems the current rate of juvenile carbon dioxide production is much less than the rate at which carbon dioxide from fossil fuel is being produced.

The apparent gradual increase in atmospheric carbon dioxide is, thus, generally ascribed to the burning of fossil fuels. There are several questions, however, that deserve consideration at this point.

First, what is the reliability of the early estimates of atmospheric carbon dioxide data? Probably, poor, in view of the precision of the early data (cf. Skirrow[1] for a summary of assessments of the data reliability), though more recent precise measurements over a short period of time do provide evidence of a gradual increase in atmospheric carbon dioxide.

Secondly, granting a gradual increase due to fossil-fuel burning, why isn't the increase greater? The atmospheric carbon dioxide seems to have increased linearly, though the industrial carbon dioxide production seems to have increased exponentially. It has been presumed that the accumulation of carbon dioxide in the atmosphere is not greater because of dissolution and accumulation in the sea. The dissolution of carbon dioxide in sea water is considered in the next section because an understanding of the process and consequences of dissolution will assist in understanding the carbon cycles.

Finally, what are the consequences of accumulation of carbon dioxide in the atmosphere? The consideration of this probably should be postponed until after we have considered the solubility of carbon dioxide in sea water.

8.4 The Solution of Carbon Dioxide in Water[1,6]

Carbon dioxide in contact with sea water participates in several equilibria (Eqs. 8-1 to 8-6). A rigorous treatment of the carbon dioxide-sea water system requires the definition and accurate evaluation of the pertinent equilibrium constants.

$$CO_{2(g)} \rightarrow CO_2(aq) \tag{8-1}$$

$$CO_2(aq) + H_2O \overset{k_1}{\underset{k_{-1}}{\rightleftarrows}} H_2CO_3 \tag{8-2}$$

$$H_2CO_3 \rightarrow HCO_3^- + H^+ \tag{8-3}$$

$$HCO_3^- \rightarrow CO_3^{2-} + H^+ \tag{8-4}$$

$$M^{n+} + HCO_3^- \rightarrow M^{n+} \cdot HCO_3^- \tag{8-5}$$

$$M^{n+} + CO_3^{2-} \rightarrow M^{n+} \cdot CO_3^{2-} \tag{8-6}$$

The hydration and dehydration of carbon dioxide (Eqn. 8-2) are relatively slow (Note 3) processes and are subject to catalysis by a variety of substances. The enzyme carbonic anhydrase is particularly effective as a catalyst and is found in many marine and fresh water algae. It seems likely that the slow processes are a significant factor in determining the exchange rate of carbon dioxide across the atmosphere-sea water interface. It appears, however, that the kinetics of the processes have been studied mainly in pure water systems. The ionization reactions (Eqn. 8-3, 8-4) are extremely rapid. The ion-pair reactions (Eqn. 8-5, 8-6) are also involved.

While it is no problem to _define_ a series of useful equilibrium constants, it is a problem to _evaluate_ the equilibrium constants. In effect, two sets of constants have been defined which might be imprecisely termed theoretical and practical.

The true first and second thermodynamic dissociation constants of carbon dioxide are

$$Ka_1 \ = \ \frac{(H^+)(HCO_3^-)}{(CO_2)(H_2O)} \tag{8-7}$$

$$Ka_2 \ = \ \frac{(H^+)(CO_3^{2-})}{(HCO_3^-)} \tag{8-8}$$

where parentheses denote activities and brackets denote concentrations of the molecular or ionic species involved.

From a practical standpoint, it is useful to define so-called apparent dissociation constants of carbon dioxide (Eqn. 8-9, 8-10).

$$Ka_1' \ = \ \frac{(H^+)[HCO_3^-]}{(CO_2)(H_2O)} \tag{8-9}$$

$$Ka_2' \ = \ \frac{(H^+)[CO_3^{2-}]}{[HCO_3^-]} \tag{8-10}$$

The apparent constants vary with the salinity as well as with the temperature because of the mixture of concentration and activities.

The situation is complicated by the fact that there are two sets of apparent constants in general use. The first set is due to Buch and coworkers,[6] using the constants as defined (Eqn. 8-9, 8-10). The second set is based on a treatment of the problem by Lyman,[6] who defined the first dissociation constant as

$$K_1^o = \frac{(H^+)(HCO_3^-)}{(CO_2) + (H_2CO_3)} = K_{L_1}' \qquad (8\text{-}11)$$

An apparent first constant, K_{L_1}', is related to K_{a_1} by the expression (Eqn. 8-12)

$$K_{L_1}' = K_{a_1} \cdot \frac{P_s}{P_o} = \frac{\alpha_o}{\alpha_s} = K_{L_1}' \qquad (8\text{-}12)$$

Here P_o and P_s are the vapor pressures of pure water and a sea water sample, respectively; α_o and α_s are the solubility coefficients of carbon dioxide in pure water and the sea water sample, respectively. The second apparent constant used by Buch or Lyman is based on the definition given previously (Eqn. 8-8).

It should be emphasized that the apparent constants do not have the same basic significance as true thermodynamic

constants and that a rigorous and theoretically unobjection-
able treatment of the carbon dioxide system in sea water has
yet to be achieved.[6]

Nevertheless, the data compiled by Buch or Lyman are
validly used to estimate the properties of the carbonate
system of a water sample. The validity rests on the fact that
the values of the parameters K'_{a_1} and K'_{a_2} or K'_{L_1} and K'_{L_2} are
determined empirically.

The apparent constants are used with pH and alkalinity
data to estimate the concentrations of bicarbonate ion, carbonate ion, dissolved carbon dioxide, total carbon dioxide, and
the partial pressure of carbon dioxide (P_{CO_2}). The pertinent
equations are summarized in Table 8-2, and derivations are
given by Skirrow,[1] Spencer,[6] and Park.[7]

The use of these constants has been assessed by these
authors,[1,6,7] and the following points should be considered.

1.   The tabulated constants were determined empirically at
     surface pressure and appropriate corrections must be
     made if the constants are applied to deep-water samples.
     This correction ($\Delta pK'_{a_n}$) is necessary because the apparent
     constants are pressure dependent. Typically, the Buch-
     Gripenberg correction has been used (Eqn. 8-13).

$$\Delta pK'_{a_n} = -C_n \times 10^{-4} \Delta Z \qquad (8\text{-}13)$$

TABLE 8-2

Pertinent Equations for Calculating

Inorganic Carbon Concentrations[7]

$$a = CA - y + 2z$$

$$c = \Sigma CO_2 = x + y + z$$

$$a(H^+) = k_1 x/y^{a}$$

$$(H^+) = k_2 y/z$$

$$x = [H_2CO_3] + [CO_2] = \alpha \, P_{CO_2}$$

$$y = [HCO_3^-] = k_1 \alpha \, P_{CO_2}/(H^+)$$

$$z = [CO_3^{2-}] = k_1 k_2 \alpha \, P_{CO_2}/(H^+)^2$$

$$x = (\Sigma CO_2 - CA) + \frac{[-B + (B^2 + 4(k-4)a^2)^{\frac{1}{2}}]}{2(k-4)}$$

$$y = [HCO_3^-] = \frac{ck - [B^2 + 4(k-4)a^2]^{\frac{1}{2}}}{k-4}$$

$$z = [CO_3^{2-}] = \frac{-B + [B^2 + 4(k-4)a^2]^{\frac{1}{2}}}{2(k-4)}$$

---

[a]k_1 and k_2 are the apparent first and second dissociation constants for carbonic acids, $k = k_1/k_2$, $B = 4a + ck - ak$, $\alpha =$ the solubility coefficient of carbon dioxide $= [H_2CO_3]/P_{CO_2}$.

Here, C_n is equal to 0.48 and 0.18 for $\underline{n} = 1$ and 2, respectively; and $\underline{\Delta Z}$ is the depth in meters.

2. These pressure corrections are probably in error because they are based on constants obtained for pure water systems and then adapted for sea water. The pressure coefficients of K_1' and K_2' have been determined by Pytkowicz and coworkers,[8] who find a considerable discrepancy between their coefficients and those of Buch and Gripenberg.[6] Further work on the temperature and pressure coefficients of the apparent dissociation constants of carbonic and boric acids in sea water is in progress.[8]

3. The effects of pressure have a significant bearing on the pH correction and the pH control of the oceans, according to Pytkowicz.[9] The Buch-Gripenberg treatment predicts a decrease of pH with depth. The Pytkowicz treatment suggests a different view because the effect of pressure not only on the dissociation constants but also on the apparent solubility product constant of calcium carbonate must be considered.

    To illustrate this view, suppose a water mass with a surface pH of 7.89 is submerged and comes in contact with sediment containing calcium carbonate. The pH will increase as calcium carbonate dissolves. Now, if this water mass is raised to the surface, it will have a pH greater than it did before it was submerged. It will also be under-saturated with respect to carbon dioxide. Atmospheric carbon dioxide will dissolve, the pH will decrease, but the final value will still be greater than 7.89. It is possible that further cycling will occur until a limiting pH is attained. The evidence which supports this view[9] includes the increase of specific alkalinity with depth, enhanced rates of solution of calcium carbonate, and variation, with depths, of calcium carbonate content in sediments.[10] According to Park,[10] however, the major process affecting the vertical distribution of pH in the subarctic waters of the northeastern Pacific Ocean is the apparent utilization of oxygen by marine organisms; carbonate dissolution affects the distribution to a lesser extent.

4. The expressions for $[CO_3^{2-}]$ and $[HCO_3^{-}]$ in Table 8-2 are somewhat misleading because the usual treatments do not include an estimate for the amount of ion-pairing with metal ions in the sea water (cf. Eqn. 8-14; see Note 2). The first detailed examination of ion-pairing was provided by Garrels and Thompson.[11] Their treatment is

$$M^{n+} + CO_3^{2-} \; \underset{\leftarrow}{\rightarrow} \; \underset{\text{ion pair}}{M^{2+} \cdot CO_3^{2-}} \qquad (8\text{-}14)$$

based upon a model system containing the four major cations and three anions (Table 8-3) and depends heavily

upon the concept of individual ion activities, the use
of the mean-salt method, and Debye-Hückel extrapolations.
It is evident (Table 8-3) that only magnesium and calcium
ions are significantly involved in ion-pairing, but
nearly all of the carbonate, one-third of the bicarbonate,
and about half of the sulfate ions are associated. The
extent of association between magnesium and sulfate ions
in artificial sea water was found to be about 11%, which

TABLE 8-3

Distribution of Major Cations as Ion-Pair Complexes

of Sulfate, Bicarbonate, and Carbonate in

Representative Sea Water[a]

Ion	Percent as Free Ion	Percent as Ion-Pair with						
		SO_4^{2-}	HCO_3^-	CO_3^{2-}	Ca^{2+}	Mg^{2+}	Na^+	K^+
Ca^{2+}	91	8	1	0.2				
Mg^{2+}	87	11	1	0.3				
Na^+	99	1.2	0.01	-				
K^+	99	1	-	-				
SO_4^{2-}	54				3	21.5	21	0.5
HCO_3^-	69				4	19	8	-
CO_3^{2-}	9				7	67	17	-

[a]Chlorinity, $19^o/oo$; pH, 8.1; pressure, 1 atm.

compares well with the value of about 10% determined by solubility measurements[12] or 9% determined by ultrasonic absorption.[13]

5.   The values of the alkalinity may be altered by the presence of dissolved organic acids (humic and tannic acids) which may be present in significant quantities in the vicinity of river runoff. The problem reportedly arises from the complexing of boric acid by the organic acid, conversion of boric acid into a "super acid" which affects the alkalinity of the sample. A significant error may arise if a standard practice is followed and carbonate alkalinity (CA) is obtained by subtracting the boron content from the titration alkalinity.

6.   The deviations between calculated and observed values of P_{CO_2} may be considerable. This is of serious concern because direct comparison of theoretical and predicted values is possible for this parameter. The deviations do not constitute an indictment of the use of the concentration expressions listed in Table 8-2. It does seem, though, that when precise values of P_{CO_2} are needed, the parameter should be measured rather than calculated. Many of the deviations reported are probably due to imprecise measurement of pH and temperature (which have a significant effect on P_{CO_2}) or to the use of pH scales which are not consistent with those used for tabulated constants.

283

On the other hand, many workers who have been aware of
these problems still have found considerable differences
between observed and calculated values of P_{CO_2}.[11] In
these instances, it may be that a state of equilibrium
had not been established or that dissolved organic matter
may have interacted with dissolved carbon dioxide.

7.   Finally, it is important to recognize that P_{CO_2} (the
partial pressure of the carbon dioxide in a given mass
of sea water) differs from p_{CO_2} (the partial pressure of
carbon dioxide in the atmosphere above the sea). As
Skirrow[1] emphasizes, equilibrium between the sea and the
atmosphere is attained only in restricted areas, and
then only in a transient sense.

8.5   The Significance of P_{CO_2}

The values of P_{CO_2} are of interest for several reasons,
most of which center around the significance of the variations
in this parameter and the possibility that the values of P_{CO_2}
serve as an indicator of chemical and physical changes.

The dynamics of the CO_2 system of the ocean can be studied
by the use of P_{CO_2} and combinations of three other parameters
(pH, carbonate alkalinity, and total carbon dioxide, ΣCO_2).[7]
Park[7] has considered the use of various combinations of the
four parameters and concludes that the combination of pH and

P_{CO_2} is currently the most precise way to study changes due to biological activity (AOU effect) and the carbonate dissolution effect. It should be stressed that the precision of the shipboard measurements (± 0.01 for pH, ± 2ppm for P_{CO_2}, ± 0.02 meq/liter for carbonate alkalinity, and ± 0.02 m$\underline{M}$ for ΣCO_2) rather than accuracy is the important consideration for these studies.[7]

The utility of the parameters is best indicated by considering two changes or effects, AOU and carbonate dissolution. As noted earlier these are two major processes affecting the CO_2 system of the ocean.

<u>AOU Effect</u>. Consider the consequences of the addition of 0.2 m$\underline{M}$ ($0.2 \times 10^{-3}\underline{M}$) of carbon dioxide by the metabolic processes of marine organisms in a hypothetical ocean condition. This is roughly the addition associated with an AOU of 0.3 m$\underline{M}$, which represents an upper limit. The ratio is based on Eqn. 7-7. The effects of the increase in carbon dioxide (Table 8-4) are: ΣCO_2 increases (by exactly 0.2 m$\underline{M}$), as does P_{CO_2}, pH decreases, and $[CO_3^{2-}]$ decreases, though the other inorganic carbon species increase. Carbonate alkalinity is presumably invariant, ignoring the effect due to a change of pH on the borate alkalinity. The equations for calculating these changes are given in Table 8-2. It was assumed[7] that the first and second apparent dissociation constants were $10^{-6.000}$ and

TABLE 8-4[7]

Effect of Addition of 0.2 m$\underline{M}$ CO_2 by

Marine Organisms to Hypothetical Ocean Condition

Parameter	Before	Change
Temperature, $^{\circ}C$	20	–
Chlorinity, $^{\circ}/oo$	19	–
pH	8.200	–0.447
Carbonate alkalinity, meq/liter	2.487	–
$[H_2CO_3 + CO_2]$, m$\underline{M}$	0.012	+0.028
$[HCO_3^-]$, m$\underline{M}$	1.889	+0.345
$[CO_3^{2-}]$, m$\underline{M}$	0.299	–0.173
P_{CO_2}, ppm	350	1,160
ΣCO_2, m$\underline{M}$	2.200	+0.2
ΔCO_2, m$\underline{M}$	0	0.2
ΔAOU, m$\underline{M}$	0	0.260

$10^{-9.000}$, respectively. The data (Table 8-4) indicate that carbonate alkalinity would be a poor choice to follow AOU changes, but it would be a good choice for carbonate dissolution. The order of sensitivity to AOU by marine organisms is P_{CO_2} > pH > ΣCO_2.

Carbonate Dissolution (Precipitation) Effect. Park[7] has considered the results of dissolving calcium carbonate under the
hypothetical ocean condition

$$CaCO_3 \; \overset{\rightarrow}{\leftarrow} \; Ca^{2+} + CO_3^{2-} \qquad (8\text{-}15)$$

If 0.1 mM carbonate dissolution occurred, carbonate alkalinity
(CA) would increase by 0.2 meq/liter, ΣCO_3 would increase by
0.1 mM, carbonate and bicarbonate concentrations would increase
(Table 8-5). Here, the best combination for detecting these
changes is P_{CO_2}-pH; other combinations, P_{CO_2}-CA, P_{CO_2}-ΣCO_2,
are less sensitive.

TABLE 8-5[7]

Effect of 0.1 mM Carbonate
Dissolution in Hypothetical Ocean Condition

Parameter	Before	Change
Temperature, $^{\circ}C$	20	–
Chlorinity, $^{\circ}/oo$	19	–
pH	8.200	+0.121
Carbon alkalinity, meq/liter	2.487	+0.2000
$[H_2CO_3 + CO_2]$, mM	0.012	–0.02
$[HCO_3^-]$, mM	1.889	+0.005
$[CO_3^{2-}]$, mM	0.299	+0.098
P_{CO_2}, ppm	350	–60
ΣCO_2, mM	2.200	+0.100

Park[7] believes the pH-P_{CO_2} combination to be the best tool for studying <u>both</u> AOU and carbonate dissolutions (precipitations). As he notes, though, the combination of choice may change as analytical methods improve. Thus, the potentiometric determination of carbonate alkalinity (Vol. 1, Chapt. 4) has an improved precision, and this may favor the use of the P_{CO_2}- CA combination to study carbonate dissolution.

8.6 Changes in Carbon Dioxide Content in the Atmosphere and the World Ocean

The problems due to increased fossil-fuel consumption were raised earlier (Section 8.3) and may be considered now that inorganic carbon equilibria have been reviewed. The atmospheric carbon dioxide level presumably has been increased during the last century because of fossil fuel burning (Callendar hypothesis), though the actual increase can only be roughly estimated because of uncertainties in early values. The assessment of the effects requires an understanding of the rates of transfer of carbon dioxide from one natural reservoir to another, and it requires some method of measuring the residence time of carbon dioxide in each reservoir. In short, three items are required: a suitable model, methods, and a forecast. These have been considered by various authors and their conclusions may be summarized here (cf. Skirrow[1]).

The proposed model. Various models have been proposed and all
have useful features. Any model suffers from certain defects
imposed by the problems of calculations. For example, most
workers assume a qualified steady-state condition: specific
activities of carbon-14 in each reservoir are constant (corrected for fractionation and allowing for recent bomb and
industrial activity). This has not been verified, though the
non-steady-state condition is difficult to treat theoretically.
The latter condition would arise from alternating periods of
approach to a state of equilibrium.

A two-layer steady-state model (Fig. 8-3) has been devised by Craig[14] and used by Bolin and Eriksson[15] to evaluate
the consequences of fossil-fuel consumption. This model dis-
regards the role of the biosphere and emphasizes the atmosphere
and two layers of the ocean; the mixed layer consists of the
strata above the thermocline, and the deep-sea layer consists
of the remainder of the world ocean. The three reservoirs are
assumed to be well mixed and exchanges presumably occur
through first-order processes. The fuller treatment includes
consideration of the biosphere and humus reservoirs. Broecker
and co-workers[16] have considered two other models: a non-steady-
state mixing model and a geographically oriented worldwide
steady-state model. The latter includes consideration of
specific water masses and geographical locations.

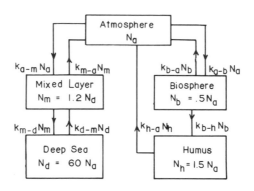

FIG. 8-3

Model of the CO_2 exchange between five carbon re
reservoirs. (After Craig,[14] Bolin and Eriksson.[15])
N represents the total amount of carbon (g/cm^2
of earth's surface); the subscripts a, m, d, h,
and b refer to the atmosphere, mixed layer, deep-
sea layer, humus, and biosphere, respectively;
k refers to the specific rate constants.

Before considering the results of the models, we should

consider the method used to evaluate residence times.

The method of determining residence times consists of analyz-

ing the radiocarbon distribution (Section 2.7) and correcting

for effects of fractionation and industrial and bomb activi-

ties. Obviously, these corrections require some assessment of

the significance of each effect and the use of model systems.

Two fractionation factors are used. Because of carbon

isotopic fractionation, the carbon-14 activity of marine

materials should be about 5% greater than that of the original standard, terrestrial 1850 wood; this assumes a complete equilibrium between the atmosphere and the sea surface. The symbols $(\alpha_{14})_{2/w}$ and $(\alpha_{14})_{s/w}$ are the fractionation factors for carbon-14 relative to standard wood for the atmosphere and marine materials, and have values of 1.037 and 1.049, respectively.

Industrial activity, after 1850 but before extensive bomb activity, should have diluted the specific activity of carbon-14 because of the addition of large amounts of $^{12}CO_2$ to the atmosphere. The dilution effect is termed the Suess effect; it was first observed by H. E. Suess in about 1953, and has been confirmed by others.[1] The effect seems to explain the progressive carbon-14 specific activity impoverishment in wood samples over the last 100 years (as selected by examining the rings of trees). The Suess effect has an average value of about -2%. Though the Suess effect is supported by good evidence, the possibility exists that it may be complicated by a superimposed natural effect of unknown magnitude. Small changes (1-2%) in specific activities of atmospheric $^{14}CO_2$ seem to be indicated (again from studies of tree rings and other samples) at times prior to intense industrial activity.[1] The Suess effect has significant implications in terms of radiocarbon dating of objects and in terms of the mixing of the world ocean. A discernable reduction in the specific activity

of atmospheric carbon should not be observed if the isotopic
equilibrium were established rapidly between the atmosphere
and the deep-sea reservoir.

A marked increase in carbon-14 activity has been observed
in the postbomb era (i.e., after about 1953) because of testing
of nuclear weapons. The effect may be tested by monitoring
atmospheric and plant levels, though the latter shows a considerable lag because of the time needed for exchange between
the upper atmosphere and the troposphere. As a result of the
production of artificial carbon-14, the specific activity of
carbon in the troposphere of the southern hemisphere had increased by about 7% in May 1957, by 16% in March 1959, and by
1963, peak increases of about 30% had been noted at some
locations.[17]

The results. The significant results of various studies
are the values of mean residence times in various reservoirs
and transfer times from one reservoir to another.

The mean residence time for atmospheric carbon dioxide is
about 5-7 years for the world ocean, though a range of values
(3-20 years) seems to exist. The rates of exchange of carbon
dioxide between the atmosphere and the sea vary with the
location because the rate depends upon temperature, turbulence,
and P_{CO_2}; the rate-determining step may be the rate of hydration of carbon dioxide (Eqn. 8-2, k_1). It appears that the
precise rate of exchange may not be significant because, from

Bolin and Eriksson's treatment,[15] the net increase of CO_2 in the atmosphere is nearly independent of the exchange rate. The capacity of the upper oceanic layer is limited; small amounts of CO_2 absorbed from the atmosphere balance much larger quantities released from the ocean (cf. Section 4.5).

The net increase in CO_2 in the atmosphere seems to be more dependent upon the residence time in the deep-sea reservoir. Using a residence time of 200 years, an 8-9% increase in atmospheric CO_2 should have occurred prior to 1953; using a residence time of 500 years, the increase should have been about 10%. Both estimates are in accord with the Callendar hypothesis, which estimates about a 10% increase. The calculated values do not depend significantly on the size of the two oceanic reservoirs. The calculated Suess (industrial or dilution) effect is about 2-2.5%[16]; and the observed value was about -3% in 1954.

The exchange processes with the biosphere and humus reservoirs are uncertain. If the mean exchange time between the atmosphere and the mixed layer is about five years, and between the mixed and deep-sea reservoirs 500 years, the atmosphere-biosphere and the biosphere-humus reservoir exchange times are estimated to be comparable, about 30 years.[16]

These and similar results have an internal consistency and the agreement between several workers is surprisingly good, in view of the limitations of the models noted earlier.

The forecasts. It is of interest to consider the forecasts that have been made for changes in the atmospheric CO_2 level during the remainder of this century. At present, the value of N_a (deviation from the atmospheric carbon-12,-13 concentrations in 1850) is about 10%. Bolin and Eriksson believe the most likely value in the year 2000 will be 25%, though it may be as much as 40% (both values are much larger than those estimated by Revelle and Suess). It is difficult to assess the consequences of these substantial increases in atmospheric CO_2, assuming they do come to pass (Note 3). Presumably, the radiational implications are immense. Based on our previous considerations, it is evident that the increase in atmospheric CO_2 would not have a long-term effect on the pH of sea water, but it seems likely that the increase would affect the geological cycle, specifically in reservoir 6 (Fig. 8-2).

8.7 Origin and Diagenesis of Marine Carbonates (Note 4)

Only three naturally occurring carbonate species are really significant in a consideration of carbonate precipitation and dissolution. These are calcite ($CaCO_3$), aragonite ($CaCO_3$), and high-magnesium calcite, $Ca(Mg)CO_3$. Calcite, the thermodynamically stable form, and aragonite, the metastable form, together with opaline silica constitute a major fraction of the total volume of recent marine carbonate sediments, this major fraction being derived almost entirely from the skeletal remains of organisms. Dolomite, $CaMg(CO_3)_2$, is another carbonate important because it is abundant among ancient marine sedimentary rocks. In theory, dolomite should precipitate before calcium carbonate, yet relatively few recent dolomite deposits have been observed. The control of calcium and carbonate ions through carbonate deposition is obvious; the control of trace metal ions by such deposition is less obvious but also very important. Three topics need to be considered in connection with carbonate deposition: the conditions of deposition and recrystallization of calcium carbonate, the dolomite problem, and control of trace element concentration.

Carbonate Deposition. Precipitation of calcium carbonate in the marine ecosystem occurs principally in two ways: first, as a constructional process either within or around the bodies of organisms; and secondly, as a chemical precipitation process in the open water. The construction process depends upon the biochemistry of the organism, and the surrounding waters need not be supersaturated with respect to calcium carbonate. The second process depends upon a state of supersaturation being attained; biochemical processes such as photosynthesis may or may not be involved. The extent to which biochemical processes are involved in carbonate deposition (both processes combined) is in dispute, but many believe that better than 90% of the carbonate arises directly or indirectly from some kind of biochemical activity.

The constructional process is typical of many organisms in a range of environment. These organisms include many multicellular invertebrates, lime-secreting algae, foraminifera, and coccoliths. The form of carbonate deposited may be a generic characteristic. This seems to be true for foraminifera and algae. The mineralogy has been related to the environment of certain molluscs, Bryozoa, and the serpulid worms. In still other instances, the mineralogy has been related in a general way to the latitude for shallow-water ecosystems. In the equatorial zone, aragonitic coral reefs are prominent; in the temperate latitudes, banks of aragonitic oysters are common, and in the Scandinavian fjords, banks of calcitic brachiopods are known.

The chemical precipitation of calcium carbonate requires a state of supersaturation, and this leads to a consideration of the solubility of calcium carbonate. The given solubility product constant, K_{sp} or K_{so}, or the apparent solubility product constant, K'_{sp} or K'_{so}, must be specified for each crystallographic form of $CaCO_3$ because each has a different free energy of formation. The calculated difference in free energy of formation ($\Delta G^o_{calcite} - \Delta G^o_{aragonite}$) of calcite and aragonite at 1 atm pressure is -272.5 kcal/mole[19]; and the measured values of ΔG^o_c and ΔG^o_a are -269.8 kcal/mole and -269.5 kcal/mole,[20] respectively. The solubility may be defined in terms of the two constants (Eqn. 8-16, 8-17).

$$K_{sp} = (Ca^{2+})(CO_3^{2-}) = [Ca^{2+}][CO_3^{2-}] + \gamma mg^{2+} + \gamma CO_3^{2-} \qquad (8\text{-}16)$$

$$K'_{sp} = [Ca^{2+}][CO_3^{2-}] \qquad (8\text{-}17)$$

Here, the species in parentheses refer to activities, those in brackets refer to molar concentrations, and γ refers to the activity coefficients. It has been estimated that the values of K_{sp} are 7.8×10^{-9} and 4.7×10^{-9} for aragonite and calcite, respectively,[18] at a salinity of 36°/oo and a temperature of 25^oC. The values of K'_{sp} are 1.1×10^{-6} and 0.6×10^{-6} for aragonite and calcite, respectively.

These values indicate several things. Aragonite should be less soluble than calcite. Also, in tropical zones, most waters in most places should be supersaturated with respect to either form of calcium carbonate, assuming normal salinity and pH of surface water. The actual extent of supersaturation is disputable, depending as it does upon the true values of K_{sp} and K'_{sp} and being able to assess the values of the activity coefficients. The degree of saturation decreases with depth as a result of greater carbon dioxide concentration (increased pressure), reduced carbonate ion concentration (decreased pH), and decreased temperature. Water at depths below about 4000-5000 m (carbonate compensation depth) are undersaturated with respect to calcium carbonate. No net accumulation of calcium carbonate occurs on the ocean floor below the carbonate compensation depth.

Thus far, only two polymorphic forms of carbonate have been considered, aragonite and calcite. What about magnesite ($MgCO_3$) and dolomite? Cloud[18] notes that magnesite should precipitate in preference to either of the major forms of $CaCO_3$. The relative degree of saturation can be estimated knowing activity coefficients and the concentrations of magnesium and calcium ions (Eqn. 8-18 a-d). The degree of saturation of magnesite should be about eight times that of calcite, if the values are correct (vide infra).

$$\frac{K_{sp}(MgCO_3)}{K_{sp}(calcite)} = \frac{(Mg^{2+})(CO_3^{2-})}{(Ca^{2+})(CO_3^{2-})} \tag{8-18a}$$

$$= \frac{[Mg^{2+}][CO_3^{2-}]\gamma Mg^{2+}\gamma CO_3^{-}}{[Ca^{2+}][CO_3^{2-}]\gamma Ca^{2-}\gamma CO_3^{2-}} \tag{8-18b}$$

$$= \frac{[Mg^{2+}]\gamma Mg^{2+} = [0.054]\ 0.39}{[Ca^{2+}]\gamma Ca^{2+} = [0.010]\ 0.27} \tag{8-18c}$$

$$= 7.8 \tag{8-18d}$$

The free energies of formation of magnesite and dolomite (ΔG^o = -246, -520 kcal/mole, respectively)[18] are also consistent with a view that both should precipitate in the marine environment. Dolomite is stable in contrast to aragonite, calcite, or magnesite and should be the ultimate transformation product.

Why doesn't magnesite commonly precipitate from the sea as a primary product in view of the high degree of saturation? Probably one major reason is that complexing of magnesium ion occurs (Table 8-3). In effect, the calculations (8-18) do not consider the fact that the effective concentration is less than 0.054 $\underline{M}$, and that the complex $[Mg^{2+} \cdot CO_3^{2-}]_{aq}$ is very stable. Moreover, it appears that the fraction of complexed calcium ion is very small, though some workers consider a calcium carbonate complex to be very stable.[18] It is reasonable, then, to ascribe the general absence of primary precipitation of magnesite and other magnesium carbonates to the effect of complexing. The dolomite problem is considered later.

The factors that affect the solubility and combination of component ions of calcium carbonate may be summarized.

1. Carbon dioxide flux is the major factor which affects the solution or precipitation of carbonates because the flux affects the pH and the carbonate-bicarbonate ion concentrations (cf. Table 8-5). Addition of carbon dioxide to the ecosystem decreases the likelihoood of carbonate precipitation because the carbonate ion is decreased (Eqn. 8-1, 8-4). Removal of carbon dioxide from the system (cf. Eqn. 8-19) increases the carbonate ion concentration and the likelihood of precipitation.

$$2HCO_3^- \;\overset{\rightarrow}{\leftarrow}\; CO_2 + H_2O + CO_3^{2-} \qquad\qquad (8-19)$$

Carbon dioxide is added through the following processes or changes: respiration, activity of bacteria, chemical oxidation, temperature decrease, and pressure increase. Carbon dioxide is removed through: photosynthetic uptake, turblence, temperature increase, and pressure decrease.

2. Complexing of calcium, magnesium, carbonate, or bicarbonate ions, presumably decreases the likelihood of precipitation and increases the tendency to dissolve. It is also possible that complexing may be involved in the apparent control of carbonate mineralogy in the marine ecosystem.

3. Physical factors such as changes in temperature and pressure alter the carbon dioxide flux and alter the solubility in the manner indicated.

4. Salinity. The value of K_{sp} for carbonate minerals is invariant with salinity. As salinity increases, the values of the activity coefficients decrease, and the degree of supersaturation is enhanced. The situation is described in some detail by Cloud for a major site of modern carbonate deposition, the Bahama Banks.[18]

Carbonate Recrystallization. Taft[21] has summarized a critical and complex problem of carbonate recrystallization. It is a curious paradox that metastable carbonates, such as aragonite and high-magnesium calcite, persist in the marine environment for extended periods of time, yet are absent or significantly recrystallized in modern sediments that are above sea level or are absent in older lithified marine sediments. Aragonite should be metastable with respect to calcite, based on the thermodynamic data and aragonite should not be preserved for extended periods of time. Yet, the results of deep borings in Eniwetok indicate the preservation of aragonite in pre-Pleistocene materials. Observations such as these indicate the existence and preservation of metastable carbonates for extended periods of time, and they may suggest one cause of such preservation: chemical control by some constituents(s) of sea water.

Taft has suggested control by metal ions is responsible for the preservation of metastable carbonates. In particular, solutions of magnesium in contact with metastable carbonates appear to be capable of preventing recrystallization (Fig. 8-4). The critical concentration ratio (CCR) is an empirical weight ratio (grams of precipitate in contact with solution/grams of magnesium in solution) that may be used to define the tendency of magnesium to prevent recrystallization. At $23 \pm 2^{\circ}C$, a CCR value of 805 prevents recrystallization; i.e., 50 ml of a 5-ppm magnesium ion solution retards the recrystallization; at $70^{\circ}C$, a 50-ppm solution is needed (CCR value of 80). The effectiveness of magnesium is indicated by the fact

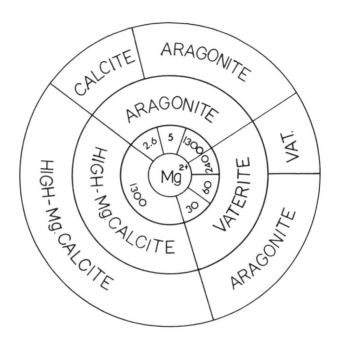

FIG. 8-4

The effect of magnesium on the recrystallization
of metastable carbonates. The diagram summarizes
pertinent relationships. For example, starting
with magnesium ion (center) 240 ppm of magnesium
ion in contact with vaterite retards recrystallization
of vaterite to aragonite. On the other hand, 2.6
ppm of magnesium ion in contact with aragonite is
insufficient to prevent aragonite from recrystalliz-
ing to calcite. Pertinent conditions described in
text. (Courtesy of W. H. Taft.)

that standard sea water contains 1300 ppm of magnesium, which
is sufficient to prevent recrystallization.

The mechanism of metal-ion control of recrystallization
is uncertain. According to Bischoff,[22] the transformation
from aragonite to calcite in contact with solution may be controlled by nucleation and growth of calcite. This view was
based on the observation that the fraction of aragonite in non-
buffered solutions transformed to calcite at $50-120^{\circ}C$ was proportional to the square of the reaction time. Other observations are consistent with this view, though the situation is
equivocal. It is probably not easy to precipitate aragonite
in the absence of seed crystals of calcite so that some nuclei
are always present. Also, the effect of noncommon alkaline-
earth metal ions has been investigated,[23] and the results are
consistent with a surface mechanism (cf. Bischoff[22]), though
the importance of control by species in solution cannot be
overlooked. The limiting concentrations of metal ion, which
retard the recrystallization of aragonite in contact with
buffered solutions, are inversely related to the observed coordinating tendency of these ions (Note 5). This observation
is consistent with control by metal ions as a surface effect.
It is also consistent with control as a solution effect
through, say, control of carbonate by metal ion complexing.
These observations indicate the need for further research;
meanwhile, they are of interest in understanding the origin

and geologic history of sites of carbonate deposition such as
at Yellow Bank, Bahamas.

In the normal shallow-water environment represented by
the New Providence Platform, recrystallization of the metastable carbonate sediments evidently does not occur because of
control by magnesium ions.[24] Recrystallization would have
occurred if the sediments had been in a low-magnesium environment (e.g., in dense sediments with low interstitial water
content and low magnesium ion content). Alternatively, recrystallization could occur in a nonmarine environment where
the metastable carbonate minerals were exposed to rainfall.
Carbon-14 determinations of carbonate-carbon indicate that
sedimentation in the Banks started about 6700 B.P. and continued without permanent exposure to the atmosphere. About 6700
B.P. the sea level must have risen sufficiently to cover most
of the Bank, though portions were probably exposed during
low tide.

Lithification of modern carbonate sediments is occurring
in situ in the Yellow Bank and seems to be closely related to
present sites of bioherm communities (algae, corals, sponges,
and sea fans).[24] It is believed that lithification occurs here
because of intimate participation of bioherms at a water-
sediment interface. Probably lithification occurs as a result
of decomposition of organic material followed by precipitation

of aragonite. Thus, according to this view, cementation is the result of a combination of organic and inorganic processes.

The mechanism of recrystallization and lithification is obviously of concern to geologists in understanding geologic history; it is less obviously of concern, but very important, in determining paleotemperatures and the ecology of the past. Certain ratios $(Sr^{2+}/Ca^{2+}, {}^{12}C/{}^{13}C,$ and ${}^{16}O/{}^{18}O)$ should be useful in interpreting the environments in which ancient sediments were deposited. The ${}^{16}O/{}^{18}O$ ratios of carbonates deposited in isotopic equilibrium with the surrounding sea water were thought to be dependent on the temperature and independent of carbonate mineralogy or the biochemistry of the species; the mineralogy and Sr^{2+}/Ca^{2+} ratios may be affected by temperature, the chemistry of the sea water, and the biochemistry of the species.[25] Actually, the preservation of the ${}^{16}O/{}^{18}O$ ratios depends upon the mechanism of recrystallization. The ratio should be preserved if solid-phase recrystallization occurs; the ratio may be significantly altered if the recrystallization involves aragonite dissolution and calcite reprecipitation. This mode of recrystallization would occur as a result of prolonged exposure of the metastable carbonate to a magnesium-poor environment (e.g., fresh-water exposure of beach rock or magnesium- and strontium-poor aragonite shells).

The Dolomite Anomaly.[24] True dolomite has not been prepared
under simulated sedimentary conditions, and contemporary formation of dolomite in sizable deposits in the marine ecosystem
is unknown. On the other hand, abundant, thicker and extensive
beds of dolomite are observed as representative of several
ages (Precambrian-Mesozoic). No unusual conditions seem to
have occurred in the past to effect the precipitation of
dolomite.

The origin of the dolomite beds remains one of the obscure
and significant problems of geochemistry. It appears
that most of the dolomite rock was formed slowly by transformation of calcium carbonate (Eqn. 8-20,8-21), not as
primary precipitate which subsequently lithified.

$$CaCO_3 + Mg^{2+} + 2HCO_3^- \rightleftarrows CaMg(CO_3)_2 + H_2CO_3 \qquad (8-20)$$

$$2CaCO_3 + Mg^{2+} \rightleftarrows CaMg(CO_3)_2 + Ca^{2+} \qquad (8-21)$$

The reactions (Eqn. 8-20,8-21) are very slowly shifted to
dolomite, which probably grows very slowly because of the
highly ordered crystal structure of dolomite. Krauskopf[26] notes
that the probability of the reactions is indicated by the
poor preservation of fossils in dolomite rock, coarseness of
grain, and characteristic cavities and pore spaces. The dolomite structure might be produced through templating, i.e.,
complex ions orienting (or serving as a template for) magnesium or calcium ions in such a way as to favor the highly

ordered dolomite structure. This hypothesis is suggested by the observation that protodolomite is produced in the laboratory at ordinary temperatures when the solutions contain high concentrations of sulfate (template?) ions. Otherwise, laboratory precipitation usually produces a mixture of hydromagnesite and calcite. This hypothesis might help explain the observation that contemporary primary precipitation of dolomite occurs in hot springs and in muds of salt lagoons undergoing marked solar evaporation. Increased temperature favors dolomite formation, but these sites may also represent the location of high concentrations of templating ions. In summary, the dolomite anomaly is the prevalence of this material in contrast to the absence of contemporary formation and difficulty of laboratory precipitation (except under unusual conditions). Much of the dolomite problem may be rationalized by noting the highly ordered nature of the dolomite crystal which can be formed only slowly at ordinary temperatures.

Control of Trace Metal Elements.[27] The low concentration of certain elements in the ocean may be ascribed to one of two causes. First, the element may occur in low concentration in the nonoceanic source (crustal rocks or in the earth's interior). One example is cesium which is present in low concentrations in crustal rocks and in the ocean. Secondly, the element may be an abundant constituent of the source domain,

but because of great reactivity in the marine ecosystem it is
present in low concentration in sea water. Aluminum is a good
example. The comparative reactivity of various elements is indicated by the use of two parameters, residence time and degree
of undersaturation.

The residence time of an element, τ, is defined as the
mean time that an element remains in sea water before removal
by some process (Eqn. 8-22).

$$\tau = \frac{A}{(dA/dt)} \qquad (8-22)$$

Here, $\underline{A}$ is the total weight of element suspended or dissolved
in the world ocean; $\underline{dA/dt}$ is the weight introduced or precipitated per unit time. Typically, it is assumed that a steady-
state condition exists (rate of river input is compensated
by rate of sedimentation) and that the time of complete mixing
is small with respect to the residence time. In general, both
assumptions seem to be reasonable if residence times are
compared on a relative, not an absolute, basis.

Elements can be arranged in three categories on the basis
of relative times (Table 8-6): I, long residence times, low
reactivity (typically alkali and alkaline-earth elements of
lower atomic weight); II, intermediate residence times,
10^3-10^6 years (commonly, those elements associated with
ferromanganese minerals in the oceans); III, short residence
times, less than 10^3 years, with residence times less than the

TABLE 8-6

Concentrations and Residence Times of

Some Elements in Sea Water[27]

Category	Element	Concentration, ppm	Residence Time, millions of years
I	Na	10,500	260
	Mg	1,350	
	Ca	400	8
	K	380	11
	Sr	8.0	19
	Li	0.17	20
II	Ba	0.03	0.084
	Zn	0.01	0.18
	Cu	0.003	0.050
	Mr	0.002	0.001,4
	Co	0.0001	0.018
III	Al	0.01	0.000,15
	Be	6×10^{-7}	0.000,1
	Fe	0.01	0.000,14
	Cr	0.5×10^{-5}	0.000,35

likely mixing time in the deep-sea reservoir (Section 8.6).
The elements are in the last category because they enter the
world oceans as solids and settle rapidly.

Degrees of undersaturation have also been used to compare
relative reactivities. The upper limit of concentration of a
metal ion should be governed by the solubility of its least
soluble compound, assuming no other chemical reactions are

involved. Then it may be argued that the reactive elements are those that are highly undersaturated; the inert elements are those that are near saturation. Krauskopf[28] has been concerned with degrees of undersaturation both experimentally and theoretically, and has considered the many assumptions that must be made and the usefulness of the concept.

Trace metal ion concentrations are controlled by two types of processes, chemical "scavenging" and concentration by organisms. Chemical "scavenging" would include the following types of reactions: (1) control by solubility insoluble compounds (Pb by $PbCO_3$, Ba by $BaSO_4$, Sr by $SrCO_3$, Mg by $MgCO_3$ are simple examples); (2) control by ion-exchange processes (Sect. 4.3); and (3) "scavenging" action of hydrous oxides, such as those of manganese and iron, which adsorb ions from solution. The latter process is involved in the formation of ferro-manganese sediments.

The concentration of trace metal elements by organisms can be spectacular, as Goldberg[27] and others have suggested. Nicholls and co-workers[29] suggested that "for any given chemical element, there will be at least one planktonic species capable of spectacularly concentrating it." Several important features of this phenomenon may be summarized.

1. Concentration factors are used to define the enrichment of trace metals in organisms. The factor is equal to the concentration (w/w) in the organism (dried at $110^\circ C$)

divided by the concentration (w/w) in sea water. Concentration factors range from 100 to 100,000 and a value of several million has been reported for titanium in the colonial ascidian _Eudestoma_ _rittori_.

2. _Specificity_, the ability to remove a given trace metal, is often a property of a given family or even a given species of organism. Goldberg[27] has noted a close parallel between the concentration factor and the Irving-Williams order for transition-metal ions. This order defines the relative coordinating tendency of certain metal ions with a variety of chelating agents (with oxygen or nitrogen donor atoms; sulfur donors may cause variations). The abbreviated Irving-Williams order of coordinating tendency is $Sc^{2+} < Ti^{2+} < V^{2+} < Cr^{2+} < Mn^{2+} < Fe^{2+} < Co^{2+} < Ni^{2+} < Cu^{2+} < Zn^{2+}$. Other metal ions may be fitted into an extended Irving-Williams order, but the position of non-transition metals varies somewhat with the ligands involved.[30]

3. The _mechanism_ of concentration does not necessarily involve a chelating process as implied by the parallel with the Irving-Williams orders. At least five general mechanisms of concentrations have been indicated by various workers (cf. Goldberg,[27] Brooks and Rumsby[31]): (1) particulate ingestion of suspended matter from sea water; (2) ingestion of elements which have been preconcentrated in food material; (3) chelation of metals

with appropriate organic chelating agents; (4) incorporation of metal ions with physiologically important
systems; and (5) uptake of metals by exchange as on
mucous membranes of oysters.

4.   Physiological effects of uptake of metal ions are of
great concern both from a standpoint of the effect on the
organism and on those who subsequently consume these
organisms. Much work has been concerned with the uptake
of elements such as strontium-90 from atomic bomb fallout
and trace metals (copper, chromium) which come as an indirect result of thermal pollution. Such studies must be
concerned with the rate of uptake, the concentration
levels, the location of the metal concentrated within the
organism, and the rate of depletion within a pollution-
free environment.[32]
Much remains to be studied concerning the control of
trace metals by chemicals and organisms, and the next few
years should see useful and interesting results of
present studies.

8.8 Summary

This chapter has considered the carbon budget and the
gross features of three carbon cycles: biological, geological,
and combined biological-geological-economic. The equilibria
involved upon dissolution of carbon dioxide in sea water have

been reviewed and some emphasis has been placed on the limitations and utilities of various parameters and equations used
to evaluate concentrations of various inorganic carbon species.
One such value is P_{CO_2}, the partial pressure of carbon dioxide
in sea water. This parameter, coupled with pH, seems to be
the most currently useful probe for indicating physical and
chemical changes involving carbon. Two important changes are
the AOU effect (due to biological activity) and the carbonate
dissolution-precipitation effect. Changes in the carbon dioxide content of the atmosphere and the ocean were considered.
The problems of carbonate deposition include understanding the
environment and requirements of carbonate deposition (and
solution), the recrystallization (and preservation) of metastable carbonates, the dolomite problem (which seems to be
understandable in terms of the complexity of the structure),
and the control of trace metal elements by organisms.

It is evident that all major cycles are intimately
associated with the intense biological cycle. Aspects of this
cycle receive special attention in the following chapter.

NOTES

1. Metasomatism is a high-grade metamorphic transformation
   that involves change of composition,e.g.,

$$CaMg(CO_3)_2 \;+\; 2SiO_2 \;\rightarrow\; CaMgSi_2O_6 \;+\; 2CO_2$$

    dolomite   quartz   diopside

The extensiveness of zones in which these changes occur varies as indicated by the progressive adjectives contact, regional, and ultra.

2.   Neglecting the effect of complex formation is probably not a serious matter when changes or relative values are of interest.

3.   Some speculative projections for 2050 have been made by Peterson.[33] These include an _average_ increase in temperature (maybe $4^{\circ}C$) in the temperate zone, more rainfall and less snow in the U.S., rise in ocean levels (perhaps by 4 ft), major increase in volcanic activity and earthquakes (producing more atmospheric CO_2), major shifts in weather in the northern hemisphere (because the Arctic Ocean would be ice-free for at least half of each year).

4.   Diagenesis refers to the physical and chemical changes sediments undergo after deposition, compaction, cementation, recrystallization, and other processes which result in lithification (conversion of newly deposited sediments into rock).

5.   The relative coordinating tendency of the noncommon alkaline earth metal ions is $Be^{2+} > Mg^{2+} > Sr^{2+} > Ba^{2+}$.

REFERENCES

1. G. Skirrow in Chemical Oceanography (J. P. Riley and G. Skirrow, eds.), Academic Press, New York, 1965, Chapt. 7.

2. H. Borchert, Geochim. Cosmochim. Acta, 2, 62 (1951).

3. G. Dietrich, General Oceanography, Interscience, New York, 1963, pp. 235-239.

4. R. Revelle and H. E. Suess, Tellus, 8, 18 (1957).

5. G. E. Hutchinson in The Earth as a Planet (G. P. Kuiper, ed.), Vol. II, Univ. of Chicago Press, Chicago, 1954, Chapt. 8.

6. cf. G. P. Spencer, Oceanog. Mar. Biol. Ann. Rev., 3, 31 (1965).

7. P. K. Park, Limnol. Oceanog., 14, 179 (1969).

8. C. Culbertsen, D. R. Kester, and R. M. Pytkowicz, Science, 157, 59 (1967).

9. R. M. Pytkowicz, Deep-Sea Res., 10, 633 (1963).

10. P. K. Park, Science, 162, 357 (1962).

11. R. M. Garrels and M. E. Thompson, Am. J. Sci., 260, 57 (1962).

12. R. M. Pytkowicz, Deep-Sea Res., 10, 633 (1963).

13. F. H. Fisher, Science, 157, 823 (1967).

14. H. Craig, Tellus, 9, 1 (1957).

15. B. Bolin and E. Eriksson in The Atmosphere and Sea in Motion (Rossby Memorial Volume, B. Bolin, ed.) Oxford University Press, Rockefeller Institute Press, New York, 1959, p. 130-142.

16. W. S. Broecker in The Sea (N. M. Hill, ed.), Vol. II, Interscience, New York, 1963, p. 88-108, and other papers in the series.

17. cf. J. D. Burton _in_ Chemical Oceanography (J. P. Riley and G. Skirrow, eds.), Academic Press, 1965, Chapt. 22.

18. P. E. Cloud, Jr., ibid., Chapt. 17.

19. J. C. Jameson, J. Phys. Chem., $\underline{21}$, 1385 (1953).

20. R. M. Garrels, Mineral Equilibria, Harper and Row, New York, 1960; R. M. Garrels, M. E. Thompson, and R. Siever, Am. J. Sci., $\underline{258}$, 402 (1960).

21. W. H. Taft _in_ Carbonate Rocks, A. Origin, Occurrence, and Classification (G. V. Chilingar, H. J. Bissell, and R. W. Fairbridge, eds.), Elsevier, Amsterdam, Chapt. 3.

22. J. L. Bischoff, Am. Mineral, $\underline{54}$, 149 (1969).

23. M. E. McLester, D. F. Martin, and W. H. Taft, J. Inorg. Nucl. Chem., $\underline{32}$, 391 (1970).

24. W. H. Taft, F. Arrington, A. Haimovitz, C. MacDonald, and C. Woolheater, Bull. Mar. Sci., $\underline{18}$, 762 (1968).

25. H. C. Wing, H. A. Lowenstam, S. Epstein, C. R. McKinney, Geol. Soc. Am. Bull., $\underline{62}$, 399 (1951).

26. K. B. Krauskopf, Introduction to Geochemistry, McGraw-Hill, New York, 1967, Chapt. 3.

27. cf. E. D. Goldberg _in_ Chemical Oceanography (J. P. Riley and G. Skirrow, eds.), Academic Press, New York, 1965.

28. K. B. Krauskopf, Geochim. Cosmochim. Acta, $\underline{9}$, 1 (1956).

29. G. D. Nicholls, H. Curl, Jr., V. T. Bowen, Limnol. Oceanog., $\underline{4}$, 472 (1959).

30. D.F. Martin and B.B. Martin, Coordination Compounds, McGraw-Hill, New York, 1964, Chapt 5.

31. R.D. Brooks and M.G. Rumsby, Limnol. Oceanog., $\underline{10}$, 521 (1965).

32. cf. B.H. Pringle, D.E. Hessong, E.L. Katz, S.T. Mulawka, J. Sanit. Engn. Div., Proc. Am. Soc. Civil Eng., $\underline{94}$, 455 (1968).

33. E.K. Peterson, Environ. Sci. Technol., $\underline{3}$, 1162 (1969).

ORGANIC PRODUCTIVITY[1-3]

9.1 Introduction

It is difficult to generalize about the photosynthesis in the marine ecosystem because it is so poorly understood in a quantitative sense. About two decades ago, it was commonly believed that, per unit area, the sea was roughly twice as productive (photosynthetically) as the land.

This view was dispelled as a result of the research of E. Steemann Nielson, who studied organic productivity during the Galatea Expedition (1950-1952). This marked the first extensive use of the carbon-14 technique for measuring primary productivity. Steemann Nielson claimed[4] in 1952, "Before the Galatea Expedition put to sea in 1950, the production of organic matter in the oceans must...be considered as completely unknown. Only the values for the production in a few northern coastal waters had been determined by reliable methods."

Estimates of the productivity of the sea vary. According to Steeman Nielson's estimates, the total net production was an average of 55 grams of assimilated carbon/m^2/year for the world ocean. The total net production was calculated as 1.5×10^{10} tons of fixed carbon per year in the 71% of the earth covered

by the seas, assuming a loss of 25% for respiration. This
value was somewhat less than the estimated value for land and
about a tenth of previous estimates for the sea. These estimates have been modified since 1952 as improvements in techniques and error analysis have been made. Presently, it
appears that the amount of organic carbon produced in the
seas per unit time is about the same as on land. Thus, the
land is more than twice as productive as the sea per unit area
per unit time. This view is subject to change.

Two important aspects, the organisms involved and the definition of photosynthesis, are considered in the following
sections.

9.2 Plants of the Sea (Note 1)

In a discussion of production of organic matter in the
primary stage of the marine food system, it is convenient to
divide all plant life in the sea into two categories:
phytoplankton and benthic (or attached) plants.

Benthic plants, algae and sea grasses, occur near the
shoreline because they are attached to the bottom and are
limited to a maximum depth (about 200 m). This is the depth
to which light penetrates with sufficient intensity to permit
adequate photosynthesis. It is generally conceded that more
than 99.9% of all photosynthesis is carried on by photoplank-
ton. This does not mean the benthic plants are unimportant.
They are ecologically significant. They are the only marine

plants that currently have economic value (for cell wall poly-
saccharides, fertilizer, stock feed, etc., cf. Section 11.4).

Phytoplankton are of direct interest from the standpoint
of photosynthesis. They are generally microscopic unicellular
plants that live suspended in sea water and occupy a three-
dimensional domain, the entire surface of the sea down to some
unknown depth. The limiting depth represents the point at
which light of suitable intensity and wavelength penetrates.
In clearest sea water, this depth is at least 100-150 m and
may be significantly deeper. Our present basic productivity
measurements cannot accurately define the lower limit. No universally accepted classification of the algae exists, and
taxonomists disagree on the position of not only certain species and genera but even certain orders (Note 2). Obviously,
despite the lack of agreement, some comment on the marine
phytoplankton species is in order. The listing used here
(Table 9-1) follows that of Smith[5]; a different and useful
arrangement is given by Silva.[6] The significant divisions may
be considered in order of increasing importance in the marine
food chain.[1,2]

1.   Division Cyanophyta. Blue-green algae are uncommon in
     marine phytoplankton, though some species may be season-
     ally abundant in near-shore and brackish areas (Calothrix)
     The importance of some species in nitrogen fixation
     (Section 7.5) has been mentioned; vast blooms of

TABLE 9-1

Some Phytoplankton Species

Division	Class	Order	Some Genera
Cyanophyta	I. Myxophyceae	I. Chroococcales	Anacystis, Chroococcus, Synechococcus
		II. Nostocales	Nostoc, Trichodesmium
Pyrrophyta	I. Dinophyceae (Desmokontae)	I. Prorocentrales	Exuviella, Prorocentrum
		III. Peridiniales	Ceratium, Glenodinium, Gonyaulax, Peridinium
Chrysophyta	I. Chrysophyceae	I. Chrysomonadales	Coccolithus, Phaeocystis, Silicoflagellates
	II. Bacillariophyceae (diatoms)	I. Pennales	Navicula, Nitzschia
		II. Centrales	Cyclotella, Skeletonema
	III. Xanthophyceae		Halosphaera

"Trichodesmium" have been noted in tropical and semi-tropical waters.

2. Division Chlorophyta. Green algae are also uncommon in marine phytoplankton. These are predominately fresh-water plants and are not included in Table 9-1.

3. Division Pyrrophyta. Dinoflagellates predominate in the division and can comprise a significant fraction of marine phytoplankton when blooms occur. Blooms of dinoflagellates are commonly called "red tides," though other organisms may be responsible.[7] Blooms of Gymnodinium breve (W. Florida, Gulf of Mexico) are a fish-killing phenomenon, and Gonyaulax catenella (California) and Gonyaulax tamarensis are associated with paralytic shell fish poisoning. The morphology and physiology of species of this division is diverse. Some species have even lost photosynthetic capability; these live phagotropically or symbiotically.

4. Division Chrysophyta. Species of the division Chrysophyta comprise a large fraction of marine nanno- and ultra-plankton (e.g., silicoflagellates) and may comprise a large fraction of the biomass (e.g., coccolithophores) in some pelagic areas. Diatoms (with the rest of the division) probably comprise the largest fraction of bio-mass of marine phytoplankton. Placement of diatoms is a matter of opinion. Silva[6] has made bacillariophyceae a

321

separate division (Bacillariophyta); Centrales and
Pennales are two classes. Also, Phaeodactylum tricornutum
(Nitzschia, Section 6.5) probably is to be classified as a
(sole) member of a sub-order of bacillariophyceae; it is
not a true diatom.

5. Cryptophyta. The above are the major divisions in terms of
providing the major constituents of marine phytoplankton.
Minor constituents of other divisions include the division Cryptophyta, which has been proposed to encompass
some species that have been included in Pyrrophyta.
Members of this division are small flagellates (typically
red-brown or blue) and may be significant in shore and
coastal waters.

9.3 Photosynthesis

This term means literally "the synthesis of compounds in
light." More precisely, though, photosynthesis is used to
designate the synthesis, in light, of organic compounds (mainly
carbohydrates) from inorganic materials, with the concomitant
liberation of heat by chlorophyll-containing plants.

The photosynthesis process may be said to be the unique
source of all living matter;of all life energy on the Earth.
It is, moreover, the source of nearly all industrial and
domestic power and heat (except wind, water, and nuclear
power) because all fossil fuels are the decomposition products
of plant photosynthesis at some past time. Photosynthesis is a

major link in the various carbon cycles described in the preceding chapter. The process is responsible for the major regeneration of carbon, oxygen, and hydrogen; only light energy
is not regenerated. The overall chemical reaction (Eqn. 9-1)
may be represented easily; here $(CH_2O)_x$ is a carbohydrate.

$$H_2O + CO_2 + h\nu \xrightarrow[\text{enzymes}]{\text{chlorophyll}} (CH_2O)_x + O_2 \tag{9-1}$$

$$\Delta H = -112 \text{ kcal/mole}$$
$$\Delta G = -115 \text{ kcal/mole}$$

The equation is misleading in several respects. It does
not emphasize that this is an "uphill" process, that it leads
to a decrease in entropy as more ordered and less probable
carbohydrate is formed. It does indicate that much of the
light energy used is stored as chemical energy (115 kcal per
mole of CO_2 reduced). It does not, however, indicate the
results of isotopic tracer experiments, that the liberated oxygen comes from the water, not from the carbon dioxide.

Moreover, the equation does not indicate the complex multi-
stage processes. These may be roughly grouped into three
phases (Fig. 9-1). Phase 1 consists of a nonphotochemical
("dark") enzyme-catalyzed evolution of oxygen from dehydro-
genated water; manganous ion is required. Phase 2 is a photochemical ("light") reaction in which hydrogen atoms (or
electrons) are transferred by light-activated chlorophyll.
This transfer is made from an intermediate of phase 1 to an

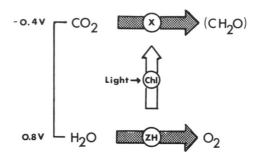

FIG. 9-1

Schematic illustration of photosynthesis as a
tripartite process.   Here, ZH and X are donor
and acceptor, respectively. (After Rabinowitch,
Ref. 17, p. 112.)

acceptor intermediate which is capable of reducing carbon

dioxide. Phase 3 consists of a series of non-photochemical

("dark") reductions of carbon dioxide.

This is a brief but general view of photosynthesis

(Note 3). The general characteristics are the same in the

plant world from phytoplankton to flowering plants, though

some minor variations in mechanism are to be expected in

various autotrophic organisms. Once photosynthesis is com-

pleted, the primary products undergo amination, polymerization,

oxidation-reduction, and other changes to produce protons,

pigments, enzymes, vitamins, cellulose, and other structural

components.

9.4 Productivity Terminology

At this point, it is useful to define some of the terminology associated with photosynthesis. Gross primary productivity is the total amount of organic matter resulting from exposure to light, whereas net primary productivity refers to the
net amount of organic matter available after subtracting losses
due to respiration and other processes. Estimation of productivity requires an estimate of the rates involved and the use
of a conversion factor. Photosynthetic rate is the rate of
"change of some substance" that results from photosynthetic
activity. Various definitions differ in terms of "change of
some substance." This may refer to (a) "increase in dry
organic matter in plants" (not practical with marine algae);
(b) "increase in the amount of oxygen in the extra-cellular
environment" (suitable for growth periods longer than a few
minutes); (c) "decrease in amount of CO_2 (or $^{14}CO_2$) in the
extra-cellular environment"; (d) "increase in number of cells."
Recording changes in oxygen production, or uptake of CO_2,
presents no great difficulty, though equating these changes
[definitions (b), (c)] to the production of organic carbon is
difficult. The rate of increase in the number of cells is not
necessarily the equivalent of photosynthetic rate.
Definitions based on oxygen change are important because an
early technique for estimating marine plankton photosynthesis
was based on changes in oxygen concentration. Photosynthetic

quotient (PQ) was defined (Eqn. 9-2) as the moles of oxygen liberated during photosynthesis (ΔO_2) divided by the moles of CO_2 assimilated ($-\Delta CO_2$). The respirator coefficient (RQ) may be defined as (Eqn. 9-3) the moles of CO_2 liberated during respiration (ΔCO_2) divided by the moles of oxygen assimilated.

$$PQ = \Delta O_2 / -\Delta CO_2 \qquad\qquad (9-2)$$

$$RQ = \Delta CO_2 / -\Delta O_2 \qquad\qquad (9-3)$$

Definitions related to unicellular algae growth. The growth cycle of unicellular algae is characterized by four phases: (1) lag, (2) exponential growth, (3) plateau, (4) death phases (Fig. 9-1). At a given instant, the change in amount of material in a phytoplankton system is (Eqn. 9-4):

$$\frac{dp}{dt} = kp \qquad\qquad (9-4)$$

Here k is a growth (or specific rate) constant and has units of time^{-1} (hr^{-1} or days^{-1}). Because most phytoplankton reproduce by cell division, the growth constant can be related to the number of cells n (Eqn. 9-5).

$$\frac{dn}{dt} = kn \qquad\qquad (9-5)$$

The growth constant is equal to 2.303 m where m is the slope of the linear exponential phase of the growth plot (Fig. 9-2). Some workers prefer to use k_{10} values, which are equal to m. The mean generation (or division) time, T_g, (Eqn. 9-6) is the time required for the population to double.

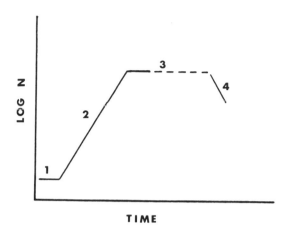

FIG. 9-2

Idealized growth cycle, log $\underline{n}$ (cells/unit volume)
as a function of time, showing four phases.

$$T_g = \frac{0.69}{k} = \frac{0.30}{k_{10}} \qquad (9\text{-}6)$$

<u>Comparison</u> <u>of</u> <u>populations</u> in cultures or nature may be done in
several ways.

1. Primary standing crop (stock) is the instantaneous amount
    of biomass present in water and may be expressed as
    mg C_{org}/m^3 or mg C_{org}/m^2, the amount of organic carbon in
    a unit volume or below a unit area.

2. The rate of photosynthesis may be expressed on the basis
    of carbon present (Eqn. 9-7, cf. Eqn. 9-5).

$$\frac{\text{mg } C/m^3/hr}{\text{mg } C/m^3} = k \ (hr^{-1}) \qquad (9\text{-}7)$$

327

3. Expressing the photosynthetic rate on the basis of chloro-
    phyll-a (Chl-a) present (Eqn. 9-8) is more convenient for
    field work.

$$\frac{mg\ C/m^3/hr}{mg\ Chl-a/m^3} = P(c) \qquad (9-8)$$

9.5 Some Physical Factors and Plankton Growth

Marine phytoplankton respond to three major variables;
two physical factors, light and temperature; and the chemical
composition of sea water. Salinity may provide an ecological
barrier to the stenohaline organisms. The effect of physical
factors is considered in this section, the effect of
chemical composition in the next.

Light

Wavelength effect. The total illumination from radiation is
about 1.6 ly/min (Note 4) in the range 3000-7500$\overset{o}{A}$. The amount
of carbon fixed per quantum of light absorbed by a cell suspension (action spectrum) is relatively uniform for all wavelengths in the visible spectrum. The action spectrum roughly
follows the absorption spectrum: Exceptions seem to be due to
the method of measurement of action spectrum, i.e., illumination of cells with roughly one wavelength at a time; but
light of more than one wavelength must be present for the cells
to have maximum utilization efficiency (Emerson effect). Evidently this effect is due to significant participation by

pigments (chlorophylls -b, -c, and peridinin, among others) as
well as chlorophyll-a.

Compensation intensity. A phytoplankton cell will not divide
in the euphotic zone unless the illumination exceeds the compensation intensity. This is the lowest light intensity needed
to sustain photosynthesis. At this intensity, the cell respiration rate and its rate of gross photosynthesis are equal.
The compensation intensity is higher with poor nutrition. It
is lower if phosphate is deficient because respiration tends to
be suppressed more than photosynthesis. Relatively few reliable data are available, according to Strickland.[2] Perhaps
the most realistic measure of compensation would be that level
at which no cell division occurred for several days under
normal conditions. Laboratory measurements suggest this value
to be 4-20 ly/day (depending on the species and temperature).
These data indicate the importance of knowing the species
being studied; evidently, some unusually low compensation intensities must be assumed for certain species of phytoplankton.[2]

Light intensity. The variation of photosynthetic rate with
light intensity (P versus I plot) is termed the intensity response and is a useful property. If accurately known, the
intensity response would be useful in predicting the photosynthesis by phytoplankton under natural conditions.

Attempts to make such predictions have had limited success because of the complexities of the property. The rate of photosynthesis by algal cells increases linearly with intensity until a "light saturation" value (a "plateau," I_{max}) is reached and the rate does not vary with intensity. At even higher intensities (supraoptimal), rate suppression may be noted at a given concentration of chlorophyll. I_{max} can vary widely, but usually is within 0.05-0.1 ly/min. Thus, a P-I plot should be determined for each species. Even this may not be enough; comparison between workers is difficult because, among other reasons (Note 5),the P-I relationship depends upon the physiological state of the cells. For example, severe rate suppression may be observed at 0.5 ly/min if nutrition is inadequate or temperatures are unsuitable, though under favorable conditions supra-optimal suppression might not be noted. Finally, the observation of supra-optimal regression may be due to difference in light sources: some workers have found repression at 0.1 ly/min with chlorophycea; others, using radiation free of ultraviolet and redlight, found no repression at intensities of 0.3 ly/min.

Effects of preconditioning on photosynthetic rate may be significant. Typically, preconditioning might refer to whether cells have existed for one or more days at low or high intensities, as would happen if a pycnocline suddenly developed in the euphotic zone (Note 6). The population would be divided into those above (higher light intensity or "sun" forms) and those

below (low intensity or "shade" forms) the transient pycnocline.

Or, the low-intensity forms could be exemplified by surface

organisms during winter months in temperate climates. The P-I

relationship may be dramatically different (Fig. 9-3). The

exact values of I_{max} for low- and high-intensity precondition-

ing are unknown under actual conditions, though they might be

of the order of 0.05 and 0.2 ly/min, respectively. The effects

indicated in Fig. 9-3 apply only for a short time , i.e., the

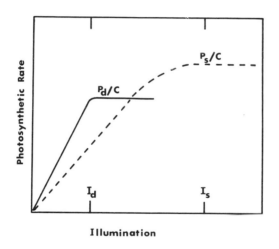

FIG. 9-3

Effect of illumination and preconditioning on
photosynthetic rate. Here, I_d and I_s refer to
the preconditioning intensity of "shade" and
"sun" forms, respectively; and P_d/C and P_s/C
refer to the photosynthetic rate per unit of
carbon or per cell for the "shade" and "sun"
forms, respectively.

low-intensity forms change within two days to the "sun" forms
when exposed to higher light intensities, and the reverse
situation also applies.

Temperature

Each species of phytoplankton seems to have an optimum
temperature, as indicated by a maximum photosynthetic rate,
P_{max}, the value obtained at I_{max}. Actually, the optimum temperature usually is seen as an optimum temperature range of
about $3^{o}C$ above and below the optimum temperature (assuming the
cells have an opportunity to adapt during a couple of days).
At higher temperatures, an abrupt, commonly irreversible,
decrease is observed. This may be due to increased demand for
nutrients, as large excesses of nitrogen and phosphorus extend
the thermal tolerance. On the other hand, membrane anomalies
(thermal anomalies) may be involved (Section 1.2). Thorhaug[8]
suggested this explanation for the irreversible plasmolysis
which occurred in algal cells (Valonia, Chara, and Nitella)
below 15 and above $30^{o}C$.

It is a matter of some regret that more is not known about
the effects of temperature because this is perhaps the most
important single factor acting on marine organisms and because
in many estuaries thermal pollution will become an increasingly important problem.

9.6 Chemical Factors

It is convenient to focus attention on certain groups of chemicals or chemical parameters. These might be divided into three groups, for convenience: gross chemical parameters, gross nutrients, and trace elements.

Gross Chemical Parameters

These parameters include such factors as salinity, pH, and alkalinity.

As noted earlier (Section 1.8), salinity can control the region in which organisms such as dinoflagellates can thrive, and in practical terms salinity can govern the penetrating of red tides. The dinoflagellate Gonyaulax tamarensis can thrive in the salinity characteristic of an estuary; the Florida red tide organism, Cymnodinium breve, typically is found in coastal waters.

Most phytoplankton can tolerate the range of pH and alkalinity found in the marine ecosystem. These two parameters affect, but do not limit, the growth of most phytoplankton.

Gross Nutrients

The effect of major nutrients (nitrogen, phosphorus, silicon) has been considered in other chapters. It may be useful to summarize the effect of these nutrients here and consider the effect of other nutrients.

333

Nitrogen. As noted earlier (Section 7.5), most, but not all, phytoplankton can utilize nitrate satisfactorily, though ammonium ion is the preferred form. The rate of photosynthesis is affected when the nitrogen levels are below a critical value, particularly at high light intensities. The limiting concentration of nitrogen which supports maximum photosynthetic rates at I_{max}, is thought to be less than 50, and may be less than 10 µg NO_3^--N/liter.[1] This minimum level is not commonly maintained, except in the tropics. Even there, available evidence indicates nitrogen concentrations can be limiting (Section 7.5), even though natural marine populations have adapted to concentrations as low as 2.8 µg NO_3^--N/liter.

Phosphorus. Probably phosphorus, though a "master element" in the terms of atomic ratios, is seldom at a sufficiently low concentration to limit photosynthetic rates of phytoplankton in the marine ecosystem. (The concentration of phosphorus in some lakes may limit the photosynthetic rate.) Unfortunately, unequivocal evidence on this point is hard to obtain for several reasons. First, problems of analysis of phosphorus exist. Secondly, some phytoplankters are able to store phosphorus for subsequent utilization. Thirdly, phosphorus is exchanged very rapidly between plant cells and the medium. Finally, some obscure auxiliary compounds seem to affect the availability of phosphorus to the cell.[1] All of these factors

complicate the problem of determining at what minimum level

phosphate concentrations limit the photosynthetic rate.

Silicon. A priori, it might be expected that the concentration

of silicon would affect only the diatom growth, and the inter-

relationship of silicon levels and diatom growth has been con-

sidered (Section 5.4). Two observations seem to indicate that

silicon concentration has a wider effect than might have been

supposed. The first is the observation that concentrations of

Gymnodinium breve seem to show a significant negative cor-

relation with silicate concentration.[9] This may indicate an

indirect effect: blooms of this organism occur in nutrient-

depleted waters, following diatom blooms.

The second observation is more startling: silicate avail-

ability in the subtropical pelagic environment seems to limit

phytoplankton photosynthetic rates, as measured by the ^{14}C

technique.[10] These are enrichment experiments: Samples of sea

water containing the natural flora of phytoplankton and other

microorganisms were treated with silicate (and other nutrients)—

omission of silicate resulted in reduced uptake of ^{14}C,

relative to that for complete enrichment.

Problems arise in interpreting these and other interesting

experiments unless the chemical composition of the sample is exactly defined and, more importantly, unless the pertinent organisms are defined. As Provasoli has noted,[11] any discussion of the fertility of given waters must be defined in terms of specific organisms or groups. Nevertheless, sufficient experiments seem to have been conducted with silicate enrichment so as to indicate the intriguing nature of the problem.

Trace Metals. Most enrichment experiments, which must usually be interpreted with some caution, seem to indicate that trace metals have two effects: (1) they may limit photosynthesis in some of the less fertile areas of subtropical pelagic waters; and (2) they may inhibit the growth of certain oceanic phytoplankton in coastal waters, where the concentrations of trace metals are greater than in the pelagic environment.

The two critical concentrations of any trace metals are unknown for marine phytoplankton. These concentrations would be: (1) the minimum concentration needed for maximum photosynthetic rate; and (2) the minimum concentration needed for observable photosynthetic rate. Actually, it is not really pertinent to define these concentrations because the form of combination, not the total concentration, of a given metal is critical for individual phytoplankton.

The form of combination of the metal ion, i.e., occurrence as a complex compound, is critical because most trace metals probably do not pass through the cell wall as free ions,

and because at the pH of sea water most transition metals
would be precipitated as hydrous oxides, which should be
ineffective in stimulating growth. Dissolved organic matter
(such as humic acids, tannins, or man-made chelating agents)
seem to stimulate growth of phytoplankters. The stimulating
effect is presumably associated with the chelating tendency
of these materials. This is indicated by the observation,
during enrichment experiments, that the addition of chelating
agents to sea water cultures can be as effective as adding
chelated metals. In some instances, however, addition of
chelating agents can cause "good" waters for phytoplankton to
become poor - possibly because of the high total concentration
of trace metals in these samples. The mechanism of incorporation of chelated metals in the cell is unknown; probably, the
metal ion, not the entire metal-chelator compound, passes
through the cell wall.

Iron. The problems of interpreting the roles of chelating
agents in growth stimulation by trace metals are magnified in
the case of iron. Iron-EDTA combinations at a pH of 8 seem to
stimulate growth of various phytoplankton, including G. breve.
What species are involved? Is the EDTA complex involved or
does it serve to assist the photodecomposition to the hydroxide. For a given microorganism, the chelating agent may be
unnecessary. At least one diatom (Asterionella japonica) seems

to utilize only particulate iron.[12] Is the particulate iron

serving as a stimulant and/or does it serve as an active sur-

face on which other growth-stimulating trace elements have been

adsorbed? The importance of iron in haemitin compounds of the

photosynthesis and oxidase systems is unquestioned, but the

specific iron compounds and the mechanisms of incorporation

are unknown.

Manganese. The concentration of manganous ion in river and

lake has been used as an index of fertility of the surrounding

land by Harvey (cf. Strickland[1]). The true ecological signifi-

cance of this element in the marine environment is unknown.

Probably, the "availability" of manganese (as perhaps in a

chelated form) rather than the total amount of manganese

would limit the growth of some phytoplankters. The main

function of manganese is as a co-factor in the oxygen-evolution

step of photosynthesis and maybe in the reduction step as well.

Other trace metal elements. Zinc, molybdenum, copper, vana-

dium, and cobalt may be essential for plant growth because they

act as co-factors for enzymes, but there seems little evidence

that the concentration of these elements limits photosynthesis

in the marine ecosystem. Some qualification is necessary be-

cause cobalt containing vitamin B_{12} (and related cobalamins)

are required by many species of marine algae. This may have

ecological significance or it may not because different strains

of diatoms of the same species may not require vitamins at all
or may require different vitamins.

9.7 Photosynthetic Rate Measurements[1,2]

The rate of photosynthesis is determined by measuring
changes that occur during the process of photosynthesis or
respiration. As indicated (Eqn. 9-1), changes in oxygen and
carbon dioxide concentrations will occur. Moreover, the changes
in certain nutrient concentrations will occur during photosynthesis. By measuring any of these changes, in theory, it
should be possible to determine the rate of photosynthesis. In
practice, however, photosynthetic rates have been measured in
three ways, mainly two. They can be measured by changes of
nutrient concentration, though this method has received comparatively little attention. Historically, the more common
approach has been to measure changes of dissolved oxygen concentration: the so-called light and dark bottle method of
Gran and others was used commonly during 1930-1955. The
changes in carbonate concentration typically are too small for
convenient measurements, but the use of radioactive carbon as
carbonate permits measurement of uptake of carbon dioxide by
phytoplankton with adequate sensitivity. The carbon-14 technique has made it possible to measure photosynthesis in oligotrophic tropical oceans.[4] This is probably the method of

choice. Unfortunately, some doubts exist as to the interpretation of measurements by this method, as we shall see in the
following discussion in which the various methods are compared.

Changes in Nutrient Concentrations. Changes in the
concentrations of nutrient salts as a means of measuring primary products have probably been used little outside of the
English Channel.[3] Basic work in the early 1920's involved
estimation of the loss of phosphate under a 1-meter square of
surface or changes in oxygen compared with changes in nitrate
concentrations. More recently, this has been studied in the
northern part of the North Sea. Here, the loss of phosphate
in the photic zone during the productive season has been measured and correction made for the regeneration of phosphate.
The correction involves an assumption that the regeneration
rate in the photic layer is the same as in waters below the
thermocline or below the photic layer where there is no uptake of phosphorus. Apparently, it is possible to obtain an
order-of-magnitude value for minimum production in a given
area of the sea. Very few concurrent measurements with the
carbon-14 technique indicate the fair agreement of this
technique with the nutrient change technique.

Oxygen Changes. The "light bottle, dark bottle" method
measures organic production in the sea in terms of changes in
oxygen concentration. Details of the method are given by
Strickland and Parsons.[13] Briefly, samples of water with the

indigenous microflora are collected from various depths and are carefully placed into BOD bottles. Some bottles are used to determine the concentration of oxygen at the start of the experiment [Winkler technique; (see Vol. 1, Chapt. 24)]. Samples in two different kinds of bottles "light" (ordinary) and "dark" (wrapped in black material, painted, or taped),are lowered to the depths at which the samples were obtained and kept there for some period of time, perhaps up to 24 hours, affixed to a line hanging down from a fixture or anchored buoy. Samples are then returned to the laboratory and the oxygen content is determined. The oxygen content in the black bottles minus that in the initial bottles corresponds to the combined rate of respiration of all the indigenous microflora. The oxygen concentration in the clear bottles minus that in the black bottles corresponds to the rate of photosynthesis by the plankton. Gross photosynthesis is determined by this technique. Net photosynthesis can be measured if it is assumed that the respiration of heterotropes or animals is the same in both light and dark bottles.

The method in principle is simple; in practice several disadvantages and certain experimental difficulties appear. First, all the problems and difficulties of the Winkler technique are ever present in the determination. Secondly, difficulties arise with enclosure of the water sample in bottles for prolonged periods. The plankton may settle and introduce errors (such as difficulty in taking up carbon dioxide). Bacteria may start growing in large quantities, thus introducing doubts as to the validity of the experiment. Thirdly, the in situ method is time consuming, even if experiments lasted from noon to sunset; it may be too expensive to use on major oceanographic vessels. Thus, a simulated in situ method is used in which the experiment is conducted in water of appropriate temperature and appropriate attenuated light (using filters). The major difficulty in this method is that low sensitivity in the field limits its use or makes it unsuitable for open ocean work and limits its application to high production rates, exceeding about 50 mg $C/m^2/day$. Other problems will be considered when all methods are considered together.

Carbon Dioxide Changes. The advantages of measuring changes of carbonate concentration in sea water due to biological activity have been considered (Section 8.4); P_{CO_2} and pH are the measurements that are most useful. It appears, however, that even with sensitive measurements of these parameters, the methods are not applicable to a study of production rates of less than about 250 mg $C/m^3/day$. The difficulty arises because sea water has a fairly high carbonate content and only a small percent of the total carbonate is used up in a day in a given area, even in eutrophic waters.

Carbon-14 Method. This is the only method that is applicable to precise measurements of photosynthetic rates in the ocean

which are in the range 2.5–25 mg C/m^3/day. The general shipboard technique developed by E. Steemann Nielsen has not
changed substantially, though it has been used by many workers
since 1952. The method consists in adding 1–25 µc of $^{14}CO_3^{2-}$
to a few hundred millimeters of sample. After photosynthesis
has occurred for several hours, the phytoplankton is filtered
onto a membrane filter and dried. There is, in effect, a
nominally zero thickness of phytoplankton resting on the top of
the filter; thus, negligible self-absorption occurs and the
radioactivity in the phytoplankton can be determined by end-
window counting. Knowing the count, the efficiency of the
counter, the total radioactivity added, and the total carbonate present, the rate of photosynthesis can be calculated.
The experimental details are given by Strickland and Parsons[13];
detailed discussion has been presented by Strickland[1,2] and
Steemann Nielsen.[3] The pertinent equation is given (Eqn. 9-9).[13]

Radiocarbon-measured photosynthesis:

$$\text{mg } C/m^3/hr = \frac{(R_s - R_b) \times W \times 1.05}{R \times N} \qquad (9-9)$$

Here, R_s and R_b are the corrected counting rates for the sample
and blank (counts per minute), respectively; W is the weight of
carbonate carbon in the water (in mg C/m^3) and is equal to the
carbonate alkalinity x 0.95 x 12,000; R is the counting rate of
the added ^{14}C sample; N is the number of hours the sample was
exposed to light; and 1.05 is an isotope-correction factor.

Problems. Some of the difficulties seem to be evident on the consideration of the available methods. Two major points of interest are the validity and direct comparison of the two methods. A controversy has raged as to whether or not the carbon-14 technique measures growth for photosynthesis because some unlabelled intracellular carbon dioxide might be used for photosynthesis in preference to fresh extracellular labelled material. The unlabelled intracellular material might arise from recently respired material. If the respired carbon dioxide was preferentially and completely assimilated, the carbon-14 technique would measure net photosynthesis; thus the true figure might be somewhere between the net and gross rates. In any case the method should not measure the same fraction of gross photosynthesis for all species. Probably any variations are thought to be relatively unimportant for most field studies. Other difficulties arise because of low carbon-14 rates. Some sources of carbonate in sea water may not come into radial carbon equilibrium,though this has not been verified. Also,not all of the photosynthetically fixed activity would be counted on the filter. For example, ^{14}C-labelled materials formed in early stages of plant photosynthesis might be excreted by plant cells.

Remarkably few direct comparisons seem to have been made between the oxygen method (light and dark bottles) and the carbon-14 technique according to Strickland.[2] When a comparison was made (cf. Ryther[15]) the two methods seemed to give nearly the same result. On the other hand, in instances, the carbon-14 uptake is less than the rate of net photosynthesis, possibly for the reasons considered above.

Measurements of Productivity in the Field. Exact determination in situ daily gross or net production beneath a portion of the sea surface probably has never been achieved and is extremely difficult to achieve for several reasons.

The first problem is perhaps an insurmountable one, sampling difficulties. In a pelagic environment, the amount of plant material varies laterally and with depth. In a practical sense, it is debatable as to whether the concept of an exact productivity is relevant. To make it useful, we must assume that a sample of the water column obtained is truly representative and that no damage is done to the organisms.

The second problem is time. Wide variations in the rate of photosynthesis exist among plankton throughout the day. Some organisms have, for example, a rate in the afternoon which is a fifth of the morning rate. This means that the rates should be conducted for a full 24 hours. On the other hand, some workers have found that in certain circumstances, the yield of a 24-hour experiment may be 20% less than short-term experiments. Possibly, very high light intensities reduce the rate of photosynthesis, and it may take some period of time before this effect diminishes. On the other hand, multi-exposure experiments are usually inpracticable and extrapolation from less than 12 hours of exposure is probably undesirable.

Thirdly, values should be obtained from the uptake of carbon-14. No way is available to estimate the additional respiratory loss during hours of darkness.

A logistic problem arises if large areas are to be surveyed. It is impracticable to measure productivity by these techniques of suspension and incubation must be used with the attendant difficulties.

The final problem: measurements in situ or in incubators may induce physiological disturbances that are not present in the true environment. Phytoplankton cells are ordinarily unconstricted in vertical motion; in contact with containers they are behaving in an unnatural way. The extent of the alteration of values is an unknown quality.

9.8 Geographical Variations in Productivity[14,15]

A detailed summary of the geographical variations is beyond the scope of this book, but it will be possible to summarize some of the major features of this subject. Additional discussion has been given by Ryther[14, 15] and Strickland.[1]

The sea is a desert, relative to moderate production on land. High production rates and high productivity, comparable to those on land, can be observed in specific instances. It should be noted that these can be maintained for only a matter of days and only in a given body of water. For example, if terrestrial plants can sink roots into a media of rich soil, they have sufficient nutrient available to grow at the maximum potential rates for periods of up to many years and forests can be developed. No forests of plankton exist in the sea in a comparable way. Solar energy falling on a square meter of surface could produce an organic yield of 10 grams of carbon per day in excess of the metabolic requirements of plants on land and a cubic meter of sea water could support a crop of no more than about 5 grams of carbon per day.

High levels of marine production can be maintained only by constant replenishing of nutrient-rich waters and these are conditions under which productivity may curiously not be favored.

This paradox arises in the following way: mixing is needed for nutrients to be resupplied to the euphotic layer. This means that turbulent action is required. Turbulence produces vertical mixing which brings nutrients to the surface but at the same time deprives plants of critically needed illumination. The vertical mixing process that carries nutrients to the sur-face also carries plants down. The depth of the wind mixed layer may exceed the photic zone by severalfold. Organisms may thus spend much time in the dark and necessarily productivity for this given water column would decrease.

It may be useful to review the variations of this wind mixing with latitudes. Mixing should be at a minimum at the equator and largely invariant with the season. Mixing should be at a maximum at 60° (N and S) and here most pronounced in the winter in the temperate zone sea water. The importance of storms is open to some debate. Some persons have suggested that gale force winds deepen the mixed layer by about 20 to 30 feet in the Gulf of Mexico,which is a relatively minor effect. On the other hand, gale force winds may be a stimulus to effective mixing in the North Sea, which has typically less stable water. In summary, two factors limit productivity - light and nutrients - though, typically, both are not limiting at the same time.

Three properties of light are of concern (cf. Sect. 1.6): incident radiation, water transparency, and penetration relative to the depth of the wind-mixed layer. Considering the effects of light and recalling the considerations of nutrient variations from previous chapters, it appears that three zones need to be considered.

The first is the tropical zone. This is characterized by high radiation, by exceptionally clear water, and by thermal stability of the water which limits transport of plants out of the euphotic zone. The second and opposite extreme is a zone roughly centered at 60° (N and S). Here, radiation is lower in

the winter, water is more turbid, and mixing is more extensive
(if this is indicated by the amount of isothermal water). In
this latitude, mixing can carry plants to depths that are five
to ten times the depth of the euphotic zones. Plant growth is
inhibited perhaps more than half the year at 60°. The third or
transition zone is centered roughly at 40° (N and S) with
characteristics intermediate between the two extrems (tropical
and 60° latitudes). Here, plant growth is inhibited during the
winter months.

In addition to light and nutrients, two other factors seem
to affect the geographical distribution of productivity. These
are the land-mass effect and grazing. Primary productivity
seems greater near the coasts of continents and islands or submerged ridges and banks than in the open ocean. The phenomenon
does not seem to be related to nutrient increases at the
coast. It seems to be observed at all latitudes. The effect,
in some instances, may be due to an increase in the amount of
standing crop, p (cf. Eqn. 9-4), rather than a change in the
growth constant, k. The value of k would be effected by lights
and nutrients; the complete history of the water mass would
govern the value of p.

For some reason grazing in the open ocean seems to be more
continuous and effective than in the coastal areas. Strickland[1]
compares the relatively poor productivity of tropical oceans to

the poor productivity of fertile but overgrazed pastures. The poor productivity of tropical oceans is analogous to under-fertilized and overfarmed land. Grazing appears responsible for patchiness that is observed in chlorophyll distribution of surface waters. The variation of chlorophyll values can be 50 to 100% in distances,though only a few miles,in waters having comparable hydrographic and nutrient properties, which suggests the local zooplankton flora superimpose grazing patterns on already overgrazed phytoplankton. At present, it is not pos-sible to describe an adequate model of zooplankton-phytoplank-ton interrelationships that will permit precise predictions of the observed productivity in the sea, but certain generaliza-ions can be made about the productivity of major oceana-graphic regions.

Some five regions can be distinguished (Table 9-2). These are tropical, semitropical, temperate, and subpolar, arctic, and antarctic seas. If the relative productivity of tropical seas is taken to be one, the productivity of the semi-tropical is about two, that of temperate and sub-polar waters roughly four, and polar waters would be extremely low in case of Arctic seas, and perhaps a value approaching four in the case of the Antarctic waters. In all of these seas wide vari-ations can be noted in specific instances. A generalized sum-mary of the sea types, the patterns, annual production and production rate is given in Table 9-2.

TABLE 9-2

Geographical Variations of Productivity

Sea Type	Productivity Characteristics	Annual Production	Rate g C/m^2/day
Tropical	Uniform: consistently low, little seasonal variation	36	0.05-0.15
Semitropical (Sargasso Sea)	Exceptional areas: Pacific equatorial, Indian equatorial		ca. 0.50 0.2-0.25
Semitropical (Sargasso Sea)	Moderate, seasonal variation	72	0.89 (max.) 0.1-0.2 (min.)
Temperate, subpolar	High, but wide seasonal variation, low winter, high summer rates; spring max.	120	0.33 (mean) 1.93 (max.) (min.)
Arctic station "Bravo"	Annual production low; summer max.	ca. 1	0.01 (mean) 0.02 (max.)
Antarctic	Higher fertility due to circulation pattern	ca. 100	

This has been a concise summary of the factors affecting the geographical variations of productivity. The chapters that follow the concepts that have been introduced will be applied In Chapter 11, the concept of productivity will be used in considering the food resources of the sea.

9-9 <u>Summary</u>

In comparison with land, the productivity of the sea in many areas is very poor and the sea in many instances can be regarded as a desert with the understanding that even deserts can have a certain measure of fertility and that no area of the sea is without some degree of fertility. Our measurements of the amount of organic carbon produced in the sea per unit time are poor, but it appears the amounts produced are about the same as on land. The land is more than twice as productive as the sea per unit area per unit time, a view that is subject to change. Sea plants fall into two categories, benthic plants and phytoplankton. The former may be of economic value; they are ecologically significant, but relatively unimportant in terms of the total photosynthesis of the sea. Probably more than 99.9% of all synthesis of the sea is carried on by the phytoplankton in five major divisions. The nature of the photosynthetic process has been summarized and terminology concerned with production introduced. The physical factors affecting phytoplankton growth are light, the wavelength, intensity, effects of preconditioning, water transparency, and radiation. The effects of temperature, salinity, and other physical properties have been considered, as have the effects of nutrients (nitrate, phosphate, silicate, and trace metals). It appears that in specific instances silicate, iron, and other trace metals may be growth limiting, as evidenced by enrichment experiments. Methods of measuring photosynthetic rate include measuring changes of nutrient concentration, oxygen, carbon dioxide, and the carbon-14 as carbonate. Of these, the carbon-14 technique is perhaps the most useful and the only one applicable to the precise measurements of photosynthetic rate in the ocean. Finally, the gross aspects of geographical distribution of productivity have been summarized.

NOTES

1. Please see Appendix A for this and other plankton terminology.

2. Prime example is the name _Trichodesmium_, which has been, and probably will be, widely used. Several years ago, Drouet showed that the proper genus name was _Skujaella_. More recently, Drouet[16] demonstrated that only one species is really involved; evidently, much variation occurs in the marine environment. The proper name is _Oscillatoria erythrae_ (Gomont) Drouet. The significance of this organism has been considered (Section 7.3). As a nitrogen fixer, it is able to thrive in waters that have been depleted of combined inorganic nitrogen.

3. Extensive treatments of this subject are available elsewhere.[17-20]

4. Illumination may be expressed as meteorological heat unit = langlies/minute (ly/min) or calories/cm^2/min; as

353

energy units: watts/cm^2 or Joules/sm^2/min; though it is

most commonly expressed as foot-candles or lux.

5. Workers may use different methods to measure light intensities or use different light sources.

6. A pycnocline is a vertical gradient of density.

REFERENCES

1. J. D. H. Strickland in Chemical Oceanography (J. P. Riley and G. Skirrow, eds.), Academic Press, New York, 1965, Chapt. 12.

2. J. D. H. Strickland, Ann. Rev. Microbiology, 19, 127 (1965).

3. E. Steemann Nielsen in The Sea (M. N. Hill, ed.), Vol. 2, Interscience, New York, 1964, Chapt. 7.

4. E. Steemann Nielsen, J. Cons. Explor. Mer., 18, 117 (1952).

5. G. M. Smith in Manual of Phycology (G. M. Smith, ed.), Chronica Botanica Co., Walthan, Mass., 1957, p. 13.

6. P. C. Silva in Physiology and Biochemistry of Algae (R. A. Lewin, ed.), Academic Press, New York, 1962, p. 827.

7. D. F. Martin, Adv. Chem. Ser., 67, (1967).

8. A. Thorhaug, Thesis, Univ. of Miami, January 1969.

9. G. A. Rounsefell and A. Dragovich, Bull. Mar. Sci., 16, 404 (1966).

10. J. H. Ryther and R. R. L. Guillard, Deep-Sea Res., 6, 65 (1959).

11. L. Provasoli in The Sea (M. N. Hill, ed.), Vol. 2, Interscience, New York, 1964, Chapt. 8.

12. E. D. Goldberg, Biol. Bull., 102, 243 (1952).

13. J. D. H. Strickland and T. R. Parsons, A Practical Hand-
    book of Seawater Analysis, Bull. 167, Fish. Res. Bd.
    Canada, Ottawa, 1968, Part V.

14. J. H. Ryther, Science, 166, 72 (1969).

15. J. H. Ryther in The Sea (M. N. Hill, ed.), Vol. 2,
    Interscience, New York, 1964, Chapt. 17.

16. F. Drouet, Revision of the Classification of the Oscilla-
    toriaceae, Monograph 16, Academy of Sciences of
    Philadelphia, 1968.

17. E. I. Rabinowitch, Photosynthesis and Related Processes,
    2 Vols., Interscience, New York, 1945-1956.

18. B. Kok and A. T. Jagendorf eds., Photosynthetic Mechan-
    isms of Green Plants, NAS-NRC, Washington, 1963.

19. M. D. Kamen, Primary Processes in Photosynthesis,
    Academic Press, New York, 1963.

20. R. P. Levine, Sci. Am., December, 1969, p. 58.

RESOURCES OF THE SEA

10.1 Introduction[1,2]

It is one of the more common notions ingrained on our popular culture that the sea is an inexhaustible supply of food, minerals, and nearly everything we would need. As we shall see, this is an incorrect belief and, as such, is a rather insidious view. Also, one tends to look at the enormous amount of materials present in the sea. To break this down into smaller terms, consider a 55-gallon barrel of sea water and assume all of the dissolved materials could be removed in some common form. The following would be obtained: common table salt, 15.25 lb, which would provide enough for the average person for two years; about 0.8 lb of magnesium sulfate, enough in theory to make a small ingot of magnesium weighing about 0.25 lb, and many other materials, including enough bromine to make antiknock scavengers for about ten gallons of gasoline. If one multiplies this 55-gallon unit by all those present in the sea, it is truly impressive. It is also impressive if we consider what is actually obtained from sea water (Table 10-1). At present about five major items are obtained from sea water.

TABLE 10-1

World Production of Chemicals from the Sea[1]

Chemical	Tons per Year	Percent of Total Production
Sodium chloride	35,000,000	29
Bromine	102,000	70
Magnesium metal	106,000	61
Magnesium compounds	609,000	6
Fresh water	142,000,000	59

The amount of materials that we obtain from the sea are impressive and the percentages are impressive also. The annual value of only the commodities listed in Table 10-1 approaches about 400 million dollars. Not only do we obtain much from the sea by extracting it as minerals from sea water, but we also obtain much from on or below the sea floor or from beaches, as indicated in Table 10-2. These materials include petroleum, sulfur, sand, heavy minerals, lighter minerals, gems such as diamonds, precious corals, and even iron and coal. One cannot argue that we have obtained much from the sea. Nevertheless, the notion that the sea is an inexhaustible supply of food and of minerals and almost everything else is a dangerous notion, because the facts speak differently.

TABLE 10-2

Annual World Production of Minerals

Extracted from the Sea Floor[3]

Mineral	Value in Millions of Dollars[a]	
	Total	Offshore[b]
Petroleum	$26,000	$3,900
Sulfur	340	37
Sand and gravel	900	150
	(U.S.)	(U.S.)
Heavy heavy minerals		
gold	1,900	*
tin	460	24
platinum	150	*
Light heavy minerals		
ilmenite	54	*
rutile	16	*
zircon	10	*
monazite	1.8	*
Diamonds	290	4
Precious coral	2	2
Subsurface deposits		
coal	18,500	35
Iron ore	4,300	17

[a]Asterisk indicates less than $500,000 excluding beach sands.
[b]Estimated 1967-1968 range.

First, much of the world's oceans are aquatic deserts in
the sense of being of relatively low productivity, relatively
poor in minerals and plant or animal life.

Secondly, sea water as an ore is relatively low grade and recovery of minerals from sea water is limited to special circumstances, even for major ingredients. Very few land minerals are mined and processed when the value is below five dollars per ton. The value of sea water depends on the ingredients.[1] Sea water is worth about 65¢ a ton as an ore for three components: table salt ($3 per ton), bromine ($460 per ton), and magnesium oxide ($100 per ton). On the other hand, as an ore for critical metals (antimony, bismuth, cadmium, chromium, cobalt, copper, gold, lead, manganese, mercury, molybdenum, nickel, silver, tin, titanium, uranium, and zinc) sea water is worth about 2¢ per 100 tons. The value of these 17 critical metals in a cubic mile of sea water, assuming they could be extracted, is about $940,000 at current values.

Thirdly, it is misleading to consider the phrase "a cubic mile of sea water." The simple phrase does not give much indication of the magnitude of the problems involved. A plant to handle or process this amount of sea water would need to process 2.1 million gallons per minute every minute of the day for an entire year. The extraction of these minerals from sea water is remote, using present technology.

This is rather a pessimistic view. It seems likely that the time will come when by one means or another we will obtain mined minerals from the sea, if not by extraction then by obtaining them from the sea bed. Though extraction of the

17 metals from the sea may be remote, it is a contemporary
problem because it requires relatively unpolluted bodies of
sea water. Locations of unpolluted sea water seem to be more
limited each day. There are other problems of concern,
including legal problems.

Who owns the sea? Who owns the sea floor? We need to
contend with problems of this type. In this chapter and the
next, we shall consider the resources of the sea and some of
the problems in obtaining these resources of the sea. These
problems can be considered in the following sections which deal
with the legal aspects of resources, sea water as an ore body,
and mining the sea floor. The following chapter is concerned
with obtaining food and other products from the sea.

10.2 Legal Aspects [2, 4]

Research in legal problems of the sea has not kept pace
with research in the utilization of the sea, though this gap
should have been closed by the United Nations Conference on the
Law of the Sea. This conference was held in Geneva in the
spring of 1958 when some 88 nations came together to formulate
and codify the law of the sea. The conference adopted four
documents concerned with (1) Convention on the territorial sea
and contiguous zone; (2) Convention on the high seas; (3) Convention on fishing and conservation of living resources on the
high seas; (4) Convention on the continental shelf. The last

document is perhaps of the greatest concern to us because the continental shelf contains the areas best suited for immediate exploitation. At the present, however, there seems to be no clear-cut definition of the outer limits of the shelves or the extent of jurisdiction of coastal nations.

The problem arises because the Convention, which was adopted in 1958 and entered into force on June 10, 1964, defines the term "continental shelf" in an equivocal manner. The continental shelf is the seabed and subsoil of submarine areas adjacent to the coast outside the territorial sea to a 200-m isobath or beyond that limit to where the depth of the superadjacent waters admits the exploitation of natural resources of such areas. There are, in effect, three kinds of continental shelves. They are far from being similar. The first is what one might term a geological continental shelf, a natural one defined by marine geologists, reflecting some association with reality. The second is a jurisdictional continental shelf, which exists on the coasts of certain countries due to governmental proclamation. The third type is a political continental shelf which is of the type defined by the Geneva Convention.

Problems arise in the application of these definitions. The geologist might define the continental shelf as being that area of the ocean floor between the mean low water line and the

sharp change in the ocean floor and the continental slope. By
this definition, little or no continental shelves exist off the
coasts of Chile, Equador, and Peru. On the other hand, these
countries do have continental shelves of the second or jurisdictional type, and have proclaimed sovereignty over the sea,
its bottoms, and resources in and on each to a minimum distance
of 200 marine miles. Obviously problems arise when there are
three definitions. In theory, the problems should have been
minimized by the third definition as provided in the Geneva
Convention. It seems not to be the case, however, and some
legal headaches have arisen because of the imprecision in the
definition. Some problems include the following:

Where is the outer edge? The Convention definition is
based on a depth of 200 m or beyond that limit to some depth
at which exploitation is possible. In effect, what does this
mean? Does this mean the very first 200-m isobath? If there
is a deep-sea irregularity in the sea floor, does this constitute a limit? Does it really preclude a second 200-m isobath in the event there is a trench (Fig. 10-1)? This problem
arises in dealing with areas that are relatively shallow and
separated by deep trenches from the mainland. One example is
the Cortez Bank about 50 miles from San Clemente Island about
100 miles from the mainland of California. The Bank is about
12 feet under water at the shallowest point, but is separated

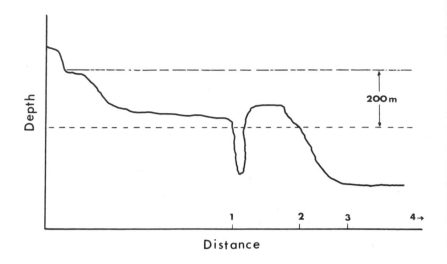

FIG. 10-1

Limits of the continental shelf indicated for a
hypothetical case: 1, first 200-m isobath; 2,
second 200-m isobath; 3 end of continental slope;
4, limit of superadjacent exploitability.

from the island and mainland by ocean floor trenches as deep

as 1000 feet. According to one view, this bank is in an area

of U.S. jurisdiction. Under the act of the Convention, is it?

In what depth of water can oil and other leases be granted?

The problem here is that resources of oil, natural gas, and

sulfur deposits presumably extend inward to a point at which

they are below the 200-m isobath, but it may be convenient to

drill at some depth which is beyond the 200-m isobath. Can leases

be granted under these circumstances? It appears that no

definite answer has been given, and each case will be considered individually upon consultation with appropriate
departments in a coastal nation.

What does the term "exploitation" really mean? Must the
development of the mineral for deposit be commercially profitable? Does the exploitation in small quantities of one
mineral (oil, sulfur, phosphorite) automatically extend the
continental shelf? These problems have not yet been solved
and seemingly are decided as above as individual cases.

What is meant by the term "natural resources"? Here the
Convention defines this term as mineral and other nonliving
resources of the seabed and subsoil along with those living
organisms which at harvestable stage are rather immobile on or
under the seabed or unable to move except in constant physical
contact with the seabed. Natural resources by this definition
are: minerals, hydrocarbons, oysters, scallops, and benthic
seaweed. On the other hand, by the same definition, swimming
fish, shrimp, nonbenthic seaweed, and anything else floating in
the water do not constitute natural resources.

What is meant by the term "superadjacent exploitable area"?
At present, there is no clear-cut definition as to how extensive this area might be except in one special instance, the
division of the continental shelf between two coastal nations
which face each other. The shelf may be divided by the nations
concerned. In the absence of some such agreement, the median

line principle would be applied: the shelf would be divided at
a point halfway between the two nations. This principle applies, however, only when the continental shelf, as defined by
this Convention, lies beween the two nations. It would not
necessarily be justifiably applied to the division of the
entire oceans.

What are the implications with regard to scientific
research? The Continental Shelf Convention provides that the
consent of a coastal state shall be obtained with regard to
any research undertaken on the continental shelf. Normally,
that coastal nation shall not withhold its consent, assuming
the request is submitted by a "qualified institution." It is
presumed that the intention of the institution is to conduct
purely scientific research concerned with the physical or biological characteristics of the shelf. The nation involved
reserves the right to participate or to be represented in that
research and the results shall be published. It is notable
that the restrictions against the coastal nations - interference with research and its implicit consent - apply to those
cases where the results are to be published. But what about a
private company conducting geophysical research on the shelf
for its own information? It appears that the protective
clauses of this Convention would not be applicable. The entire
operation might be subject to the jurisdiction and control of
the coastal nation. How extensive this control jurisdiction

is to be is unclear due to the imprecise definition of the
outer edge of the continental shelf. It also appears that even
for "qualified institutions" there may be problems as to
exactly what types of research can be conducted. For instance,
seismic operations that involve no physical contact can be
conducted, but evidently core drilling cannot normally be
conducted according to the strict interpretation of the Convention. Finally, though it is obvious perhaps that certain
private companies might be excluded on the grounds of non-
publication of the research, what institutions are to be
placed under the category "qualified institutions"? Is it
possible these will be strictly educational institutions, that
there will be no military association, directly or indirectly?
Must the research be wholly financed by the local institution
without any governmental support that might have any military
associations?

These quite obviously are problems that need to be resolved before extensive exploration or exploitation of continental shelves are undertaken by foreign nationals. If
there are problems that are concerned with who has what rights
on the continental shelves, these are relatively well defined
when compared with the legal problems, the rights on the pelagic sea floor. The ability in the contemporary mining industry
for a company or a man to gain exclusive control over a specific
mineral deposit to develop it as seen fit, is a fundamental

aspect of the mining industry. Presently, it seems that any

such controls over mineral deposits in the seabed of the

pelagic environment is most unlikely.

Consider the problem of the mining of manganese nodules

(Section 10.4) that are possibly continuous over thousands of

square miles of the ocean floor. These deposits have been

known for about 100 years and have been explored by many

scientists. The nodules vary considerably in composition from

one location to another on the sea floor. According to Mero,[2]

there are at least 15 characteristics of these deposits that

have a bearing on the economics of mining the deposit, and so

for most efficient mining these fifteen factors will have to

be assessed. For a given location the operation of mining may

be remarkably different in design from that needed for another

location. Before any miner would begin to work the manganese

nodule deposits, he would have a considerable capital invest-

ment, with a considerable amount of time between exploration of

the deposit and the time of working. This miner obviously

would like to have some assurance that he can mine these de-

posits. From what country will he obtain a franchise that will

grant him the right to mine this deposit exclusively, to

warrant the operation?

The only Convention that seems to have any bearing on the

matter is the Convention on Fishing and Conservation of Living

Resources of the High Seas which, among other things, provides for the right of all nations to engage in fishing on the high seas, subject to treaty obligations and the interests and rights of coastal states as described earlier. Such a Convention is clearly contrary to mining tradition and the concept of a mineral position, but it does raise the question of which nation will grant that franchise. Is Switzerland, for example, to be denied rights to any of the riches from the sea? The application of the Fisheries Convention is viewed by some as being logically applied to the mining operation. Miners, however, have not been the hunters that fishermen have been in the past. It well may be that in the future they shall have to be.

The alternative is to revise the Convention to make it applicable to mining minerals from the sea, to indeed grant franchises. According to one view, this seems most unlikely. Any change in international law covering the franchise would take a minimum of ten years and more likely fifty years.[2] These, then, are some of the implications of the legal problems of the resources of the sea: problems concerning research; problems concerning definition of the continental shelf; and problems concerning who, if anyone, controls the resources of the high seas.

10.3 Mining Sea Water

As Shigley[1] has noted, the ocean is the largest continuous ore body available for exploitation. As an ore body it has

369

some unique features and consequently some unique problems. The unique features include the magnitude of the resources. The total mineral reserve is 50×10^{15} tons or 330,000,000 cubic miles of sea water. The second unusual feature is that this is the only ore body that is being replenished at a rate greater than its consumption, as rivers of the world deliver more dissolved salts than are removed by man each year. Shigley[1] has noted a third unusual feature: extraction plants have the curious distinction of being possibly the only mining operation that has to protect itself against its own raw materials during hurricanes and typhoons. This is one major problem. There are in addition at least five other major problems. These are:

1. Overburden. In land operations, overburden must be removed before mining operations occur. In sea water mining, the overburden is fresh water or water with low salinity at the surface which must be removed before mining. This is removed by a wall in front of the pump intake which in theory holds back the fresh water and favors water of higher salinity from the bottom. Mixing, however, does inevitably occur and the overburden then represents a continuous problem of contamination.

2. Purity. Undiluted uncontaminated sea water along coastal regions is much rarer than one might believe and along the U.S. coastline there appear to be relatively few

areas where undiluted non-polluted sea water can be
obtained. This is indicated in Fig. 10-2, which shows
the variation of offshore salinity along the Gulf Coast
and dramatically indicates the effect fresh water from
the Mississippi River has on salinity for nearly 150
miles of coastline.

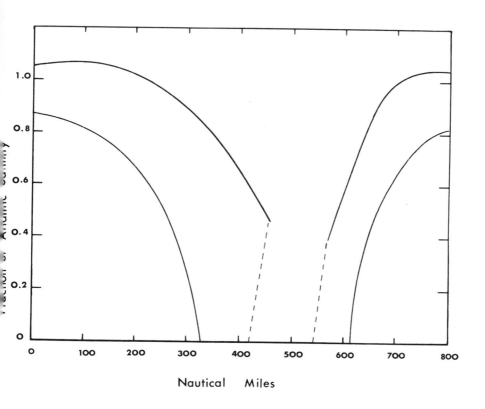

FIG. 10-2

Offshore salinity range as a function of nautical
miles of coastline from Brownsville, Texas to
Pensacola, Florida. (After Shigley.1)

371

3. **Hazards** of storms are obvious problems, but the hazards of creatures and energy are perhaps more subtle problems. Sea water contains creatures that corrode steel, foul and plug intake tubes, and perhaps even attack sea water miners. Energy is a hazard in the problems of waves, tides, and currents which tend to attack any sea water mining structures.

4. **Ore costs** tend to be very low in terms of components that can be extracted from sea water, which, by present technology, require eminently large volumes of water to be processed except perhaps for the five items noted in Table 10-1.

5. **Volume requirements**. The magnitude of the problems of extracting the components from sea water is indicated when we consider the number of cubic miles needed to supply the U.S. annual requirements for certain elements. This assumes 100% recovery (Table 10-3). These numbers (Table 10-3) take on sobering significance when it is noted that each cubic mile of sea water represents about 1.1×10^{12} gallons and when this figure is prepared with the predicted value of world desalination operations. The installed desalination capacity for 1978 is predicted to be 14×10^9 gallons per day or about 0.001 cubic mile of water. In effect, then, no element present in a concentration less than that of bromine can be expected to be extracted from sea water by present technology.

TABLE 10-3

Volumes of Sea Water Required to Supply

U. S. Annual Needs[1]

Elements	Cubic Miles per Year to Supply U.S. Needs
Strontium, magnesium, chlorine sodium, bromine	0.25
Potassium, sulfur	1.5
Boron, iodine	5
Thorium, fluorine	50
All others	100

6. <u>Location</u> is probably of greater importance together with the availability of power or materials than with the availability of unpolluted sea water of high salinity. The development of a large chemical manufacturing complex of which sea water extracting activities are a small part may make the sea water extraction processes more favorable. The source of sea water is probably less critical than one might expect. For example, effluents from sea water desalination would be slightly more valuable as a source of minerals than typical sea water. Typically, desalination plants produce a volume of fresh water roughly equal to the volume of effluent. The concentration of salts in the effluent is roughly twice that

of the original source sea water. Using these effluents, to produce salt, for instance, would not affect harvesting costs, though the area required for evaporation would be reduced 50%. Using them for the production of bromine would leave the cost of all materials roughly the same, though the higher temperature and salinity of the effluent would be beneficial. For production of manganese, the higher salinity of effluent would permit some savings in settling-tank construction, but this is a minor fraction of the equipment needs; the raw materials and power requirements would be essentially unchanged.

The foregoing problems and the evident limitation of the number of substances that can be removed from the sea by extraction may lead to a view of pessimism. They certainly do lead to the question of what new technologies we might expect that would permit compounds other than the major six components to be extracted from sea water. There appear to be three types of processes that might be used. These are: use of specific ion-exchange resins; the recovery of suspended matter in sea water, and the concentration of the specific chemicals by organisms.

Specific ion-exchange resins presumably could be developed which would be selective for some valuable element such as silver or uranium in the presence of large excesses of other ions as would be the case in sea water. Though progress is

being made in this connection there are still major difficulties and the selectivity is far inferior to what would be
needed.

Many elements are present in sea water combined in the
form of suspended particulate matter. Such elements as lead
and iron, as we have noted previously, are present in sea water
as particulate forms. At present, the economics of filtering
these particles is prohibitive. The difficulty of separating
the organisms from the particulate matter is enormous, but
improved separation techniques may be developed in the future.
Since many of these materials seem to be present as colloidal
dispersions and thus carry some electrical charge, it is
possible that an electrostatic process might be used, such as
the analogy to the Cottrell precipitation process which is now
used to recover certain precious trace elements in land
operations. Frothing might also be a useful technique.

The recovery by marine organisms is a technique that is
promising and has been known for some time. As noted earlier
(Section 8.6) marine organisms are capable of concentrating
certain elements in a very dramatic way, sometimes up to one-
millionfold. At first glance, it seems unlikely that we
would raise organisms for the simple and sole process of concentrating certain trace metals. The idea, however, is not
without merit nor is it without precedent. Seaweeds, for
instance, have been used in the past as a source of potassium

and as a source of iodine. The seaweed <u>Laminaria</u> is able to concentrate iodine from sea water by a factor of 100,000, and prior to the discovery of iodine in Chilean deposits most iodine was obtained from seaweed. At one time, seaweed was also used as a source of potassium. Even now, in many localities, particularly those near the sea, seaweed is still used as a fertilizer. If the past is thus a guide to the future, it seems likely that one organism or another may well be used to effect concentration so that the total volume of material to be processed becomes very small.

10.4 <u>Mining the Sea Floor</u>[2,5]

The primary consideration in mining the sea floor is a pragmatic one: is it profitable? At present, there is a great deal of enthusiasm in mining the sea floor and there is an understandable tendency to forget this pragmatic economic consideration applies. A ton of sulfur, a pound of tin, a ton of iron, an ounce of gold all have values that are independent of the origin of these materials or elements. Anything that is mined from the sea must be mined economically in competition with continental resources in the face of improved land mining techniques.

Three major types of mining occur in the sea. Solution mining has already been considered (Section 10.3). The second type is on-bottom mining, which today mainly involves conventional dredging operations for sand, gravel, oyster shells, and tin. The third type of mining involves sub-bottom mining the recovery of minerals from beneath the floor of the ocean. Coal is not always included in this category because it is mined from shafts that are started on land and extend outwards. In some instances, the same is true of tin. Examples of the third type of mining include mining gas, oil, and sulfur. Some examples of this type of mining operation may be considered.

The only contemporary offshore production of sulfur is that to be found off the Louisiana coast where the Gran Isle deposit is being mined by the Freeport Sulphur Company, which uses a modification of the Frasch process. Heated sea water is used instead of fresh water. The water is heated to a temperature of about $180^{\circ}C$ and pumped under pressure into the sulfur deposit where it melts the sulfur; the sulfur is then frothed by compressed air and forced into a pipe which is placed within the pipe that transports the water to the formation. The sulfur deposit is roughly 2000 ft below sea level and the structure on which the mining operation occurs is a steel platform, an artificial island, which cost about $30,000,000, is about one-half mile long, and rises about 60 ft above the Gulf waters. Sulfur is frequently found over salt domes, a fact which suggests that three conditions are required: a shallow dome, a thick cap over it, and the presence of hydro-carbons that would have provided an energy source for species of sulfate-reducing bacteria.[5] Texas and Louisiana have shallow

377

salt domes. Mexico may well have potential offshore salt
domes opposite domes in the Tehuantepec Isthmus area. Offshore
sulfur may be found ultimately in salt domes over the southern
half of the Red Sea, the northern Caspian Sea, the Persian
Gulf, and possibly off Australia's northwest shelf and Africa's
west coast.

Mining offshore resources of sulfur is economically
feasible because of the rapidly growing shortage of immediately available sulfur. The shortage is such that since 1962
sulfur supplies have been withdrawn from inventories and in
turn these have declined where they contain at times perhaps
a three-month supply. Because of the shortage of sulfur,
higher prices are stimulating development of various sources
of production, including offshore production. About 50% of
the increased use of sulfur is in the production of phosphate
and fertilizers.

An explosive increase of interest in seeking petroleum
offshore has occurred during the past few years, primarily as
a result of repeated success in exploratory work. At present,
20 countries are producing or are ready to produce subsurface oil and gas. Hundreds of companies of various sizes
are exploring the continental shelves of about 70 countries.
The ever-increasing exploratory effort is occasioned because
of the success of the past. The volume of the offshore oil
reserves presently is about 85 million barrels, about 20% of

the world total reserves. The proved world oil reserves, 425

million barrels, represents a 33-year supply at current pro-

duction rates, which may seem adequate, but it is estimated

that in two decades, the world consumption of oil will be

nearly four times that of today. The use of petroleum gas

will increase perhaps five times in the same period. Estimated

ultimate world potentials, and these are only estimates, are in-

dicated in Table 10-4.

The data in Table 10-4 indicate potentials of offshore oil

reserves, relative to land reserves, on the basis of reasonable

estimates and raise the question of the problems of land versus

marine operations.

Weeks[5] has compared land and marine operations and the

major features may be summarized as follows: The total costs

TABLE 10-4

Estimated Ultimate World Potentials[5]

Class of Source	Offshore	Land[a]
Petroleum liquids	700	1,500
Petroleum gas	350	800
Secondary oil recovery	350	1,000
Heavy oil sand	200	700

[a] Millions of barrels of oil.

379

for land operations are less than for offshore operations;
the offshore costs are generally higher with respect to producing operations, rather than mining operations. Geological
and geophysical costs involved in the mining operations are
significantly lower offshore, relative to the land operations.
Drilling rates in the offshore formations of the offshore
basins are the highest. In addition, platforms for producing
operations in 200-400 ft of water may cost between two and four
million dollars. These same platforms, however, also provide
a base for drilling as many as 10 to 24 productive wells, and
total construction and handling costs may be spread over large
volumes.

With these facts in mind, it might seem that offshore
costs would be prohibitive. The factor that makes offshore
mining economically feasible and profitable is that marine
sediments tend to be more prolific and the offshore success
ratio is greater. Most of the world's offshore oil and gas
reservoirs are and probably will be found in relatively young
sediments of the Mesozoic-Tertiary age which have a record of
greater average yield on a per well, per acre, or per discovery basis than the older paleozoic sediments. An example
of the high offshore success ratio is to be found in Nigeria.
Here the wildcat success was about 17 discoveries out of 20
wildcat operations, as compared with the moderate success

found on the land portion of the east Africa basin. Also, the record of success is remarkable in Lake Maracaibo, Venezuela. Here most of the oil and greater average yields per well or per acre have been obtained offshore during the past 40 years. Finally, in Australia's Bass Strait, a major discovery was made in the first well drilled in the continent's off shore. During the preceding 40 years, 140 dry holes were drilled on the land portion of the same basins.

At present, some of the major problems have not been solved. These include the problems of pollution, which have attracted widespread attention, and problems of ownership of offshore resources, which have been discussed earlier (Section 10.2). The importance of these problems will be magnified in years to come as we exploit more offshore resources or subsea floor developments.

Methods

Mining the ocean bottom will be essentially a dredging operation in the future. Four types of dredges are or will be in operation. These are: the ladder bucket dredge, the surface pump hydraulic dredge, the wire line dredge and the air-lift hydraulic dredge. The economic working depths, the advantages, and limitations of each are compared in both Table 10-4 and Fig. 10-3. The ladder bucket dredge consists of an endless chain to which buckets are attached. The chain

TABLE 10-5

Comparison of Types of Dredges for Recovering

Minerals on the Sea Floor

Dredge	Economic Working Capacity, ft	Advantage	Limitation
Ladder bucket dredge	150	Great digging ability, low horsepower per unit of solids, continuous operation	Depth, use to near shore
Surface pump hydraulic dredge	200	Great production capacity relative to investment	Depth, use in low-wave current velocity areas
Wire line dredge	500	Flexibility, operation under various conditions	Control
Air-lift hydraulic dredge	1000	Extreme simplicity	Compressed air vs depth cost

is drawn around the periphery of the ladder. It is a continuous process with the serious disadvantage that it is impractical to use in offshore dredging where wave motion and strong currents could cause damage to the mechanism resting on the seabed. Wire methods and the air-lift hydraulic dredge seem to be well suited to working areas of high-current velocities or areas with high ocean waves. Probably, the air-lift dredge will be one of the most featured deep-seabed mining operations; the serious limitation is the cost of

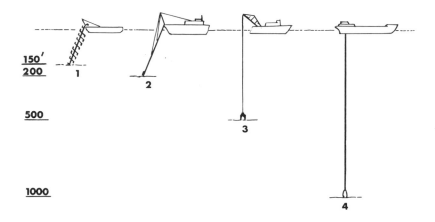

FIG. 10-3

Dredge types and economical operating depths:
1, ladder bucket type; 2, surface pump hydraulic
dredge; 3, wire line type type; 4, air-lift
hydraulic dredge.   (After Mero.[2])

supplying compressed air, which increases exponentially with

the depth of dredging.

Minerals[2,6]

This brings us to the question of what materials are and

will be mined on the sea floor. Some of the most important

items from the standpoint of the tonnage mined will be sand

and gravel. For example, in the United States alone, over 500

million tons of sand and gravel are produced annually. Much

of this is sold at prices of less than one dollar per ton. Over

90% is used in construction and, of necessity, is limited to

local or regional markets. Many beaches have been mined now
and there is more extensive use of seabeds. In addition, such
items as monazite sands, tin, gold, phosphorite deposits,
Red Sea deposits, and manganese nodules are likely to be exploited in the future. These are considered in the following:

Monazite is a phosphate mineral with the general formula
(Ce, La, Y, Th)(PO$_4$). Major production areas of monazite are
found in placer deposits of Florida, South Carolina, Idaho,
India, Brazil, and Union of South Africa. Recently, monazite
sand processing plants were established in southern Australia
to process sands from heavy mineral placers on the coast and
maybe in offshore sands. Here, monazite sands have been sold
for about $170.00 per ton, but the rare earth minerals which
can be extracted from these sands should sell for $1,400.00
per ton.

Exploration and exploitation of the _tin_ minerals are
occurring in four major offshore sites - Indonesia, Malaysia,
Thailand, and Cornwall, England. Many sites of tin deposits
represent the placer deposits of drowned river valleys.
These deposits arise from the series of the following events.
At some time in the recent geological past, the ocean level
was lowered perhaps several hundred feet. During this time,
rivers flowed over considerable areas of what is presently the
ocean floor. Placer deposits probably formed along the beds
of these rivers. When the ice cap melted and sea levels rose

to their present levels, the river valleys became submerged
and filled in with sediments. Such river valleys extend as
much as 300 miles seaward from present shorelines.

Placer deposits of drowned river valleys may also be
promising sources of gold according to recent studies. The
gold-bearing beaches have yielded five million ounces of gold
and currently there is exploration on the submerged beaches
and stream channels off the coast of Cape Nome. In addition,
deposits have been discovered off the coast of Oregon, where
concentrations of gold range from 5 parts per billion to perhaps 150 parts per billion with the grain size of gold 40 to
250 microns in diameter. The gold is associated with heavy
mineral sands which may be former beach placers formed during
an earlier age. The gold content is low, but a higher grade
material may be present at a lower depth.

If the exploration work is any indication, it appears that
experienced mining people regard offshore phosphorite as more
of a mineral curiosity than a possible source of phosphorus for
the future.[7] Based on projected needs, the world capacity of
phosphate by 1975 must be nearly twice that of the 1965 demand.
On the other hand, no new major phosphate projects seem to be
developing with more geographical advantages than the present
sources. According to Overall,[7] economic exploitation of offshore phosphorite deposits may become a reality much sooner
than many expect. Unless present producers, such as those in

Florida, recognize this as the threat it is, they could lose sizable markets in Japan, Mexico, Malaysia, and emerging countries.

There appear to be two or three areas in the world where an offshore mining operation might be considered on the basis of the extensive exploration.[7] The first location is the 40-mile bank of San Diego, California, which apparently has a phosphorite concentration of five million short tons. The second location is the Santo Domingo Bay, Baja California, where the phosphorite deposit exceeds 70 million metric tons of 28% rock. A third area, some 75-80 square miles off the 25-mile stretch of shoreline near Savannah, is scheduled to be leased, and may be exploited. The deposits are lower grade than deposits onshore in Florida and North Carolina and contain 70 and 120 ft of overburden which would have to be dredged to get at the deposits.

Red Sea Deposits[8,9]

One of the more interesting and exciting discoveries of recent date has been the discovery of four undersea "pools" of hot, high specific-gravity brines in Red Sea deeps. At least four "hot spots" have been discovered. These are named after the oceanographic vessels that discovered them and have been termed the Discovery Deep (1964), Atlantis II Deep (1965), Chain Deep (1966), and Oceanographer Deep (1967). The first three are located in an area about 10 x 10 miles, roughly in the center of the Red Sea west of Mecca. The fourth is about 340 miles north of the first three discoveries near the entrance to the Gulf of Aquaba.

The deposits have several interesting features. All are hot-brine deposits associated with heavy metal deposits. The water in all four deeps is highly saline and contains about 8 to 10 times as much salt as is commonly found in the ocean. The waters are reducing, contain little or no dissolved oxygen and are typically acidic with the pH as low as 4. The temperature of the Atlantis Deep is $56^{\circ}C$ and the salinity is about $260^{\circ}/oo$. It has been estimated that the Atlantis II Deep alone contains 1.5 million dollars worth of gold, copper, zinc, and silver in 10 meters of sediment. The dollar value of iron and manganese has not been considered in this figure, and probably it is a conservative figure. Even so, this conservative figure would exceed the total mined ore of the Coeur d'Alene district in Idaho since the initiation of mining in the 1870's. In addition to the potential value of the sediment, another interesting ore body, as it were, would be the brine pool associated with each deep. This is indicated by the data (Table 10-6) comparing this ore body with others.

The economic potential of the Red Sea deposits is clearly recognized, as are the legal problems.[6] The first three deeps appear to be clearly in international waters, about 50 miles from the coastlines of Saudi Arabia and Sudan. In February

TABLE 10-6[8,10]

Chemical Composition of the Selected Waters[a]

Element	Normal Sea water	Red Sea Atlantis Deep	Geothermal Brine Well (Imperial Valley, Calif.)
Specific gravity	1.027	1.196	1.264
Na	10.80	105.0	64.0
K	0.39	3.61	32.00
Mg	1.30	0.95	0.92
Ca	0.411	6.44	51.00
Cl	19.50	195	234
Fe	1×10^{-6}	0.070	4.0
Mn	1×10^{-6}	0.086	2.5
Zn	5×10^{-6}	0.003	1.23
Cu	2×10^{-6}	0.001	0.013

[a]Units, grams/liter at 20°C.

1968, Crawford Marine Specialists, Inc., San Francisco, petitioned the United Nations for an exclusive three-year exploration lease, including a renewable option. This lease would cover a 39-square-mile tract in order to explore area deposits. In July, 1968, Red Sea Enterprises, an international consortium lay claim to the deposits through an announcement in the London Daily Express, and an area of some 270 square miles roughly opposite Port Sudan was designated as the holdings. The justification for this procedure was that there was no governmental

body with authority to grant leases for the areas involved.
This issue is not likely to be resolved soon, but is likely to
be a recurring problem. The Red Sea "hot deep" area is
probably not the only one in the world producing the hot-brine
phenomena. Grice[8] has suggested that other likely areas might
include the Gulf of Aden, the Gulf of Aquaba (as indicated by
the finding of the Oceanographer Deep), and the Gulf of
California.

Manganese Nodules

Manganese and iron oxides or ferromanganese minerals occur
as coatings on exposed rocks as slabs or nodules, and as
micronodules in a variety of physical forms and sizes. These
relatively high rates of supply would be accompanied by a high
surface and a relatively rapid accumulation. A second process
of accumulation seems to be operating in those areas where
there is a low rate of iron oxide deposition. In bottom waters
with high dissolved-oxygen concentration, some surface other
than ferrous oxide may provide the site of oxidation of manganese, and then accretion would occur.

The rates of accumulation are not uniform nor continuous,
nor are they rapid. The measured rates seem to be between 0.n
and 0.0n $mm/10^3$ years. If this rate is correct, it would mean
that a 4-cm-diameter nodule would have required about 800,000
years to form, if the rate is 0.1 mm per 10^3 years. This
assumes that the rate is relatively uniform and that accretion

is occurring typically over one-half of the surface area of the nodule at a given time. On the other hand, the sediment most commonly associated with manganese nodules, the red clays, form the slowest of all pelagic sediments and have appearance rates of roughly 0.1 cm per thousand years. If the two rates are correct, it would imply that the red clays should bury the nodules. Evidently, some process maintains the nodules at the surface of their associated sediments.

The ferromanganese minerals have a range of composition; average values are listed in Table 10-7.

TABLE 10-7

Average Composition of Major Constituents of

Ferromanganese Minerals

Constituents	Weight Percentage
MnO_2	31.7
Fe_2O_3	24.3
SiO_2	19.2
Al_2O_3	3.8
$CaCO_3$	4.1
HCl-insoluble	26.8
H_2O	12.0

The data in Table 10-7 do not indicate the maximum and the minimum values, which have been given by Mero.[2] The maximum materials were first discovered on the Challenger Expedition (1873-1876) as black hydrous manganese dioxide materials. They are a form of pelagic sedimentation. They comprise a relatively small volume of the total oceanic sediments, though from an economic standpoint they are probably the most important sediment to be found on the deep-ocean floor. It appears that in some areas they may cover the entire sea floor, almost as a pavement. Deposits of manganese nodules are widespread in the Pacific Ocean. They appear to be less widespread in the Atlantic and Indian Oceans. In the Atlantic Ocean, the major deposit seems to be on the Blake Plateau off the coast of the Carolinas and Florida.

The physical characteristics, the mode of formation, the composition, the distribution, and the mining of ferromanganese minerals have been subjects of much interest and an excellent summary has been provided by Mero.[2] Some points of interest follow.

The significant physical characteristics are size, shape, color, and density. The ferromanganese minerals are found as grains (0.5 mm in diameter), which comprise a major component of red clays, as organic oozes, as coatings (up to 10-15cm thick) on exposed rocks, and as nodules. The nodules may be slablike or spherical and often have nuclei. The nucleus may be a carbonate, phosphate, zeolite, clay, some form of silica, or almost any hard object. There is a range of sizes 0.5–25 cm in diameter; those without nuclei tend to average about 3 cm in diameter, though this may be a function of the equipment used for dredging. Typically, the ferromanganese materials are earth-black or blue-black; those with high iron content tend to be reddish brown. Most are dull in appearance, but some (particularly those from the Blake Plateau) have a vitreous lustre. The density is about 2.5 g/cm^3; the range is 2.7 to 3.7. One of the largest nodules ever recovered weighed 850 kg.

The formation of ferromanganese minerals presents a remarkable process of concentration. Iron and manganese are present in a concentration of about $10^{-7}\underline{M}$ in sea water and are concentrated to 15–19% in the minerals. A crucial aspect of the process is the oxidation of manganese. Most of the manganese in the minerals is present as the tetravalent form, though an estimated 90% of manganese in sea water is present as divalent manganese. A general oxidation process has been proposed by Goldberg and Arrhenius[11] (Eqn. 10-1). Another

$$Mn + 2OH^- + 1/2\ O_2 \rightarrow MnO_2 + H_2O \qquad (10\text{-}1)$$

critical aspect is the evident need for a reaction site.

Two accumulation processes seem to be involved. The first involves a surface or reaction site of ferric oxide on which

manganese is deposited and oxidized. The amount deposited
depends upon the rate of supply of ferric oxide. The maximum
and minimum values for MnO_2, for instance, are 63.2 and 11.4
respectively, and the corresponding values for Fe_2O_3 are 42.0
and 6.5. Moreover, there is an enrichment of minor elements
in the ferromanganese minerals - vanadium, for example, tends
to be concentrated in these materials by a factor of up to
10 times that found in the deep-sea sediments.

Moreover, certain ferromanganese minerals tend to have
relatively high concentrations of nickel and copper, and still
others have relatively high concentrations of cobalt. The
high concentration of the three metal elements would be a
weight percentage of about 1% on a detrital mineral-free basis.
For manganese, a high concentration would be one in excess of
40% by weight, and a high concentration of iron would be one
for which the manganese-iron ratio was less than the unity by
Mero's definition.[2] The ferromanganese minerals vary in the
composition of the nickel, copper, and cobalt. These variations have been related to the specific regions in which
minerals are found.

Mero,[2] for instance, has recognized four regional variations in the composition of Pacific manganese nodules. The
"A" regions are characterized by high iron concentrations and
tend to lie along the continents, generally with notably
few exceptions. The "B" regions characterized by a high

manganese to iron ratio or a high manganese concentration, are found in roughly two areas in and near the Gulf of California and southern regions centered in latitudes 10° and 30° off the western coast of South America. "C" regions are characterized by high nickel and copper concentrations and are found in those parts of the Pacific Ocean that are farthest removed from land, either continent or island. Finally, the Mero "D"region, characterized by high cobalt concentrations, tends to be found centered on topographical highs in the central Pacific. Actual analyses have been summarized by Mero.[2] The tonnage estimates of nodules in the southwestern Pacific basin are roughly 10^{11} tons of nodules in a 10^{7}-km^{2} area or 17×10^{11} tons for 17×10^{7} km^{2} for the whole Pacific Ocean.[2] Other estimates, however, have been obtained that are about 1/20 of this value.[2]

The percentage of the nodules in the Pacific Ocean that may be economical to find is difficult to assess. Even if only 1/10 of one percent of the nodules in the Pacific Ocean were economical to mine, the reserve of metals in these nodules would be measured in terms of thousands of years at the present rates of utilization.

The ferromanganese minerals are probably the most promising of the exploitable seabed minerals, assuming three problems can be solved. First, economical methods of lifting

the minerals from the sea floor must be devised; probably some
form of hydraulic air-lift dredging will be used, though other
methods (including submarine tractors) have been proposed.[2,12]
Secondly, methods must be devised to process the minerals com-
petitively with land-based sources. Finally, legal problems
may not arise until a successful exploitation is under way, but
such problems will have to be solved. It seems likely that
serious exploratory operations will be undertaken during the
next five years. Ultimately all problems will be solved to
some extent, and mining of the nodules will be a commercial
success by 1980-1985.

10.5 Summary

Some of the mineral resources of the sea have been considered. Solving the legal problems of mineral position in
the marine ecosystem may be one of the major obstacles to ex-
ploiting these resources. Three types of mining are involved.
Solution mining is an extraction process. The details of
extracting salt, bromine, and magnesium from the sea have
been considered by Shigley,[1] and Mero.[2] Bottom mining is
mainly limited at present to mining sand and gravel, gold, and
tin. Sub bottom mining has attractive advantages for obtaining oil, gas, sulfur and, maybe, phosphorite. In the future,
hot-brine deposits and manganese nodules probably will be mined.

REFERENCES

1. C. M. Shigley, Ocean Industry, November 1968, pp. 43-46.

2. J. L. Mero, The Mineral Resources of the Sea, Elsevier, Amsterdam, 1964.

3. Chem. and Eng. News, May 26, 1969, p. 15.

4. D. S. Browning, Ocean Industry, Feb. 1968, p. 52.

5. L. G. Weeks, Ocean Industry, June 1968, p. 43.

6. Anon., Ocean Industry, November 1964, p. 43.

7. M. P. Overall, Ocean Industry, November 1968, p. 51, and other papers in the series.

8. C. F. Grice, Ocean Industry, March 1968, p. 52.

9. E. T. Degens and D. A. Ross, eds., Hot Brines and Recent Heavy Metal Deposits in the Red Sea, Springer-Verlag, New York, 1969; E. T. Degens and D. A. Ross, Sci. Am., April 1970, pp. 24-42.

10. A. R. Miller, C. D. Densmore, E. T. Degens, J. C. Hathaway, F. T. Manheim, P. F. McFarlin, R. Pocklington, and A. Jokela, Geochim. Cosmochim. Acta, 30, 341 (1966).

11. E. D. Goldberg and G. Arrhenius, Geochim. Cosmochim. Acta, 26, 417 (1958).

12. J. B. Herbich, Ocean Industry, January 1969, p. 48.

FOOD FROM THE SEA

11.1 Introduction

The previous chapter considered mineral resources of the sea. This chapter will be concerned with the organism and the natural product resources of the sea. The importance and magnitude of these resources may be overlooked, but a proper perspective may be gained by considering a few significant facts. About 80% of the species of animals are to be found in the sea, some species exclusively so. About 40,000 species of molluscs, about as many Crustacea, and perhaps 20,000 species of marine fishes, as well as the largest animals and the largest plants, are found in the sea. The only source of food for mankind is agriculture and fisheries or what might be termed aquaculture. The latter has been overlooked in view of the importance of agriculture, yet the products of fisheries are nearly indispensable. Not long ago, the fishery products constituted less than 3% of the world's food supply,[1] though in countries such as Norway and Japan such products represented a much more important food factor, up to perhaps 10%. The value in terms of the world's protein supply might be somewhat higher, about 5%.

The variety of products obtained from the sea or potentially obtainable from the sea is almost unbelievable. Some
six or seven groups of products might be noted. First,
obviously, the tremendous abundance of species of fish. Obviously, the fishery is used mainly as food for man, though
nonedible or trash fish has been made into oil, fertilizer,
meal, and currently into fish-protein concentrate (FPC). Swim
bladders, at least from certain fish, have been made into
isinglass. Some fish skins and waste materials have been used
for the manufacture of glue. Leather has been obtained from
some kinds of fish, notably shark and a few others, though the
more obvious sources were seal fur and walrus hide. Crustacea
(lobsters, crabs, and shrimp) are widely valued as food products, though 100 years ago the blue crab was nearly unknown as
an edible quantity. Within the last 20 years, frozen shrimp
has become extremely popular in the U.S. and other countries,
resulting in a marked expansion of this industry. Edible
products are more widely used than would normally be believed.
Seaweeds or kelp are utilized as food probably only in
Oriental countries to any extent, though phycocolloids obtained
from macroscopic algae find extensive uses in medicine,
preparation of media for bacterial growth, as dispersing agents,
as well as many other uses (Section 11.4).

In this chapter we shall consider the development of the
sea as a source of food and vegetable matter, and chemicals

obtained from extracts from this material, as well as the sea
as a source of drugs and new products.

11.2 Food from Land and Sea

Interest in aquaculture (husbandry of aquatic animals)
has increased recently because of forecasts that world food
supply in the year 2000 will be seriously deficient in many
regions. In fact, pessimists have warned that wide-scale
famine will occur as populations in many countries increase
more rapidly than agricultural productions. Brown[2] has summarized the world outlook for conventional agriculture and has
noted the possibility that there may be slowdowns near for some
major food crops in some agriculturally advanced countries.
For these areas where per acre yields have been increasing for
some time, some evidence indicates the rate-of-yield increase
is now slowing. In other words, we may be pushing yield levels
past the middle of an S-shaped logistic curve (Fig. 11-1).
Though this cannot be determined with any certainty, it must
be taken into consideration for future planning. If it is indeed a fact, additional pressure will be placed on less-
developed countries to meet future increases in food needs.
Brown[2] concludes that the worldwide demand for food will
continue to be strong in the coming decades because of two
forces: (1) a rapidly growing population; and (2) a rapidly
rising income in much of the world, which results in increases
in demand for food even more intensive than those that have

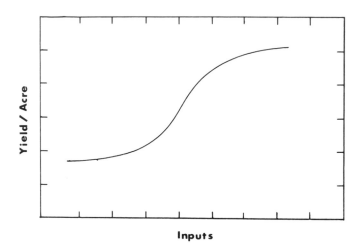

FIG. 11-1

Schematic representation of S-shaped
yield curve.   (After Brown.[2])

occurred in the past.   At present, a conventional agriculture

has assured an adequate food supply for only the economically

advanced one-third of the world and must assure an adequate

food supply for the remaining two-thirds, where the population

is now increasing at the rate of a million persons per week.

These problems can be overcome to an extent by achieving

dramatic gains in land productivity, but this would require

massive investment of capital and, moreover, a widespread

adoption of new technology.   The effectiveness of these changes

may be limited by the fact that we have not been able to bypass

the process of photosynthesis in growing our food. The upper
levels of the S-shaped yield curve (Fig. 11-1) are determined
by the dependence on photosynthesis. A grim limitation to the
effectiveness of conventional agriculture may be approaching
rapidly. For this reason, some persons have considered the
possibilities of aquaculture.

Aquaculture appears to be a particularly promising answer
to the problems of world food supply, as indicated by the
growth of 8% per year in the fish harvest during the last
decade.[3] Presently, the annual world fish harvest is about
53 million metric tons. This value is expected to increase
for some time, though estimates of the possible total sus-
tained yield vary from 120 to 2,000 million metric tons. Just
how optimistic we can be about the possibility of abundant food
from the sea is subject to considerable conjecture because most
extrapolations have been based upon scanty data on primary productivity and upon incomplete information concerning food
relations of many harvested organisms.

There are six major problems which need to be considered.
First, the photosynthetic production in the ocean, which is
after all a limiting factor, is comparable to that on land,
though the area of the ocean is nearly three times that of
land, and great regional variations in productivity exist
in both areas. Second, our present international laws, based on

the concept of freedom of the seas, are probably diametri-
cally opposed to wise use of the seas for aquaculture. Third,
fishermen are probably likely to remain hunters rather than
herders, unless some remarkable change in management practices
occurs. Fourth, fishermen obviously prefer to sell food
fish (fresh fish) rather than so-called trash fish, because
the price is much higher. Currently, however, there is an
increasing tendency to produce fish meal from trash fish or
other fish as potentially an efficient source of inexpensive
protein for human diet. Fifth, we do not now farm the sea
in the efficient way that we farm the land and a considerable
tradition of hunting must be overcome in most areas of the
world. Finally, these areas that would be most suitable for
aquaculture, namely the continental shelves, are precisely the
areas that are the most polluted and, in addition, are subject to local controls that may not necessarily be the most
favorable for aquaculture.

One of the problems, the lack of data, has been considered by Emery and Iselin.[4] They have applied a strict
classification of food resources to both land and sea. These
classifications represent increasing stages of technology:
gathering (on land, berries and nuts; in the sea, seaweed);
farming, where seeds are planted, plants tended, then harvested (on land), i.e.,conventional agriculture; and in the sea,
probably cultivation of algae. For animals, the first stage

is hunting animals for food; the second stage is herding
(selected breeding, culling, controlled slaughter, and non-
destructive utilization of by-products). Applying these
categories strictly, oysters, clams, and fish can be herded,
though not farmed. This in itself, of course, would be an
improvement over the hunting. A comparison of the tonnage
and dollar value on land and sea during 1964 is presented in
Table 11-1.

The data in Table 11-1 suggest some interesting conclusions. The total annual value of food resources taken from
the world ocean is estimated to be about $4,700,000,000 with

TABLE 11-1

Tonnage and Dollar Value of Human Food Produced

from Land and Sea during 1964[4]

| | Tonnage (millions per year) | | | | Dollars (billions per year) | | | |
| | U.S. | | World | | U.S. | | World | |
Activity	Sea	Land	Sea	Land	Sea	Land	Sea	Land
Gathering	.01	2	.02	100	.02	.1	.04	5
Farming	0.0	230	.01	2,000	.0	17	.01	100
Hunting	1.6	1.3	29	27	.3	.6	4.4	11
Herding	.01	85	.6	520	.01	22	.2	120

N.B.: In 1964, U.S. population, 190,000,000; world population,
3,220,000,000.

another $3,600,000,000 for mineral resources. In contrast,
236,000 million dollars of food products and 73,000 million
dollars of mineral resources are obtained from the land.
Based upon the productivity of the sea versus that of the land,
it might be expected that the potential of the ocean would be
236,000 million dollars. If this were the case, the actual
recovery for 1964 would be about 2% of the potential value.

The data in Table 11-1 do not indicate some of the
problems that we face. These problems include problems of
esthetics and tradition: taste, customs, prejudices regarding
food, religious restrictions, and the like. Moreover, can the
ocean supply many more and intensive fisheries? The question
has been raised that maybe overkill has been obtained with
regard to oysters, lobsters, sardines, tuna, whales, abalone,
just as it has for certain animals on land (e.g., elephants,
passenger pigeons, etc.).[4] According to some pessimistic
views, hunting in the ocean has reached a practical limit,
though it seems likely that problems of basic conservatism in
the design of hunting boats and equipment may be overcome, and
efficiency may be increased. If the pessimism is justified,
the only way of increasing food resources of the ocean is by
aquaculture, the cultivation of the plants through farming
and the animals through herding. Two areas, then, need to be
considered: husbandry of aquatic animals and cultivation of
plants in the sea.

11.3 Husbandry of Aquatic Animals[3-5]

There are several general features of the husbandry of
aquatic animals. First, it is more like herding than hunting.
Secondly, it does resemble agriculture inasmuch as it relies
upon some ownership or at least some rights in areas of production, in ponds or in sections of bays or other large bodies
of water. Thirdly, it is currently practiced mainly in fresh
or brackish waters. Some efforts are being made to extend the
practice to the ocean, but mariculture is, however, still in
its infancy. Finally, as now practiced in the western world
at least, aquaculture produces primarily what can be called
luxury foods. These products (trout, oysters, shrimp) bring
good returns because they are luxuries. In developing
countries, raised fish bring good returns because animal protein is generally scarce. Luxury foods, however, become
necessities when they can be mass produced. A typical example is the broiler-chicken industry in the United States
and western Europe.[3]

The organisms now prominent in aquaculture include bi-
valve molluscs, mainly oysters of the genera Ostrea and
Crassostrea, shrimp, and a limited number of fish species.
The last includes carp (Cyprinus carpio), trout (especially
rainbow trout), salmon, southeast Asian milkfish, mullets, and
the yellow tailed fish in Japan. Some culturing of marine
fishes is being attempted in Great Britain with plaice and

sole; in the Unites States with pompano, Pacific sardine, and extensively with mackerel; in Japan with pelagic fishes. The extent of aquaculture is about two million metric tons (mainly fish); mainland China alone reports an annual production of 1.5 million metric tons of carp and related fish.[3] The two million metric tons represent about 4% of the total world catch, though this is obtained from much less than 1% of the world's waters.

Bardach[3] has indicated the characteristics aquatic animals should have to be productive for husbandry. First, the animal should reproduce in captivity or semiconfinement. Secondly, the larvae and/or eggs should be hardy and capable of being raised (and/or hatched) in a controlled environment. Thirdly, young larvae should be able to take extraneous feeds from early stages or should have food habits that can be satisfied by processes designed to increase natural foods. Finally, the animals should gain weight rapidly and nourish themselves either entirely or mainly from available or cheaply supplied food.

Very few, if any, aquatic animals have all of these desirable characteristics, and the development of aquaculture or mariculture will depend upon overcoming four major problems: (1) selective breeding; (2) raising aquatic larvae; (3) full use of the water column; (4) feeding operations. Bardach[3] has

considered these problems and summarized them in some detail;
some aspects are reviewed here.

Relative to the breeding of terrestrial animals, the
selective breeding of aquatic animals has received comparatively little attention. The first text on fish culture was
written by Fan Li in 475 B.C. in China, but only two aquatic
animals have been subjected to extensive genetic control: carp
and several species of trout. The limited selective breeding
is the result of peculiar problems of aquatic animals.
Isolation of the pairs of animals may be difficult because of
the spawning habits. Usually only one mating occurs per year.
Many different-sized animals of the same age may be found
together because of the overriding influence of the environment on the growth of many aquatic animals. Moreover, many
require specialized environmental or even social conditions
for mating and reproduction.

Some advantages of breeding fishes may be noted. The
fishes may be treated with pituitary hormones (hypophyzation)
to induce spawning. Also, mass offspring of the breeding
fishes assists a mass selection of desirable specimens.
Finally, the ease with which many species hybridize is an
advantage. An example is the hybridization of steelhead or
sea-going rainbow trout. Hybrid, hatchery-fed rainbow trout
at the University of Washington School of Fisheries (Seattle)

have grown to nearly three times the length of the typical trout as a result of over thirty years of selective breeding.

The raising of aquatic larvae has many peculiar problems. The dangers of bacterial infection must be controlled by ultraviolet radiation of the water. Tanks are constructed without corners to minimize problems of encountering solid objects. Temperature, salinity, and pH must be controlled. Even the size of the food offering must be controlled as in the instance of raising plaice and sole larvae in captivity experiments in Britain. The quantities of food required can be enormous; plaice larvae, before settling, consume 200 brine shrimp nauplii per day. Certain larvae have very limited mobility. Sardine larvae, for instance, search in only one cubic centimeter of water per hour, so they require at least four food organisms per hour to replace energy lost in body functions and swimming. This means that if 2000 such larvae were to be raised in 500 gallons of water, about 8700 food organisms would need to be supplied during a 12-hour day.

The logistical problems are complex and have been solved in interesting ways. For example, a high-wattage underwater lamp connected to a submersible water pump is used to attract copepods from large distances to the pumps, where the copepods are sucked up with water transported to the surface. Water enriched with copepods is passed through a series of filters which concentrate the food organisms and the appropriate

filtrate is pumped to a storage tank. A series of filters re-
moves organisms larger than a certain desired size. Also,
good larvae growth has been achieved in some instances with
nonliving substitute food such as corn flour. It is hoped
that this type of substitution will be feasible in more instances.

Effective and economical aquaculture should utilize the
entire water column, if possible, and utilize it in all
dimensions. There are at least three examples where this
method has been successful.

One example is based on the food habits of several species.
In China and other Asian countries, ponds are stocked with
common carp, grass carp, silver carp, and bighead carp.
The first is a bottom feeder. The second and third feed on
plants (even banana leaves), bean meal, and rice bran from
external supplies. The last species uses the plankton in the
fertilized ponds.

The second example is the cultivation of oysters, particularly as practiced in Japan. Here, seed oysters collect on
scallop shells which are suspended on wires hung from bamboo
framework that rests on the bottom. At appropriate times,
the oyster sprat are collected and about 200 sprat per shell
are typically obtained. The shells are cleaned, culled, and
restrung on heavier wires and suspended from bamboo rafts.
The technique not only uses the water column efficiently, but

protects the oyster from many predators (starfish, oyster drills). This is a highly intensive and efficient method of operation. The harvest amounts to about 20 metric tons per hectare (but only 1/4 of the area covered by rafts). The average harvest is about 5 metric tons of shucked oyster meat per hectare of well-managed leased oyster grounds in the U. S.

The third example is the cultivation of mussels using hanging culture in the bays of Galicia (Spain). A peak of 300 metric tons per hectare is obtained here. In contrast, the minimally managed common-property resource technique in the U. S. yields 0.001 metric ton or less per hectare.

Fertilization of bays, fjords, or enclosures should lead to favorable cost-benefits ratios in aquaculture, based on the experience with fresh or brackish ponds. Some sewage ponds, notably those in Munich, have been used to produce carp, though the chief disadvantage of the method (large tracts of land) may make it obsolete as land values rise. It may be that sewage can be used effectively in the bays or other en-closures. Finally, thermal pollution, which seems to be a threat, may be used to advantage in maintaining the temperature of enclosures at desirable values. Martino and Marchello[6] have quantitatively evaluated the possibility of using industrial waste heat for convectively pumping up nutrient-rich deep water for fish-farming applications. Thermal-nutrient pumping uses the natural convective flow that arises from buoyancy forces.

Nutrient-rich water from the sea floor is carried to the surface through a large vertical pipe. The flow is accomplished
by injecting waste heat-transfer fluid directly into the pipe
so that it mixes with rising water from the ocean floor. The
limiting factor becomes the cost of pipe required to deliver
the heat-exchange water to the nutrient pump.

True mariculture is still in its infancy, though experiments in several locations indicate that it is perfectly
feasible. At present it is difficult to say where or under
what conditions mariculture will become economically solid.
Emery and Iselin[4] point out that most of the projects have been
concerned with laboratory aspects (photosynthesis, plant physiology, biochemistry). Few projects have been concerned with
making direct tests in planting and harvesting in the ocean.
They ask[4] the interesting question, "How well did early man
understand photosynthesis and biochemistry when he improved
and adapted to farming the primitive corn and other wild
plants that he encountered in his gathering stage of
development?"

11.4 Cultivation of Plants

Previous sections were concerned with the hunding or herding of animals. This section is concerned with the utilization of plants of the sea. Most of the productivity of the
sea is associated with microscopic unicellular plants which
cannot be economically used as food by human beings. This is

regrettable because it is quickly apparent from the food pyramid (Fig. 11-2) that farming is much closer to the energy source on the inefficient pyramid than is the hunting of fish. One might expect greater rewards from farming than from hunting. Farming of the ocean or plants has a major obstacle, the problem of harvesting. The cost (in energy units) of harvesting microscopic plants exceeds the value (in energy units) that can be recovered by eating or burning the crop. There are two approaches which may be used: (1) to utilize the microscopic plants in some more economical fashion; or (2) to use other plants.

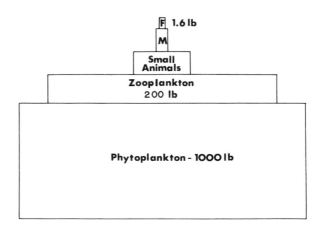

FIG. 11-2

Food pyramid (scale representation). F refers to food fish (large predators); M, medium predators.

Three examples should indicate that microscopic plants can be used, if not directly as food for human beings, at least indirectly. First, microscopic algae have been used as food for oysters and bivalves, and algae of a suitable size and lacking indigestible cellulose cell walls serve well as food for larvae (Section 11.3). Secondly, algae, bacteria, and yeast have been grown on organic waste products. For instance, nutrient-rich effluents from sewage are utilized as food for efficient protein producing plankton.[7] This is particularly significant in certain areas (e.g., Southern California) where recycling or multiple use of water is an economic necessity. The cost of protein produced from waste effluents approaches $0.03 per lb; that from agricultural plant protein $0.10 per pound. High yields of protein are produced by algae (30–50 tons per acre per year) relative to protein yields of conventional agriculture (3–5 tons per acre per year). The third example, the food value of one red tide organism <u>Gonyaulax polyedra</u>, has been demonstrated.[8] The protein content is about 27.5%, and the amino acid distribution is comparable to that of casein, the principal protein of milk. Chicks that feed on a dried red tide diet have growth rates that are similar to those of chicks on a casein diet.[11] These examples indicate the potential use of microscopic plants. The problems of harvesting these remain, though batch operation or a concentration operation, such as used to harvest copepods, may be feasible.

413

The second approach is utilization of macroscopic algae ("seaweeds") as food products. A fair amount of macroscopic algae is harvested from the sea. The amount about a decade ago was thought to be 750,000 tons, with a gross value of $30,000,000 in the western world alone.[9] Present totals are thought to be at least double what they were at that time.[9] The use of some species of microscopic algae as direct sources of food has been known since ancient times. Some 75 different kinds were used regularly as food or as relishes during the 19th century in Hawaii. Classifications of edible microscopic algae are given in Table 11-2. For example, Phorphyra (purple latha) is a red algae that has been harvested for its

TABLE 11-2

Classification of Edible Algae[9]

Type	Example
Green algae	Enteromorpha intestinalis E. flexuosa
Red algae	Asparagopsis sanfordiana Porphyra Dulse (Phodymenia palmata) Irish moss (Chrondrus crispus)
Brown algae	Haliseris plagiogramma Ascophyllum nodosum

food value for centuries. The industry associated with farming
this alga is thought to be over $17,000,000 annually, with an
average annual income per acre of $350, where it is raised in
Tokyo Bay and other places in Japan.

Algae have four major uses: as food, medicines, sources of
algin or alginic acid and related extractives, and as sources of
certain chemicals.

As food, seaweeds (like celery and lettuce) have little
nutrient value, containing as they do a high percentage of indigestible carbohydrates.[9] However, they contain various
vitamins, minerals, and trace elements. For example, the
amount of vitamin C in some brown and red algae is thought to
be comparable or greater than that in a lemon.[9] Thiamine,
niacin, riboflavin, and iodine are also abundant in brown
algae (seaweed meal and powder). In fact, A. nodosum (Table
11-2) is used to make seaweed meal and powder, which are used
as supplements of dried milk because of the vitamins and trace
elements. Dulse may be eaten raw, or with fish and butter, or
cooked with soups. Irish moss is used in making soft jellies
or even dried and eaten like popcorn in parts of western
Europe, western Canada, and New England. Marine algae have
been used as fodder for livestock, particularly near the North
Sea, and in some areas these cattle graze directly on the seaweed at low tide. Dulse, for example is fed to goats, cows,

and sheep. Also, a brown alga (<u>A</u>. <u>nodosum</u>) has been used as fertilizer in certain areas of Europe.

The use of seaweeds for medicinal purposes was begun in the Orient as long ago as 3000 B.C. They have been used by the Japanese and the Chinese in the treatment of goiter and by the Romans for a variety of purposes, including the prevention of scurvy. The British also used <u>Porphyra</u> to prevent scurvy. Several red algae (especially Irish moss) have been used in the treatment of intestinal and stomach disorders, apparently because of the anticoagulant and antibiotic properties of colloidal extracts (<u>phycocolloids</u>) of these materials.

Industrial uses of seaweed date from the 17th century in Europe. Brown algae (<u>laminaria</u>) were used as a source of potassium and sodium, which were subsequently used in the soap, glass, and porcelain industries. Though production of soda from seaweed ended about 1810 (it was at this time that iodine was discovered in seaweeds), kelp burning continued until about 1870. Presently, only Japan produces iodine from seaweeds. The production of potassium salts from seaweed shows a cyclic trend. Demands in World War I caused the industrialization of giant kelps (<u>Macrocystis pyrifera</u>) in Pacific North America. Mechanical methods of harvesting were developed and over 400,000 tons were harvested annually. Production ceased after the war because it was no longer economically feasible to obtain potassium from kelp. In the mid-1920's, the kelp

industry was reestablished because of the value of organic
constituents (phycocolloids).

11.5 Phycocolloids

These substances comprise a group of naturally occurring
organic constituents of cell walls of algae that are sometimes
termed "hydrocolloids" because they form colloidal dispersions
in water. They are cell wall components or storage substances
of all seaweeds. The phycocolloids commercially obtained are
only from certain brown and red algae.

The major phycocolloids are algin (algenic acid), obtained
from kelps and rockweeds; agar, obtained from various red
algae; and carrageenan, obtained from red seaweed, Irish moss,
and other related seaweed. The agar industry originated in
Japan in about 1670, and as such was the first seaweed product
to become an important item of commerce. The Japanese are
still the major producers of agar. Since the early 1940's,
however, agar has been produced by Britain, Denmark, Australia,
the United States, the Soviet Union, New Zealand, India, and
South Africa. Carrageenan is an agar-like extractive, but does
not meet agar specifications as in the U.S. Pharmacopoeia, and
differs sufficiently from agar so the two are not competitive.
Each of the three main groups of phycocolloids has specific
characteristics that can be varied and utilized for specific
applications.

The major value and uses of phycocolloids depend on their colloidal properties. They are used as stabilizers, emulsifiers, and controllers of texture, flavor, moisture, and color. Humm[10] has enumerated the extensive uses of seaweed extractives, particularly the various forms of carrageenan. They are used in food, drugs, and cosmetic preparations and their applications. Specific examples are given (Table 11-3) though these are but a few uses. In chocolate milk, for instance, as

TABLE 11-3

Examples of Uses of Carrageenans as Additives

Category	Examples
Foods	Bread, canned meats, cheeses, chocolate milk, confections, dehydrated mixes, fruit cakes, fruit juices, ice cream, icings, low-calorie and other health foods, mayonnaise, meringues, pie fillings, salad dressings, sauces, soups, syrups, whipped toppings
Drugs	Constipation remedies, dental-impression compounds, pill coatings, surgical dressings
Cosmetics	Cold cream, hand cream, hair dressings and sprays, permanent wave preparations, shaving cream, suntan lotions, toothpaste
Other	Insecticides, lubricants, oil-well drilling needs, tobacco, vehicles for bacterial innoculum, water-base paints, wine and beer clarification

little as 0.4% carrageenan prevents the chocolate from
settling. In toothpaste, the moisture, consistency, and the
foaming capacity are controlled and permit a long shelf life
without noticeable change. In canned meats and dog and cat
foods, the seaweed extractive maintains a desired moisture content and prevents mushiness caused by vibration during transit.
In hand creams and other cosmetic materials, the extract
stabilizes an oil-water emulsion. In water-base paints, the
extract maintains a high viscosity, which permits one coat to
carry sufficient pigment to cover without running or sagging.
Some surgical threads are being made of derivatives of algenic
acid because these materials will be dissolved and need not be
removed.

Algin is obtained, in the United States at least, mainly
from _Macrocystis_, of which about 2.5% of the total weight is
algin. The giant kelp is harvested in protected beds on the
California coastline by means of large motor-driven barges
that are equipped with mowers. These harvesters cut the kelp
about 1 meter below the water surface, and several tons of
seaweed can be harvested in a day. Carrageenan is obtained
mainly from Irish moss and species of _Gigartina_. Presently,
about 10 million pounds of the moss are processed in New
England and the Canadian maritime states. The moss is gathered
by means of long-handled rakes (3-5 yards). These rakes are
used to scrape the long blades of moss from the rocks where

they grow. More than one crop may be harvested during the May-
September season under ideal conditions, though raking is
limited to times of low tides and to shallow waters. Irish
moss is worth about 12-13 cents per pound (dry weight), though
the purified colloid is worth over one dollar a pound. The
harvesting of agar-producing seaweed (agarophytes) is also done
by hand, though various rakes and mechanical tools have been
used. Agar is obtained mainly from the genus Gracilaria (and
constitutes about 30-35% of the dry weight of most species).

The extraction of agar may be of particular interest because of its fundamental use to microbiologists as a medium
for bacteriological cultures. Obviously, the source of agar
would be a commercial product, but the extraction procedure
given here indicates how it may be obtained.[10] The agar may
be isolated from Gracilaria. Procedures for other related seaweeds would differ. Roughly 40 grams of thoroughly washed and
thoroughly dried Gracilaria are suspended in a liter of sea
water and the pH is adjusted to 5.5 to 6.0 and the liquid is
cooked in a pressure cooker at 15 pounds for 15 minutes. The
hot agar solution is poured through several layers of cheese-
cloth followed by filtration through coarse filter paper. It
is particularly helpful to use a steam pressure apparatus
in filtration. The material may be dehydrated and purified by
allowing the extractive to freeze, by placing a block of ice on
a screen, and allowing the ice to thaw at room temperature. As

thawing takes place, about 85% of the water will run free along with roughly the same proportion of soluble impurities (salts, sugars, amino acids, pigments). Water that remains in the agar can be removed by evaporation. Culture medium from Gracilaria agar is made by bringing the pH of the filtered and concentrated material to 7 and pouring the contents into a sterile petri dish.

The sources of the phycocolloids are mainly red algae of the phylum Rhodophyta. The chemical complexity (Fig. 11-3, 11-4) of the phycocolloids is great. Some recent findings on the structure of carrageenan have been summarized by Mueller and Rees[13]; their observations should provide a useful departure for future studies. Little likelihood exists that these materials will be made synthetically - at least in the near future. As a result, the only source of the seaweed extractives will continue to be the red algae.

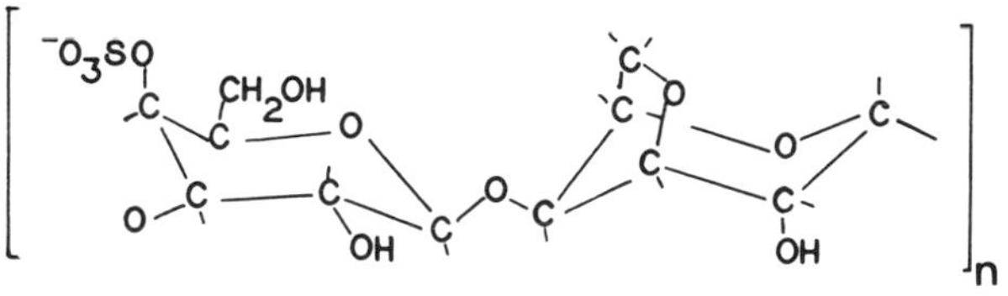

FIG. 11-3

Idealized representation of (kappa) carrageenan. Carbon-bonded hydrogens omitted for sake of clarity.[13]

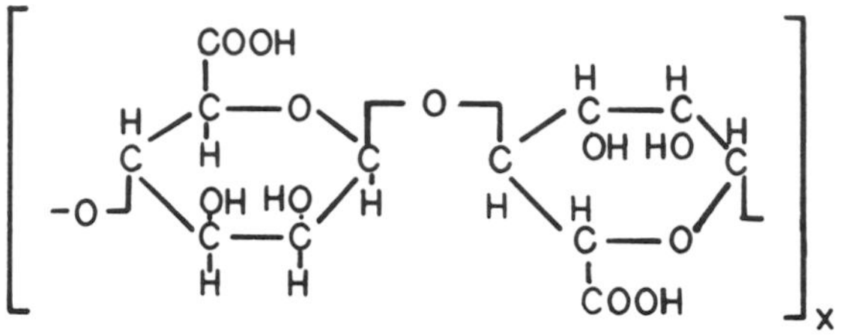

FIG. 11-4

Idealized representation of alginic acid.[15]

11.6 Drugs from the Sea

Apparently, little attention has been given to a critical aspect of food resources of the sea: the association of bio-toxins with marine organisms. A survey by Halstead[11] reveals the fantastic array of biologically active chemicals present in the marine plants and animals, evidently throughout the entire phylogenic series. Some marine biotoxins are ten thousand times more toxic than sodium cyanide, some three thousand times more toxic than some synthetic war gases. One toxin (from the dinoflagellate, Gonyaulax catenella) is thought to be 160 thousand times more potent than cocain in producing action potentials in nerves and voluntary muscles. The lethal activity approaches botulinum toxin of food poisoning. The problems of biotoxins have been known for many years, one example being paralytic shellfish poisoning. The problem of interaction of food and biotoxins in this manner is likely to be increased as we utilize more and more fresh fish for fish protein concentrate. Apparently, little or nothing is known about how or why marine biotoxins occur, though excellent summaries of this problem have been provided by Halstead,[11,14] Sieburth,[17] and Marderosin,[15] among others.[11,12,16,18] The gross features of the problem are described in the following section.

Some Origins of Marine Poisons[14]

Random toxicity. The flesh of certain fishes may become toxic to humans without warning and without any notable regularity in season or habitat. Though these fish may be valuable during nontoxic times, the general appearance and behavior of any fish do not indicate any evidence of the toxic nature of the flesh. For example, in the Line Islands during 1943-1945, food fish suddenly caused violent biotoxications, though these same fish had previously been eaten with impunity. This is an example of ichtyosarcotoxism, which is caused by cisuatoxic and cluteotoxic fishes. In one instance, the onset of ciguatera fish poisoning in the central Pacific was allegedly caused by the sinking of ships which had been heavily loaded with certain metals and substances that caused the outbreak. Halstead[14] noted, "The serious nature of this problem has not been given the recognition it deserves either by fisheries or public health organizations."

c

423

Environmental pollution. The discharge of industrial
waste into the sea may constitute a miniature barrier to the
effective use of protein resources of the sea. The devastating
outbreaks of Minamata disease in Japan is an example of this
type of toxication, as is the accumulation of copper in oysters
living near electric power generating stations. The latter
is a consequence of thermal pollution; the source of copper is
ascribed to condenser tube corrosion problems within the generating stations.

Mutual toxicities can arise because of the existence of
food chains. For instance, if a shellfish injests a toxic
dinoflagellate (G. breve, G. catenella, and others), it can concentrate the toxin mechanically and pass it to those who ingest
the shellfish. Schantz[19] and Shilo[20] summarized some of the
problems of paralytic shellfish poisoning due to algal toxins.
The responsible organisms are typically certain species of
dinoflagellates of the genera gonyaulax, e.g., G. catenella
(along the Pacific Coast of the U.S., Canada, and Alaska), G.
tamarensis (in estuaries of the St. Lawrence River and the Bay
of Fundy). The host organism may not be noticeably disturbed
by the uptake of the toxic dinoflagellate, but it can be lethal
to persons who ingest the host during the period of uptake.
Within 0.5-3 hours after consuming a few toxic shellfish, the
patient feels a numbness in the lips and fingertips, paralysis
ascends, and ultimately death due to respiratory paralysis may

occur within three to twenty hours. Prognosis is good if the victim survives for 24 hours.

Venomous organisms are found in great abundance in the marine environment.[11] These have a venom gland and some device which delivers the venom (nematocyst, stinging cell which is active or passive). Moreover, different parts of marine organisms can be toxic: skin, blood, gonads, etc. Ichtyocrinotoxic fishes are those that have glandular skin secretions not associated with a spine or sting. The box fish, trunk fish, puffer fishes, and some specialized serranids would be included in this group.[16] Trunk fishes, of which the Hawaiian box fish is an example, secrete a fish-killing toxin (ostracitoxin), a choline chloride ester of a fatty acid.[16]

Seaweed fungi which live on seaweed can be hazardous because some seaweed is processed, particularly in Norway, and converted into seaweed meal. A number of symbiotic (living together), parasytic, pathogenic, or saphrophytic fungi are found. Various studies have been conducted on the effects that processing has on the microflora of Norwegian seaweed meal, and standard procedures have been devised for monitoring the quality of this material.

Marine bacteria. Properties of variant strains of marine bacteria constitute one aspect of marine microbacteriology which urgently needs intense exploration because these strains are pathogenic to humans - superficial cuts or scratches result in severe septicemia or cellulitis for which common antibiotics seem to be ineffective.

   Marine food toxications. Consumption of fresh marine food (squid, octopus, fishes, etc.) has been the cause of many food poisoning cases. For example, in Japan during 1958–1960, about 2000 outbreaks involving 20,000–30,000 persons were reported. Fish or fish products were involved in each instance. Causative agents were not determined in about 80% of the cases. About 60% of the diagnosed cases involved bacteria; most of the remainder were thought to be caused by naturally occurring biological poisons of an unknown nature.

The Promise of Drugs From the Sea

   It is an interesting paradox that the biotoxins described previously may serve as a deterrent to the use of marine foods, but they can also serve as an extremely valuable pharmaceutical resource. As Halstead[14] notes, the noxious by-products of one industry can very well become the valuable primary product of another. Only about 1% of the biotoxic substances of thousands of marine organisms have been studied, even in a cursory manner. Of those that have been studied, perhaps a dozen have been evaluated to the point of determining chemical and pharmacological properties. Marine biotoxins have many types of biological properties. They are fungicides, growth inhibitors, antibiotics, and antitumor agents; they have antiviral, hemolitic analgesic, cardioinhibitory, and other properties. For example,

tetrodotoxin from puffer fish is highly toxic to all verte-
brates (the lethal dose to mice is less than 10 micrograms per
kilogram). It has been used for some time as a narcotic to
relieve the agony of terminal cancer in Japan.

A second paradox arises. Since the field of drugs from
the sea is promising based on past studies, it is a relatively
untapped field from the standpoint of pharmaceutical manufacturing firms. The groundwork (obtaining, extracting biotoxins from marine organisms, and evaluating their potentials
as drugs) seems to be conducted in university and basic
research centers, although about one-third of the pharmaceutical
houses of the U.S. are interested in drug research on marine
organisms. The paradox has an economical basis according to
Miloy.[18] It costs about $40,000 to find a compound that may
be useful as a drug. The second step, developing this
potential drug to a commercial product, may cost about
$7,000,000. About one out of 2500 compounds investigated be-
comes marketable. Despite this obvious economic obstacle toward the utilization of drugs from the sea, much research is
going on that does indicate the promise of drugs from the sea.

Miloy[18] has proposed two broad categories to encompass
the biotic substances of the sea: (1) antibiotics, which are
used to control and destroy disease-causing organisms; and
(2) systematic drugs, which in the broadest sense are substances other than food that are intended to affect the

structure or function of the body of animals or man. Systematic drugs act directly on parts of the body to relieve pain,
stimulate, relax, cause healing, and alter rates of biochem-
cal reactions.

Sieburth[17] has noted the problem of semantics associated
with the noun "antibiotics" and prefers to use the term "antibiosis by secondary plant materials." He uses Webster's
definition of antibiosis, "The antagonistic association between
one organism and the metabolic product of another." The term
"secondary plant materials" embraces those substances such as
sulfonium compounds, terpenes, polyphenols, and alkaloids
"whose occurrence is secondary and sporadic, but may be
specific in wide or narrow taxonomic groupings."[17] In contrast,
primary plant substances are involved in essential metabolism
and nutrition of plants. Some workers have preferred to use
the term "ectocrines," which are biologically active excretory
products of marine organisms that have effects in marine
ecology. The secondary plant materials that affect antibiosis
seem to fall into three major categories, according to
Sieburth.[17]

The first category is allyl sulfides, such as those
pungent materials that are involved when scale tissues of
onions are crushed. These materials are highly toxic to the
smudge fungus and serve a protective function. The red alga,
Polysiphonia fastigiata, (lanosa) liberates methyl sulfide.

The precursor of this compound is dimethyl-beta-propiothetin (dmpt), $(CH_3)_2\overset{+}{S}CH_2CH_2COOH$. Enzymatic hydrolysis of dmpt yields dimethyl sulfide and acrylic acid. The latter compound also has antibacterial activity, which was first observed in antarctic studies of "bacteriologically sterile" penguins. These birds eat a crustacean whose diet is an alga that contains the antibiotic acrylic acid.

A group of polyphenols represent a second class of compounds that effect antibiosis. These materials are found in certain varieties of onions that evidently also provide resistance to onion smudge fungus. A group of polyphenolic "materials," notably tannins, have been found where there is antibacterial activity, e.g., absence of frond-tip fouling in healthy plants of the Sargasso Sea. Different species of Phaeophyra have polyphenols which may be related to the known astringent taste and protein-precipitating activity. These polyphenols may act as repellents and thus protect plants

These two classes of the secondary plant materials have been best studied. All other substances seem to fall into a third category of which the best studied class seems to be neutral volatile terpernoid hydrocarbons. These substances seem to be related to the relative freedom of gorgonian sea fans from predation and epibiosis, though it must be appreciated that the cause-effect relationships here are difficult to establish.[17]

The potential usefulness of drugs that have been or may be isolated from the sea is difficult to assess. Few have become commercially available, and an economic barrier, described earlier, may limit commercial utilization of marine drugs for some time. These substances are and will be utilized in basic research because of their interesting and varied pharmacology. The range of possibilities is suggested by a comparison of some of the known marine biotoxins (Table 11-4). There is every hope that they will have beneficial uses.

11.7 Summary

The general topic, of food from the sea encompasses a range of important topics and disciplines: fisheries, mariculture, husbandry of fishes and plants, chemicals and products that can be extracted from fish and plants, as well as drugs and antibiotics. It is evident that the sea is much less fertile and available as a food source than is popularly believed. Coastal waters probably offer the most promise for increasing any food supply through husbandry of fish, shellfish, and plants. These waters, however, are most susceptible to being polluted, a danger that may be overcome by utilization of waste products, either chemicals or heat. The ubiquitousness of marine food products is best exemplified by the wide utilization of phycocolloids in our foods. The demand for these complex materials is increasing, but their complexity should limit conventional synthesis and favor managed

TABLE 11-4

Some Marine Biotoxins[16]

Property	Ostracitoxin-Pahutoxin	Tetrodotoxin-Tarichatoxin	Ciguatoxin	Saxotoxin[19,20]
Source organism	Boxfish, Ostracion lentiginosus	Puffer, Sphoeroides	Moray eel, Gymnothorax javanicus	Dinoflagellate G. catenella
Source organ	Skin mucous secretions	Viscera, gonads and skin	Viscera and muscle	
Empirical formula	$C_{23}H_{44}NO_5Cl$	$C_{22}H_{33}N_7O_{14}$	$C_{35}H_{65}NO_8$	$C_{10}H_{17}N_7O_4$
Chemical classification	Choline chloride ester of a fatty acid	Heterocycle	Lipid containing quaternary nitrogen, hydroxyl & carbonyl functions	Purine base with carbonate moiety
Ichyocidal	Yes	No	No	Yes
Toxicity to mammals, MLD to mice µg/Kg	Weakly toxic	Highly toxic to all	Moderately toxic to warm-blooded vertebrates	Toxicity to man 1-4 mg
	<200,000	<10	<1,000	<10
Hemolytic	Yes, causes agglutination of RBC	No, resembles local anesthetic, causes respiratory failure & neuromuscular block	No	Not a cholineesterase inhibitor; resembles tetrodotoxin
Other effects	Muscarinic type activity on nerves		curare-like effect on nerve-muscle end plate	
Ecological significance	Repellent (?)	Repellent (?)	Unknown	Repellent (?)

431

cultivation of macroscopic algae. The utilization of other
marine extracts, drugs and antibiotics from marine organisms,
is limited by an economic barrier, the cost of commercial
development. This will not limit the utilization of these
materials in basic research, and their potential usefulness
remains one of the great untapped resources of the sea.

REFERENCES

1. D. K. Tressler and J. McW. Lemon, Marine Products of
   Commerce, Reinhold, New York, 1951.

2. L. R. Brown, Science, 158, 604 (1967).

3. J. E. Bardach, Science, 161, 1098 (1968).

4. K. O. Emery and C. O'D. Iselin, Science, 157, 1279 (1967).

5. A. McKee, Farming the Sea, Souvenir Press, London, 1967.

6. P. A. Martino and J. M. Marchello, Ocean Industry,
   April, 1968, p. 37.

7. J. L. Potter, Ocean Industry, May, 1969, p. 94.

8. S. Patton et al., Science, 158, 789 (1967).

9. A. C. Mathieson, Oceanology International, January-
   February 1969, p. 37.

10. H. J. Humm, On the Economic Potentialities of Florida Red
    Algae, Mimeo., USF Marine Science Inst., 1968; C.S. Kim
    and H. J. Humm, Bull. Mar. Sci., 15, 1036 (1965).

11. B. W. Halstead, Poisonous and Venomous Marine Animals of
    the World. Vols I-III, U. S. Government Printing Office,
    Washington, 1965, 1967, 1968.

12. H. D. Freudenthal, ed., Drugs From the Sea, Marine
    Technology Soc., Washington, D.C., 1968.

13. G. P. Mueller and E. A. Rees, ibid., p. 241.

14. B. W. Halstead, ibid., p. 229.

15. A. der Marderosin, ibid, p. 19.

16. D. A. Thompson, ibid., p. 203.

17. J. McN. Sieburth, in Microbiology of the Sea, (M. R. Droop and E. J. F. Wood, eds.), Vol. 1, Academic Press, New York, 1968.

18. L. F. Miloy, Ocean Industry, June 1968, p. 74.

19. E. J. Schantz, J. Med. Pharm. Chem., 4, 459 (1961).

20. M. Shilo, Bact. Revs., 31, 180 (1967).

APPENDIX

Plankton Terminology[1,2]

Organism Terminology

Plankton (individually, plankters) are passively drifting
or weakly swimming organisms that are suspended in marine or
fresh waters. The size range is enormous with microscopic
plants at one end of the range and jellyfishes (which may have
bells that are six feet across) at the other end.

Phytoplankton are members of the plant subdivision of
plankton.

Zooplankton are members of the animal subdivision of
plankton. They are the main consumers of phytoplankton and are
the main food source for many larger animals, including baleen
whales. Various crustaceans, certain protozoans, mollusks,
as well as the eggs and larvae of ncktonic animals belong to
this category.

Nekton are active swimmers and are organisms that have
sufficient mobility to maintain their position against local
water movements. This category includes fish and marine
animals.

Detritus is suspended matter that is incapable of reproduction. In this text and others, detritus is defined as
being of organic origin (from phytoplankton, zooplankton, or

435

nekton. The term is used by many, however, as a synonym for
debris or suspended matter that arises from disintegration of
rock.

Location Terminology

Oceanic refers to the portion of the pelagic division that
extends seaward from the edge of the continental shelf.

Neritic refers to that portion of the pelagic division that
extends from the approximate edge of the continental shelf
landward to mean low water. The term is used for plankton of
the coastal waters. If primary productivity is being considered, the neritic province might extend to as much as 160 km
seaward of the continental shelf edge.

Allochthonous is used to denote exotic populations, that is
plankters that have developed outside the area of study.

Autochthonous is used to denote endemic populations, those
that have developed within the area of study.

Life-Cycle Terminology

Holoplankton or permanent plankton are organisms that form
spores during their life cycles and spend their complete life
cycle in the floating state. These organisms are commonly
oceanic.

Meroplankton do not spend their complete life cycle in the
floating state. They comprise, mainly, the developmental stages
(larvae and eggs) of nekton and the benthos (bottom-dwelling
organisms).

Size Classification Terminology

Classification varies among workers; the values given here are approximate and follow a standard usage.[1]

Microplankton are plankton that fall within a size range 60 μ - 1 mm (50-500 μ, according to Strickland[2]). Most phytoplankters fall within this group and the next.

Nannoplankton (or nanoplankton) are sometimes called centrifuge plankton because most specimens will pass through nets and are collected by centrifugation of water samples. They fall within the range 5-60 μ (5-50 μ, according to Strickland[2]).

Ultraplankton include bacteria and smaller flagellate forms whose largest dimension is less than 5 μ (0.5-10 μ, according to Strickland's classification[2]).

Nutritional Requirement Terminology

Autotrophic organisms manufacture their food from inorganic compounds and require few organic compounds for normal growth or reproduction.

Heterotrophic organisms use preformed organic compounds to supply their constituent carbon and may obtain constituent phosphorus, nitrogen, and sulfur from organic sources.

Auxotrophic (mixotrophic) organisms use inorganic compounds but also require some organic compounds for normal growth and reproduction.

Abundance Terminology

Eutrophic refers to bodies of water that contain an abundance of nutrients. Typically, these are coastal waters with marked upwelling. The term also refers to a fertile region in which plankton are abundant.

Oligotrophic pertains to bodies of water containing some nutrient matter and typically refers to sparsely populated, less fertile waters (as in the tropics).

Tolerance Terminology

Euryhaline refers to organisms that are adaptable to a wide range of salinity; they normally inhabit salt water.

Stenohaline refers to organisms that are capable of normal growth and reproduction only within a narrow range of salinity.

Eurythermic --Capable of tolerating a wide range of temperature.

Stenothermic - Capable of tolerating only a narrow range of temperature.

REFERENCES

1. Glossary of Oceanographic Terms (B. B. Baker, Jr., W. R. Deebel, R. D. Geisenderfer, eds.), 2nd ed., Special Publication 35, U.S. Naval Oceanographic Office, Washington, D.C., 1966.

2. J. D. H. Strickland in Chemical Oceanography (J. P. Riley and G. Skirrow, eds.), Vol. 1, Academic Press, New York, 1965, Chapt. 12.

AUTHOR INDEX

Numbers in parentheses are reference numbers and indicate that
an author's work is referred to although his name is not cited
in the text. Numbers underlined show the page on which the
complete reference is listed.

A

Abelson, P. H., 244(13), 266
Adams, J. A. S., 107, 109, 110
    (6), 142
Aldrich, D. V., 30(22), 37
Aleem, M. I. H., 254, 266
Alexander, G. B., 152(9), 180
Allen, J. A., 103
Årén, K., 190(6), 222
Armstrong, F. A. J., 148(3),
    153, 155(3), 165(3), 166(3),
    168(3), 172, 173(30), 174,
    175(3, 31), 179, 180, 181,
    188(2), 203(13), 204, 208,
    209(19), 211(2), 212(22),
    213(19b), 214(2), 217(2),
    219(19), 220, 221-223
Arrhenius, G. O. S., 143, 195
    (11), 222, 392, 396
Arrington, F., 303(24), 306(24),
    316

B

Bada, J. L., 237, 265
Baker, B. B., jr., 435(1), 437
    (1), 438
Bardach, J. E., 401(3), 405(3),
    406(3), 432
Barker, N. F., 44(4), 74
Benson, B. B., 231, 232, 246(5),
    248, 249(5), 265
Bent, H. A., 103, 103
Berger, W. H., 170, 181
Bialek, E. L., 15(11), 37
Bickley, F., 121(11), 123(11),
    143, 146(1), 162(1), 163(1),
    164(1), 166(1), 171(1), 172

(1), 180
Bischoff, J. L., 303, 316
Bissell, H. J., 300(21), 316
Bolin, B., 230(4), 232(4), 265,
    289(15), 290, 293, 315
Borchert, H., 270(2), 315
Bowden, K. F., 40(2), 41(2),
    51(2), 51(8), 74
Bowen, V. T., 310(29), 316
Bradley, D., 15, 19, 37
Brannock, W. W., 152(10), 180
Bricker, O. P., 121(11), 123
    (11), 143, 146(1), 162(1),
    163(1), 164(1), 166(1),
    171(1), 172(1), 180
Broecker, W. S., 315
Brooks, R. D., 311, 316
Brown, L. R., 399, 400, 432
Browning, D. S., 396
Brust, H. F., 203(14), 205(14),
    222
Budge, K. M., 252(18), 266
Burton, J. D., 74, 75, 292(17),
    316
Butler, E. I., 173(30), 174,
    179, 181, 209(19), 213(19b),
    219(19), 222

C

Carlucci, A. F., 255, 266
Carrier, G. F., 55(10), 56(10),
    74
Chatt, J., 256(25), 266
Chen, C.-H., 181
Chilingar, G. V., 300(21), 316
Christ, C. L., 166(23), 181

Claussen, W. F., 132(22), 143
Clymo, R. S., 152(12), 180
Cloud, P. E., Jr., 298(18), 299 (18), 300(18), 316
Cooper, L. H. N., 168(26), 181, 209(18), 210(18), 213(18), 222
Cox, R. A., 12, 13(9), 14(9), 15(10), 18(10), 19(20), 21 (10), 29(10), 37
Craig, H., 289, 290, 315
Culbertsen, C., 280(8), 315
Culkin, F., 12(9), 13(9), 14(9), 37
Curl, H., Jr., 310(29), 316

D

Danford, M. D., 11, 36
Davey, C. B., 9(4), 36
Deebel, W. R., 435 (1), 437(1), 438
der Marderosin, A., 422(15), 423, 433
Dietrich, G., 22(16), 26(18), 28(18), 29, 30(16), 32, 33 (16), 37, 270(3), 271, 315
Dietz, R. W., 193, 222
Degens, E. T., 386(9), 388(10), 396
Densmore, C. D., 388(10), 396
Dragovich, A., 200(12), 201, 202 (12), 222, 335(9), 354
Droop, M. R., 423(17), 428(17), 429(17), 433
Drost-Hansen, W. 7(2), 8(2), 9, 11(2), 20(14), 35, 36, 37
Drouet, F., 353, 355
Dugdale, R. C., 211, 223, 251, 258(26), 266
Duxbury, A. C., 173(29), 175, 181
Dyrssen, D., 190(6), 222

E

Emery, K. O., 46, 47, 193(8), 222, 227, 228(2), 230(2), 243, 265, 266, 402, 403(4), 404(4), 405(4), 411(4), 432
Emmel, E. V. M., 239(9), 265
Epstein, S., 305(25), 316
Eriksson, E., 230, 232, 265,

289(15), 290, 293, 315
Ewing, M., 153(13), 154, 155 (13), 180

F

Fairbridge, R. W., 300(21), 316
Fan, P.-F., 165, 181
Fanning, K. A., 179, 181
Fisher, F. H., 283(13), 315
Fleming, R. H., 41(3), 44(3), 45(3), 47(3), 50(3), 62(3), 73(3), 74
Frank, H. S., 11, 37
Freudenthal, H. D., 423(12), 432

G

Garrels, R. M., 106(4), 121, 123(11), 142, 143, 146(1), 160(18), 162(1), 163, 164 (1), 166(1, 23), 171(1), 172(1), 180, 181, 281, 284 (11), 296(20), 315, 316
Geen, G. H., 205, 222
Geisenderfer, R. D., 435(1), 437(1), 438
Gleuckauf, E., 129(19), 132(19b), 142(19), 143
Goering, J. J., 250, 251(15), 266
Goldberg, E. D., 155(16), 156 (16), 157(16), 158(16), 165(16), 181, 307(27), 309 (27), 310, 311, 316, 338 (12), 354, 392, 396
Goldschmidt, V. M., 107, 109, 112(5), 142
Golterman, H. L., 152, 180
Grice, C. F., 386(8), 388(8), 389, 396
Griffin, J. J., 155(16), 156(16), 157(16), 158(16), 165(16), 181
Guillard, R. R. L., 335(10), 354
Gupta, R. S., 248(14), 249, 266

H

Haimovitz, A., 303(24), 306(24), 316
Halstead, B. W., 413(11), 422,

423(11,14), 425(11), 426, 432, 433
Harder, W., 33(23), 37
Hargrave, B. T., 205, 222
Hathaway, J. C., 388(10), 396
Hemley, J. J., 122, 143
Herbich, J. B., 395(12), 396
Heron, J., 204, 222
Hessong, D. E., 312(32), 316
Heston, W. M., 152(9), 180
Hill, M. N., 40(1), 74, 195(11), 214(23), 222, 223, 317(3), 336(11), 340(3), 343(3), 345(15), 346(15), 355, 354
Hobson, L. A., 154, 181
Hoering, T., 241, 266
Holland, H. D., 122, 123(12), 130(20), 143, 162(20), 181
Hood, D. W., 123(15), 143
Horn, M. K., 107, 109, 110(6), 142
Hornig, D. F., 10, 36
Humm, H. J., 418, 420(10), 432
Hutchinson, G. E., 241(10), 245, 266, 273, 315

I

Iler, R. K., 152(9), 180
Iselin, C. O'D., 402, 403(4), 404(4), 405(4), 411(4), 432

J

Jacobs, M. B., 153(13), 154, 155 (13), 180
Jagendorf, A. T., 353(18), 355
Jameson, J. C., 296(19), 316
Jerlov, N. G., 21(15), 23(15), 37
Johansson, B., 190(6), 222
Johnson, M. W., 41(3), 44(3), 45(3), 47(3), 50(3), 62(3), 73(3), 74
Johnston, R., 26(18), 28(18), 29, 37
Jokela, A., 388(10), 396
Jorgensen, E. G., 167, 181

K

Kamen, M. D., 353(19), 355
Kanamori, H., 108(7), 143
Katz, E. L., 312(32), 316
Kennedy, G., 15, 37
Kester, D. R., 280(8), 315
Ketchum, B. H., 209(20), 211 (20), 214(23), 222, 223
Kim, C. S., 418(10), 420(20), 432
Kinne, O., 29, 37
Kirkbright, G. F., 190(5), 222
Klement, A. W., Jr., 191(7), 199(7), 204(7), 206(7), 222
Kok, B., 353(18), 355
Korson, L., 9, 36
Krauskopf, K. B., 148, 149(5), 150(5), 180, 195(10), 220(10), 221, 222, 306, 310, 316
Kuenzler, E. J., 209(20), 211 (20), 222
Kuiper, G. P., 241(10), 245(10), 266, 273(5), 315

L

LaFord, E. C., 45(5), 46(5), 74
Lee, A. J., 26(18), 28(18), 29, 37
Lemon, J. McW., 397(1), 432
Levine, R. P., 353(20), 355
Levy, H. A., 11, 36
Lewin, J. C., 151(7), 152, 167, 168, 170, 180, 181
Lewin, R. A., 319(6), 321(6), 354
Lisitzin, A. P., 154, 180
Livingstone, D. A., 160(17), 161(17), 162, 181
Lowenstam, H. A., 305(25), 316

M

MacDonald, C., 303(24), 306(24), 316

MacIssac, J. J., 258(26), 266
MacKenzie, F. T., 106(4), 121,
    123(11), 142, 143, 146(1),
    160(18), 162(1), 163, 164(1),
    166(1), 171(1), 172(1), 180
    181
Malone, T. F., 129(19), 132(19b),
    142(19), 143
Manheim, F. T., 388(10), 396
Marchello, J. M., 410, 432
Martin, B. B., 311(30), 316
Martin, D. F., 127(17), 141(17),
    143, 303(23), 311(30), 316,
    354
Martin, J. H., 253(19), 266
Martino, P. A., 410, 432
Mathieson, A. C., 414(9), 415(9),
    432
May, B. Z., 200(12), 201, 202
    (12), 222
McCartney, M. J., 12(9), 13(9),
    14(9), 37
McClellan, A. L., 2(1), 36
McFarlin, P. F., 388(10), 396
McGary, N. B., 173(29), 175, 181
McKee, A., 405(5), 432
McKinney, C. R., 305(25), 316
McLester, M. E., 303(23), 316
Mero, J. L., 357(2), 368, 369(2),
    376(2), 383(2), 391, 393,
    394(2), 395(2), 396
Meyer, C., 122(13), 143
Miller, A. R., 388(10), 396
Miller, R. J., 9(4), 36
Miller, S. L., 237, 265
Millero, F. J., 9, 20(14), 36,
    37
Miloy, L. F., 423(18), 427, 433
Morris, A. W., 27, 37
Mueller, G. P., 421(13), 433
Mulawka, S. T., 312(32), 316
Munk, W. H., 55(10), 56(10), 74
Murta, K. J., 152(10), 180

N

Nason, N., 254, 266
Nelson, L. A., 9(4), 36
Nemethy, G., 11, 37

Neumann, G., 60(13), 74
Newcombe, C. L., 203(14), 205
    (14), 222
Newton, M., 15, 37
Nicholls, G. D., 310, 316
Nielsen, E. Steemann, 317(3),
    339(4), 340(3), 343, 354

O

Odum, E. P., 77(1), 97(1), 100,
    103, 234, 265
Odum, H. T., 123(15), 143
Oppenheimer, C. H., 229(3),
    230(3), 232(3), 254(20),
    264(3), 265, 266
Orowan, E., 108(8), 143
Orr, A. P., 204(15), 222
Orr, W. L., 227, 228(2), 230
    (2), 243, 265, 266
Overall, M. P., 385(7), 386(7),
    396

P

Park, P. K., 123(15), 143,
    278(7), 279(7), 281(10),
    284, 285(7), 286(7), 287
    (7), 288, 315
Parsons, T. R., 340, 343(13),
    355
Patton, S., 413(8), 432
Peterson, E. K., 314, 316
Pierson, W. J., Jr., 60(13),
    74
Pimentel, G. C., 2(1), 36
Pocklington, R., 388(10), 396
Pomeroy, L. R., 191, 199(7),
    204, 206(7), 222
Potter, J. L., 413(7), 432
Prakash, A., 29(21), 30, 37,
    127(18), 143
Pringle, B. H., 312(32), 316
Provasoli, L., 336, 354
Pytkowicz, R. M., 123, 143,
    280(8), 281(9), 283(12),
    315

Q

Quist, A. S., 11, _37_

R

Rabinowitch, E. I., 324, 353(17), _355_
Rakestraw, N. W., 239(9), _265_
Rashid, M. A., 127(18), _143_
Ray, S. M., 30(22), _37_
Redfield, A. C., 101, _103_, 132(21), 136(21), _137_(21), 139(21), _143_, 183(1), 184(1), 193(1), _195_(1), 214(23), 218(1), _221_, _223_
Rees, E. A., _421_(13), _433_
Remsen, C. C., 255(22), _266_
Revelle, R., 273(4), 274(4), _315_
Richards, F. A., 129(19), 132 (19b), 142, _143_, 173(28), _181_, 214(23), _223_, 231, 232, _246_(5), 248, _249_(5), _265_
Richter, D. H., 122(13), _143_
Rigler, F. H., 190, 191, _222_
Riley, J. P., 27, _37_, 40(2), 41(2), 51(2), _67_, _74_, _75_, 129(19), 132(19b), 142, _143_ 148(3), 153, 155(3), 165(3), 166(3), 168(3), 172(3), 175 (3), _180_, 317(1), 319(1), 334(1), 335(1), 338(1), 339(1), 343(1), 346(1), 349 (1), _354_, 435(2), 437(2), _438_
Rittenberg, S. C., 227, 228(2), 229(3), 230(2, 3), 232, 243, 264(3), _265_, _266_
Ritter, D. F., 160(19), 179, _181_
Rogall, E., 151(8), 170, _180_
Ross, D. A., 386(9), _396_
Rounsefell, G. A., 335(9), _354_
Rumsby, M. G., 311, _316_
Russell, F. E., 30(22), _37_
Ryther, J. H., 335(10), _345_, 346(14, 15), _354_, _355_

S

Sackett, W. M., _143_
Saruhashi, K., 177, _181_
Saunders, P. R., 30(22), _37_
Schantz, E. J., 424, 431(19), _433_
Scheraga, G. H., 11, _37_
Schink, D. R., 179, _181_
Schultz, V., 191(7), 199(7), 204(7), 206(7), _222_
Sears, M., 193(9), 194(9), 195(9), 220(9), 221(9), _222_
Shepard, F. P., 193(8), _222_
Shigley, C. M., 357(1), _358_ (1), 360(1), 369, 370, 371, 373(1), 395, _396_
Shilo, M., 424, 431(20), _433_
Shishkina, O. V., 112(9), _143_
Sieburth, J. McN., 423, 428 (17), 429(17), _433_
Siever, R., 148(6), 149(6), 150(6), 151, 171(6), _180_, 296(20), _316_
Sillén, L. G., 105(1), 106(3), 109(3), 110(3), 111(1), 113(1, 2, 3), 114(1), 116 (1, 2), 119, 120, 125, 126, 135, 140(2, 3), _142_, 147, 148(2), 152(2), _180_, 193 (9), 194(9), 195(9), 220, 221(9), _222_, 227(1), 230, 231, _265_
Silva, P. C., 319, 321(6), _354_
Skirrow, G., 40(2), 41(2), _51_ (2), 67, _74_, _75_, 129(19), 132(19b), _142_(19), _143_, 148(3), 153, 155(3), 165 (3), 166(3), 168(3), 172 (3), 175(3), _180_, 270(1), 273(1), 274, _275_(1), 278 (1), 284, 288, 291(1), _315_, 317(1), 319(1), 334(1), 335(1), 338(1), 339(1), 343(1), 346(1), 349(1),

315, 317(1), 319(1), 334(1),
335(1), 338(1), 339(1), 343
(1), 346(1), 349(1), 354,
435(2), 437(2), 438
Smith, A. M., 190(5), 222
Smith, G. M., 319(5), 354
Smith, R. C., 24(17), 37
Snodgrass, F. E., 64(14), 75
Solórzano, L., 188(3), 189(3),
221
Spencer, G. P., 275(6), 277(6),
278(6), 280(6), 315
Steelink, C., 127(16), 143
Stefansson, U., 173(28), 181
Stewart, W. D. P., 256(24),
265(24), 266
Stöber, W., 148(4), 150(4), 180
Strickland, J. D. H., 188(3),
189(3), 221, 255, 266, 317
(1, 2), 319(1, 2), 329(2),
334(1), 335(1), 338, 339(1,
2), 340, 343(13), 345, 346,
349, 354, 355, 435(2), 437
(2), 438
Stromel, H., 56(11), 58(11), 74
Suess, H. E., 273(4), 274(4),
315
Sverdrup, H. U., 41(3), 44(3),
45, 47(3), 50(3), 62(3),
73(3), 74
Swindale, L. D., 165, 181

T

Taft, W. H., 300, 303(23), 303
(23), 305(24), 316
Takeuchi, H., 108(7), 143
Thomas, C. C., 229(3), 230(3),
232(3), 254(20), 264(3),
265, 266
Thompson, D. A., 423(16), 425
(16), 431(16), 433
Thompson, M. E., 281, 284(11),
296(20), 315, 316
Thorhaug, A., 332, 354
Tibbitts, S., 212(22), 223
Tressler, D. K., 397(1), 432
Tucker, J. J., 44(4), 74

U

Uyeda, S., 108(7), 143

V

Vaccaro, R. F., 229(7), 235,
238(7), 239, 240(7), 252,
253(7), 254, 256, 259(7),
265
Voipio, A., 67, 75

W

Wall, F. W., 102, 103
Wall, T. F., 10, 36
Watson, S. W., 254, 255(22),
266
Weaver, C. E., 163(21), 181
Weeks, L. G., 376(5), 377(5),
379(5), 396
West, T. S., 190(5), 222
White, D. E., 152(10), 180
Williams, J., 56, 67(9), 73(9),
74
Wilson, J. T., 108(8), 143
Wilson, W., 15, 19, 37
Windom, H., 155(16), 156(16),
157(16), 158(16), 165(16),
181
Wing, H. C., 305(25), 316
Wood, E. J. F., 423(17), 428
(17), 429(17), 433
Woolheater, C., 303(24), 305
(24), 316
Wooster, W. S., 26(18), 28(18),
29, 37
Wunsch, C., 73(17), 75
Wyrtki, K., 58(12), 59, 74

Y

Yasuo, M., 177, 181

Z

Zobell, C. E., 252(17, 18),
266

A

Action spectrum, 328
Advective processes, defined, 39
Agar, 417, 420, 421
Alginic acid, 417, 419, 421
Ammonia, liberation of, 252-253
Amplitude, A, defined, 42
Anerobic, defined, 142
Anoxic, defined, 142
Anoxic environment, 246-248
Antibiotics, 428-430
AOU effect, 247, 285-286
Apatite, 193-195, 199, 220-221
Apogean tides, 50
Apparent dissociation constants,
    277-279
Aquaculture, problems of, 401-
    404
Argon, concentration in atmos-
    phere, 129
  origin of, 128
Assimilation, defined, 103
Atmosphere, composition of,
    128-129
  primordial, 134-135
Authigenesis, 165

B

Bacteria, ammonia oxidizing,
    253-255
  denitrifying, 251-252
  desulfovibrio, 101
  thiobacilli, 101
Bacterial action, and phosphorus
    concentration, 203-205
Bar, defined, 36
Benthic plants, 318-319
Biogeochemical cycles, and
    energy flow, 99
  defined, 98
  examples of, 98-100, 134-139,
    145, 185, 235
Biological activity, and
    phosphorus, 200-202, 205,
    210-211

Biological activity index, 207-
    208
Biological oxidation, 130
Biotoxications, 423
Brine deposits, see Red Sea
    deposits
Buffer capacity, and silicate
    minerals, 121-124
  controls of in sea water,
    120-122
  of sea water, 119-124

C

Callendar hypothesis, 288, 293
Carbon, biogeochemical cycle
    of, 270-273
Carbon budget, 269-270
Carbon cycles, 270-275
Carbon dioxide, equilibria of,
    275-284, 290-300
  changes and photosynthetic
    rates, 342
Carbon dioxide exchange, con-
    sequences of, 292-294,
    299-300, 314
  model of, 290-291
Carbon-14, assumptions in use
    of, 70
  methods, 342-346
  use of in mixing analysis,
    69-70
Carbon reservoirs, 270, 289-
    290
Carbonate dissolution, 287-288,
    299-300
Carrageenan, 417-419
Catenation, 267
Chlorite, 116, 164
Chondritic substance, 140
Ciguatoxin, 431
Circulation, four-layer model
    of, 59
Clay minerals, reactions of,
    163-166
Coefficient of adiabatic
    compressibility, defined, 18

Coefficient of compressibility,
  and sea level, 18
Commodities, from the sea,
  value of, 358
Communities, marine, types, 77
Compensation intensity, 329
Compressibility, of sea water,
  17-20
Conduction, defined, 8
Constituent-chlorinity ratio,
  and mixing, 67
Continental shelf, definitions,
  362-363
Convection, defined, 81
Coordination entity, defined,
  141
Coriolis force, 54, 73
Currents, density, 58-60
  measurement of, 60-63
  ocean, 53-63
  surface, general patterns of,
    55-58
  surface, map of, 56
  tidal, 51
  wind, 54-55

D

DDT, 79
Decibar, defined, 36
Denitrification, 230-232, 245-
  252
Density currents, 58-60
Denudation, 160-162, 179
Diagenesis, defined, 314
  of marine carbonates, 294-307
Diatoms, 167-171, 179
Dielectric constant, defined,
  35
Diffusive processes, defined,
  39
Dissolved phosphorus, 187-191
  analysis of, 189-192
  forms of, 187-189
Dissolved salts, amounts added
  by rivers, 105-106
Dissolved silicon, analysis of
  151-152

concentrations of, 147
forms of, 147-148
interaction with marine
  sediments, 179-180
Diurnal variations, of
  phosphorus, 203
Dolomite, formation of, 306-
  307
Dredging, 376-377, 381-383
Drugs, from the sea, 422-431

E

Earth's crust, relative
  abundance of elements in,
  184
Economics, of sea water
  mining, 369-376
Ecosystem, defined, 77
  marine, constituents of, 77-
    78
  marine, energy flow in, 94-
    101
  marine, representation of,
    79
  marine, subdivisions of,
    77-78
Ectocrines, 428
Eddy diffusion, see turbulent
  mixing
Edible algae, 414-416
Ekman meters, 61
Ekman spiral, 54, 73
Elements, relative abundance
  in earth's crust, 184
El Niño, 72-73
Emerson effect, 328
Enantiomers, 267-268
Energy, defined, 80
  degradation of, 96
Energy flow, 92-101
  representation of, 95
Energy transfer sequence, 96
Enthalpy, 83-84
Enthalpy change, see heat of
  reaction
Entropy, and the food chain,
  96

as a thermodynamic parameter,
89-91
characterized, 89
Equilibria, of marine carbonates, 298
Equilibria, of phosphorus
compounds, 193-194
Equilibrium, and free energy,
92-94
calculations involving, 92-93
examples of, 91-92
Equilibrium constant, uses of,
92-94
Eutrophic, 265
Extinction, of light, in sea
water, 23-25

F

Ferromanganese minerals, 389-
395
Food chain, 96
Food pyramid, 412
Fossil fuel consumption, see
Callendar hypothesis
Free energy, change in, 89
defined, 88
Frequency, of a wave, defined,
42

G

Galatea Expedition, 317
Geneva Convention, 361-369
Geochemical balance, 107-108
Geomagnetic electrokinetograph
(GEK), 62
Glauconite, 116
Gold deposits, 385
Gonyaulax catenella, 422, 424,
431
Gonyaulax tamarensis, and humic
acid, 127
location, 333
salinity growth curve, 29-30
Guano, 186, 196, 244-245
Gymnodinium breve, 424
location, 333
salinity tolerance of, 30

Gyral, 55-57
Gyres, see gyral

H

H, see enthalpy
Heat, defined, 81
Heat of formation, 102
Heat of fusion, defined, 35
Heat of reaction, applications
of, 84-86
defined, 84
measurement of, 86-88
Heat of vaporization, defined,
35
Homeostatic mechanisms, 79
Human food, dollar value of,
403-404
Humic acids, 127
Husbandry, of aquatic animals,
405-411
Hydrogen bond, consequences of,
2-5
defined, 2
Hydroxyapatite, 193-195, 199,
220-221
Hypophyzation, 407

I

Ice, idealized structure, 5
Igneous rocks, formation of,
108-110
Illite, 116, 141, 163-164
Illumination, units of, 353-
354
Internal waves, 45
Ion-pair complexes, 275, 281-
282, 300
Iron, dissolved, 127
master variable plot, 126
Iron equilibria, 127
Iron paradox, 124-127

J

Jurassic sediment, 141

K

Kaolinite, 116, 156

L

L-alanine, 268
"Law of the Minimum," 136–137
Legal aspects, of the sea, 361–369
Liebig, law, 136–137
Lithification, defined, 314
    of marine carbonates, 301–307

M

Main constituents, of sea water, 26–27
Manganese, and ecological significance, 338
Manganese nodules, 389–395
Marine biotoxins, 426–431
Marine carbonates, 294–307
    types, 294–295
Marine drugs, 422–431
Marine ecosystem, ratios of elements in, 136–138
    variations of phosphorus in, 208–220
    variations of silicon in, 172–177
Marine species, 397
Material balance, of selected elements, 109
Maxima, for phosphate, 210
Metasomatism, 272, 313–314
Michaelis-Menton kinetic expression, 258–260
Microscopic plants, indirect use as food, 413
Mid-Atlantic Ridge, 108, 157
Midocean rift, 108
Minerals, from the sea, 359, 383–386
Mining, of sea floor, 376–395
    of sea water, 369–376
Mixing, assessment of, 66
Mixture models, of water, 10–11
Model ocean, 110–117

Montmorillonite, 116, 155–157
Muscovite, 116

N

Natural resources, defined, 365
Neap tide, 50
Net production, defined, 103
Nitrate, variations in coastal waters, 261
Nitrification, 226, 253–255
Nitrogen, and volcanic activity, 237–238
    assimilation of, 257–259
    atmospheric input, 238–241
    biogeochemical cycle of, 232–237
    distribution of, 259–262
    electrically fixed, 240–241
    growth limitation of, 259–260
    oxidation states of, 225–226
Nitrogen budget, 228–232
Nitrogen-15, and denitrification, 239–240, 250
Nitrogen fixation, 255–256
Nitrosocystis oceanus, 254–255
Nutrient budget, 228

O

Ocean currents, 53–63
Oil, potentials of, 378–381
Oligiotrophic, 265, 258, 438
Optical properties, of sea water, 21–25
Ostracitoxin, 431
Oxidation processes, 130
Oxidation states, defined, 263–264
    of nitrogen, 226
Oxygen, and sulfate-reducing bacteria, 130–133
    in atmosphere, 128–133
Oxygen changes and photosynthetic rates, 340–342
Oxygen-minimum layer, 250–252
Oxygen-poor environments, 246–

252
Oysters, culture of, 409–410

P

Pahutoxin, 431
Paralytic shellfish poisoning,
    424–425
Partial molal volumes, of sea
    water, 19–20
Particulate phosphorus, 192–199
P_{CO_2}, significance of, 284–288
pE, and iron paradox, 124–127
    and nitrogen, 133
    and nitrogen compounds, 231
    and phosphate, 198
    defined, 124
Perigean tides, 50
Petroleum, potentials of, 378–
    381
pH, defined, 117
    of sea water, 117–124
    of sea water, controls of,
        119–123, 280–281
Phaeodactylum tricornutum, and
    phosphorus, 210–211
Phase, defined, 81
Phillipsite, 116
Phosphate-bearing formations,
    201
Phosphorite, deposition of,
    195–199
    offshore deposits, 385–386
Phosphorus, and bacterial
    action, 203–205
    and biological activity, 200–
        202, 205, 210–211
    as a master element, 179,
        183–184
    biogeochemical cycle of,
        184–187
    biogeochemical cycle, repre-
        sentation of, 185
    control of, in the sea, 193–
        195
    dissolved, analysis of, 189–
        192
    horizontal distribution of,

215–217
    limitation in the sea, 211
    particulate, 192–199
    variations in marine eco-
        system, 208–220
    vertical distribution of,
        213–215
Phosphorus compounds, pertinent
    constants, 193–194, 220–221
Phosphorus-nitrogen ratio, 137–
    138, 217–219
"Phosphorus paradox," 192
Photochemical decomposition,
    of water, 130
Photosynthesis, 130–131, 322–
    324
    schematic representation of,
        324
Photosynthetic rate, 325–328
    measurement of, 339–346
Phycocolloids, 417–421
Phytoplankton, analyses of, 137
    oxidation of, 137–138
    terminology of, 435–438
Phytoplankton growth, and
    chemical parameters, 333–
    339
Phytoplankton species, 319–322
Plimsoll line, 16, 35–36
Pollution, of the sea, 79, 370–
    373
Polyphosphate, 188, 212
Preconditioning, 330–332
Productivity, and depth, 319
    estimates of, 317–318
    geographical variations in
        346–351
    measurements in field, 345–
        346
    terminology of, 325–328
"Protobiotic soup," 134
Pycnocline, 330, 354

R

Radiation, in transfer of heat,
    81
Radioactive tracer studies,
    and mixing, 69–71

Recrystallization, of carbon-
    ates, 300-307
Red Sea Deposits, 386-389
Red tide, 72, 127
Reflection, of sea water, 21-22
Refraction, of light in sea
    water, 22-23
Regulatory process, of oxygen
    132-133
Residence time, defined, 308
    of carbon dioxide, 293-294
    of selected elements, 308-310
River runoff, and nitrogen,
    241-242
    and phosphorus variation,
    200-202
River transport, and silicon
    cycle, 159-162

                    S

S, see entropy
Salinity, definitions of, 26-29
    distribution of, 29-34
Saxotoxin, 431
Sea, defined, 72
Sea-floor spreading, 108-110
Sea water, as a buffer, 118-124
    as an ore, 360-361
    compressibility of, 17-20
    extinction in, 22-25
    main constituents of, 26-27
    mean values of, 111
    optical properties of, 21-25
    partial molal volumes of, 19-
    20
    pH, 117-124
    real versus model, 113
    refraction of light in, 22-23
    velocity of sound in, 20-21
Sediments, and nitrogen re-
    generation, 242-244
    relative thickness of, 105
Seiches, 47
Sigma-t, curve, 68
    defined, 15
Silica, solubility, 148-151
    solubility, representation of,
    178

Silicate minerals, 116
    and cation concentrations,
    121-125
    and pH control, 120-124
Silicon, control of, in the
    sea, 166-171
    distribution in marine eco-
    system, 172-177
    incorporation into organisms,
    166-167
    particulate, 153-159
    seasonal variations of, 173-
    175
Silicon cycle, processes of,
    145-147, 159-172
    representation of, 146
Silicon solubility, factors
    affecting, 148-151, 166,
    171-172
Size-metabolic relationship,
    97
Solvation, defined, 6
Solvolysis, defined, 7
Sorption, and phosphorus, 206-
    207
Specific gravity, computation
    of, 14
Specific gravity anomaly,
    application of, 16
    defined, 15
Specificity, 311
Specific volume, defined, 12
Spring tides, 50
Stability, defined, 68-69
Standard state, 102
Standing crop, and energy flow,
    97
    defined, 96
Standing waves, see seiches
Streptococcus faecalis, growth
    optima of, 9
Sulfate reducers, 101
Sulfate-reducing bacteria, and
    atmospheric oxygen, 130-133
Sulfide-oxidizing bacteria, 101
Sulfur, mining of, 377-378
Sulfur cycle, 99-101, 133
Superadjacent exploitability,
    limit of, 363-366

Surface, of earth, versus depth, 40

Surface currents, general patterns of, 55-58
  map of, 56

Swell, defined, 72

System, defined, 81

T

Tarichatoxin, 431

Tetrodotoxin, 431

Thermal anomalies, and water structure, 7-10

Thermal pollution, 410-411

Thermocline, defined, 664
  seasonal variations, 65-66
  types of, 64-66

Thermodynamics, 81-82
  first law, 82
  second law, 90-92

Thermohaline circulation, model of, 58

Tidal currents, 51

Tides, classes of, 49
  defined, 47
  origin of, 48

Tin minerals, 384-385

Trace metal elements, and physiological effects, 312
  and phytoplankton growth, 336-339
  control of, 307-312
  residence times of, 308-310

Trophic level, 97

T-S diagrams, 67-68

Tsunamis, 72

Turbulent mixing, 51-53

U

Uniformist models, of water, 10

Upwelling, 63-64
  and phosphorus, 197

V

Velocity, of a wave, defined, 43

Velocity of sound, in sea water, 20-21

Venomous organisms, 425

Vertical distribution, of salinity, 33-34

W

Water, abnormal properties of, 3-5
  bond angle of, 1-2
  density of, 12-17
  errors in evaluation of density, 12-13
  physical properties compared with those of methane, 4
  temperature of maximum density, 3-6
  theoretical models of, 10-11
  thermal anomalies of, 7-10

Water mass, defined, 67

Water type, defined, 67

Wave, characteristics of, 41
  characteristics of, observed and computed values, 44
  defined, 41

Wave action, kinds of, 40

Wave height, H, defined, 41

Wave length, defined, 41

Wave period, T, defined, 42

Waves, internal, 45-45
  "long," 46-47
  progressive oceanic surface, 44
  standing, 47

Weathering, 105-106, 145

Westward intensification, 56

Wind currents, 54-55

Wind structure, and effects on surface currents, 57

Work, defined, 81

Y

Yield curve, 399-400

Z

Zonal distribution, of salinity, 31-33